Modern University Algebra

MARVIN MARCUS
HENRYK MINC

University of California, Santa Barbara

THE MACMILLAN COMPANY · NEW YORK
COLLIER - MACMILLAN LIMITED · LONDON

First Printing

Library of Congress catalog card number: 66-19712

THE MACMILLAN COMPANY, NEW YORK
COLLIER-MACMILLAN CANADA, LTD., TORONTO, ONTARIO

PRINTED IN THE UNITED STATES OF AMERICA

To
Rebecca, Robert, Ralph,
and Raymond

Preface

This book is intended for use in a one-semester or two-quarter course in algebra at the freshman or sophomore level. We assume only that the student has completed the standard high school courses in algebra and trigonometry, although the latter is not essential. At the University of California, Santa Barbara, this material has been used to replace the one-semester course which is ordinarily entitled "Advanced College Algebra" or "Theory of Equations." In this department such a course has traditionally been taught to second semester freshmen or beginning sophomores and is a requirement for all mathematics majors. It is generally agreed that some of the material in a classical course in the theory of equations is no longer pertinent to the educational requirements of mathematics and science majors. In Chapter 4 of this book, however, we have tried to retain those important parts of the theory of equations that bear some relation to other branches of mathematics—for example, linear algebra, numerical analysis, and modern algebra.

The goal of this book is to include those important topics in algebra that are usually assumed to be too elementary to be incorporated in a serious treatment of "modern algebra" (à la van der Waerden or Jacobson) and too advanced to be called "college algebra" in the ordinary sense. It is hoped that this material will prepare the student for subsequent courses in linear algebra, modern algebra, and some parts of analysis—for example, the theory of convex sets and convex functions. Our experience at Santa Barbara has been that many students majoring in the social sciences, as well as in the natural sciences, have found this material to be useful. This is particularly true of Chapters 2 and 3, on combinatorial analysis and convexity.

We have not tried in any sense to develop an axiomatic treatment of the material contained herein; rather, we have tried to penetrate significantly into the actual subject matter of the topics that we have dealt with. It is perhaps best to illustrate our viewpoint by example. In Chapter 2, on combinatorial analysis, we use the fact that a positive integer can divide another positive integer to yield a unique quotient and a nonnegative remainder. This fact is familiar to every fifth-grade student and thus we feel that it can safely be used in Chapter 2, although it is not until Chapter 4 that we give a systematic treatment of elementary number theory, including the Division Algorithm.

Again, we assume in Chapter 1 that the student is acquainted with the most elementary aspects of the "greater than" relation between real numbers although we do not investigate the theory of inequalities until Chapter 3.

It has been our experience that axiomatics at an elementary level is an inappropriate approach to the study of mathematics. There are altogether too many important, new, and exciting ideas in mathematics and the student may not be able to afford the time for a lengthy contemplation of material such as the Peano axioms for the integers. In our opinion, it is much more important to know something about convex sets, convex functions, and the classical inequalities than to be preoccupied with an interminable sequence of trivial results culminating in $(-1) \times (-1) = 1$.

The experienced teacher will see from looking at the table of contents that many of the topics that are covered here seem quite advanced for the ordinary student for whom this text is intended. The Frobenius-König theorem, the Minkowski inequality, and the basis theorem for symmetric polynomials are examples of topics that might well be deferred to a more advanced course. However, we have presented this material at a level which we feel makes it accessible to students with backgrounds such as we have described above. Of course, we also include much of the traditional material, such as de Moivre's theorem, greatest common divisors, and the remainder theorem for polynomials.

The four chapters are essentially self-contained and, in the main, independent of one another. Chapter 1, "Numbers and Sets," deals with the elementary language of mathematics: induction, summation and product notation, composition of functions, elementary theory of cardinality. Chapter 2, "Combinatorial Analysis," gives a fairly complete theory of permutations on a finite set. In this chapter we also introduce the concept of an incidence matrix and we motivate the definitions of matrix product and sum by their combinatorial applications. Although we state and prove the important elementary properties of matrices, we do not attempt to give a systematic treatment of linear algebra and the theory of matrices in this text. Chapter 3, "Convexity," has as its goal the investigation of important and classical inequalities for real numbers; for example, the arithmetic-geometric mean inequality, the triangle inequality, and Minkowski's inequality. It is in this chapter that our treatment is somewhat novel. We do not make the development dependent on calculus, and it should be interesting to the knowledgeable reader to see that most of the important aspects of this subject can be done completely independently of the techniques of analysis. Chapter 4, " Rings," unifies the theory of polynomials, integers, and complex numbers by regarding them as similar algebraic structures. The last section, on the theory of equations, lies on the boundary between analysis and algebra, and because of this, some of the arguments that are used in the development of the Sturm theory have a strong analytical flavor. The single item that is used from analysis, the least-upper-bound axiom, is explicitly stated and the immediate consequence of this axiom that polynomial functions attain their maxima and minima on closed intervals is also explicitly set out.

Every section of the book ends with a true-false quiz and a set of exercises. A complete set of solutions and explanations is provided in the "Answers and Solutions" at the end of the book. We have taken the attitude that any serious student will make a genuine attempt to solve some of the more difficult questions by himself and that, if he is unsuccessful, the immediate accessibility of a solution can only serve to reinforce the learning process. The authors have found in teaching this material that the first three chapters can be covered without difficulty in about three quarters of a semester. This means that in an ordinary one-semester course a certain amount of material in Chapter 4 would have to be omitted. We suggest omitting Section 5 and parts of Section 6; in particular, the Sturm theory. Also, for the better-trained high school graduate, much of the material in Chapter 1 will be repetitious and could therefore be covered rather quickly or omitted altogether. We would suggest that a minimum syllabus for a course at this level should include the first three sections of Chapter 1, Sections 1 and 2 of Chapter 2, all of Chapter 3, and Sections 1, 2, 3 and parts of 4 and 6 in Chapter 4. Such a selection of material can be easily covered in a quarter.

The authors are pleased to express their thanks to Dr. David Outcalt, Mrs. Ruth Afflack, and Miss Elizabeth Rau for their many helpful criticisms.

M. M.

H. M.

Contents

1

Numbers and Sets

1.1 Mathematical Induction

This book is intended for use in an algebra course at the freshman or sophomore level. Any student who has successfully completed the standard high school courses in algebra has sufficient preparation to proceed with this subject matter. Our raw material will be numbers: *real numbers, rational numbers, integers and natural numbers.* May we recall that a rational number is a real number of the form p/q where p and q are integers, $q \neq 0$. We use the term natural number synonymously with the term positive integer. The natural numbers are also called *counting numbers*, since the sequence 1, 2, 3,... is used in enumerating objects or events. The sequence of natural numbers is infinite; that is to say, given any number in this sequence we can conceive of a natural number which immediately follows it.

Many propositions in mathematics are proved or disproved by considering all possible cases. This often cannot be done if the proposition involves the infinite sequence of natural numbers since the number of cases to be considered may well be infinite. However, we sometimes can prove such propositions by using the *principle of mathematical induction*. This principle is inherent in the concept of natural numbers, and we do not attempt to prove it by means of simpler mathematical notions.

Principle of Mathematical Induction   *Let a proposition $P(n)$ be either true or false for every natural number n. Suppose that*
   (i) *$P(1)$ is true,*
   (ii) *the truth of $P(k)$ implies the truth of $P(k + 1)$ for all k.*
Then $P(n)$ is true for all natural numbers n.

Although, as we said, we shall not prove the principle of induction, we can argue the plausibility of this principle. Suppose that both induction hypotheses hold. Then, by (i), $P(1)$ is true. It follows from (ii) (with $k = 1$) that $P(2)$ is

1

true. Another application of (ii) (with $k = 2$) shows that $P(3)$ is true. And so on.

Before we give examples of the use of induction we introduce some notation.

Definition 1.1   (Σ and Π notation)   *The symbols $\overset{\cdot}{\Sigma}$ and Π are used as an abbreviated notation for addition and multiplication. If $a_1, a_2, \ldots, a_m$ is any finite collection of numbers or other mathematical entities for which addition (multiplication) is defined then*

$$\sum_{i=1}^{m} a_i = a_1 + a_2 + a_3 + \cdots + a_m \tag{1}$$

and

$$\prod_{i=1}^{m} a_i = a_1 a_2 a_3 \cdots a_m. \tag{2}$$

These definitions can also be stated as follows:

$$\sum_{i=1}^{1} a_i = a_1 \quad \text{and, for } m > 1, \quad \sum_{i=1}^{m} a_i = \left(\sum_{i=1}^{m-1} a_i \right) + a_m; \tag{3}$$

$$\prod_{i=1}^{1} a_i = a_1 \quad \text{and, for } m > 1, \quad \prod_{i=1}^{m} a_i = \left(\prod_{i=1}^{m-1} a_i \right) a_m. \tag{4}$$

The definitions (3) and (4) are rigorous versions of (1) and (2) and, in fact, define the symbols

$$\sum_{i=1}^{m} a_i \quad \text{and} \quad \prod_{i=1}^{m} a_i$$

inductively. Thus, for example,

$$\sum_{i=1}^{4} a_i = a_1 + a_2 + a_3 + a_4, \qquad \prod_{i=1}^{4} a_i = a_1 a_2 a_3 a_4,$$

$$\sum_{i=1}^{4} (2i + 1) = (2 \times 1 + 1) + (2 \times 2 + 1) + (2 \times 3 + 1) + (2 \times 4 + 1) = 24,$$

$$\prod_{i=1}^{4} (2i + 1) = (2 \times 1 + 1)(2 \times 2 + 1)(2 \times 3 + 1)(2 \times 4 + 1) = 945,$$

$$\sum_{i=1}^{4} b^i = b + b^2 + b^3 + b^4, \qquad \prod_{i=1}^{4} b^i = b b^2 b^3 b^4 = b^{10},$$

$$\sum_{j=1}^{4} a_i b_j = a_i b_1 + a_i b_2 + a_i b_3 + a_i b_4 = a_i (b_1 + b_2 + b_3 + b_4),$$

$$\prod_{t=1}^{4} a_i^t = a_i a_i^2 a_i^3 a_i^4 = a_i^{10}, \qquad \prod_{i=1}^{4} a_i^t = a_1^t a_2^t a_3^t a_4^t.$$

We are now in a position to give examples of the use of the principle of mathematical induction.

EXAMPLE 1.1

Prove that

$$\sum_{i=1}^{n} (2i - 1) = n^2. \tag{5}$$

We use induction on n. If $n = 1$ then both sides of (5) are equal to 1 and thus (5) is true for $n = 1$. We assume now that (5) is true for $n = k$ and show that this assumption implies that (5) holds for $n = k + 1$. Now, if

$$\sum_{i=1}^{k} (2i - 1) = k^2$$

then

$$\sum_{i=1}^{k+1} (2i - 1) = \sum_{i=1}^{k} (2i - 1) + (2(k + 1) - 1)$$

$$= k^2 + 2k + 1$$

$$= (k + 1)^2.$$

Thus we have proved by induction that (5) holds for all n.

Suppose we can prove that a proposition $P(h)$ is true for some fixed h and that the assumption of $P(k)$ being true implies that $P(k + 1)$ is true for any $k \geq h$. Then clearly $P(n)$ is true for all $n \geq h$.

EXAMPLE 1.2

Prove that if a is any positive number then

$$(1 + a)^n > 1 + na \tag{6}$$

for any natural number n, $n \geq 2$. Again, we use induction on n. For $n = 2$ we check directly that

$$(1 + a)^2 = 1 + 2a + a^2 > 1 + 2a.$$

Assume that

$$(1 + a)^k > 1 + ka.$$

Then it follows that

$$(1 + a)^{k+1} = (1 + a)^k(1 + a)$$

$$> (1 + ka)(1 + a)$$

$$= 1 + (k + 1)a + ka^2$$

$$> 1 + (k + 1)a.$$

Thus (6) holds for $n = 2, 3, \ldots$.

As our next application of the principle of induction we prove the binomial theorem. Before we do this we shall introduce the notation for factorials and binomial coefficients.

Definition 1.2   (Factorial)   *If n is any nonnegative integer we inductively define the number n!, called n-factorial, by*

$$0! = 1 \quad and, \ for \ n > 0, \quad n! = (n-1)! \, n.$$

Using more suggestive, if somewhat vaguer, notation,

$$n! = 1 \times 2 \times 3 \times \cdots \times n$$

$$= \prod_{i=1}^{n} i, \quad n > 0.$$

Definition 1.3   (Binomial coefficient)   *If n and r are integers, $0 \leq r \leq n$, we define*

$$\binom{n}{r} = \frac{n!}{(n-r)! \, r!}.$$

The number $\binom{n}{r}$ is called the binomial coefficient n over r.

The following properties of binomial coefficients follow immediately from the definition:

$$\binom{n}{r} = \binom{n}{n-r}, \tag{7}$$

$$\binom{n}{r} + \binom{n}{r+1} = \binom{n+1}{r+1}. \tag{8}$$

For example, we can establish (8) by computing

$$\binom{n}{r} + \binom{n}{r+1} = \frac{n!}{(n-r)! \, r!} + \frac{n!}{(n-r-1)! \, (r+1)!}$$

$$= \frac{n! \, (r+1) + n! \, (n-r)}{(n-r)! \, (r+1)!}$$

$$= \frac{n! \, (n+1)}{(n-r)! \, (r+1)!}$$

$$= \frac{(n+1)!}{(n+1-(r+1))! \, (r+1)!}$$

$$= \binom{n+1}{r+1}.$$

Formula (8) suggests a method for constructing a table of binomial coefficients:

n \ r	0	1	2	3	4	5
0	1					
1	1	1				
2	1	2	1			
3	1	3	3	1		
4	1	4	6	4	1	
5	1	5	10	10	5	1

This table is called the *Pascal Triangle*.

Theorem 1.1   (Binomial theorem)   *If a and b are real numbers and n is a natural number then*

$$(a + b)^n = \sum_{r=0}^{n} \binom{n}{r} a^{n-r} b^r. \tag{9}$$

Proof.   We use induction on n. Formula (9) clearly holds for $n = 1$. We assume that (9) holds for $n = k$; i.e., that

$$(a + b)^k = \sum_{r=0}^{k} \binom{k}{r} a^{k-r} b^r.$$

We shall prove that this assumption implies the truth of (9) for $n = k + 1$. We use our assumption to compute

$$(a + b)^{k+1} = (a + b)(a + b)^k$$

$$= (a + b) \sum_{r=0}^{k} \binom{k}{r} a^{k-r} b^r$$

$$= \sum_{r=0}^{k} \binom{k}{r} a^{k-r+1} b^r + \sum_{r=0}^{k} \binom{k}{r} a^{k-r} b^{r+1}.$$

Now, set $t = r + 1$ in the second sum. It becomes

$$\sum_{t=1}^{k+1} \binom{k}{t-1} a^{k-t+1} b^t$$

which is, of course, equal to

$$\sum_{r=1}^{k+1} \binom{k}{r-1} a^{k-r+1} b^r.$$

Therefore,

$$(a + b)^{k+1} = \sum_{r=0}^{k} \binom{k}{r} a^{k-r+1} b^r + \sum_{r=1}^{k+1} \binom{k}{r-1} a^{k-r+1} b^r$$

$$= \binom{k}{0} a^{k+1} + \sum_{r=1}^{k} \left(\binom{k}{r} + \binom{k}{r-1} \right) a^{k-r+1} b^r + \binom{k}{k} b^{k+1}$$

$$= \binom{k+1}{0} a^{k+1} + \sum_{r=1}^{k} \binom{k+1}{r} a^{k+1-r} b^r + \binom{k+1}{k+1} b^{k+1},$$

where we have used (8) and the fact that $\binom{m}{m} = \binom{m}{0} = 1$ for any natural number m. Thus

$$(a + b)^{k+1} = \sum_{r=0}^{k+1} \binom{k+1}{r} a^{k+1-r} b^r$$

and the proof by induction is complete.

Quiz

Answer **true** or **false**:

(In what follows, r and n are positive integers.)

1. $\sum_{t=1}^{4} t^t = \sum_{t=2}^{5} (t+1)^{t+1}$.

2. $\prod_{k=0}^{5} \cos (k\pi/6) = 0$.

3. $\sum_{k=0}^{5} \cos (k\pi/6) = 0$.

4. If $r < n$, then $\binom{n}{r} = \prod_{t=1}^{r} \dfrac{n-t+1}{t}$.

5. For any r, $(r^2)! = (r!)^2$.

6. For any r, $\binom{2r}{r} \geq 2^r$.

7. If a and b are nonzero real numbers and $(a+b)^n = a^n + b^n$, then $n = 1$.

8. If $2r + 1 < n$ then $\binom{n}{r} < \binom{n}{r+1}$.

9. $\binom{n}{r} < \binom{n+1}{r+1}$ for all $n > r \geq 0$.

10. For real numbers the coefficient of $x^4 y^2$ in the expansion of $(x+y)^6$ is $\binom{4}{2} = 6$.

Exercises

1. Compute the following numbers:

(a) $\sum_{t=2}^{5} (-t)^2$; (b) $\sum_{t=1}^{4} (2t)$; (c) $\sum_{k=2}^{2} \frac{1}{k}$;

(d) $\sum_{n=0}^{3} (-1)^n \frac{2^{2n}}{(2n)!}$; (e) $\sum_{s=1}^{20} s^2 / \sum_{t=1}^{20} t^2$;

(f) $\sum_{s=1}^{4} s! / \sum_{t=2}^{4} t!$; (g) $(\prod_{s=1}^{10} s!) / (\prod_{t=3}^{10} t!)$;

(h) $\prod_{i=1}^{4} (2i-1)$; (i) $\prod_{i=1}^{15} \frac{2i-1}{2i+1}$.

2. Write out the following expressions in full:

(a) $\sum_{n=1}^{4} (-1)^n \frac{x^{2n-1}}{(2n-1)!}$; (b) $(1-x)^6$;

(c) $(1-x) \sum_{t=0}^{5} x^t$ $(x^0 = 1)$.

3. Find the value of $\binom{21}{19}$.

4. If $\binom{n}{3} = \frac{10}{21} \binom{n}{5}$, find n.

5. Find the coefficient of x^{17} in the expansion of $(x-2)^{20}$.

6. Prove that $\sum_{r=0}^{n} \binom{n}{r} = 2^n$ and that $\sum_{r=0}^{n} (-1)^r \binom{n}{r} = 0$.

7. Expand the expression $(x-1/x)^7$ in decreasing powers of x.

8. Show that $n^n \geq (n+1)!$ for $n \geq 3$.

9. Prove that $\binom{n}{r} = \binom{n-2}{r} + 2\binom{n-2}{r-1} + \binom{n-2}{r-2}$.

10. For a fixed n find the greatest value of $\binom{n}{r}$.

11. Prove that $(n/2)^n > n!$ for $n \geq 6$.

1.2   Sets

The concept of *set* is a ubiquitous one in mathematics. It is, however, usually left undefined. By a set of mathematical objects, which we call the *elements* of the set, we understand the *totality* (or the *collection*, or the *aggregate*, or the *class*) of these elements. For example, we can speak about the set of natural numbers, the set of real numbers, the set of integers greater than 4, the set of points inside a given circle, the set of solutions of an equation, and so on. It is also convenient in mathematics to consider the *empty set* (or the *null set*), that is, the set that does not contain any elements. For example, the set of all real solutions of the equation $x^2 + 2 = 0$ is empty. We denote the empty set by $\varnothing$.

If a mathematical object x is an element of the set X we say that x *belongs* to X and write

$$x \in X.$$

If x does not belong to X we write

$$x \notin X.$$

A set is well defined if for any given mathematical object it is determined either that the object belongs, or that it does not belong to the set. In some cases we may not know whether a particular object belongs, or does not belong to a given set. For example, we do not know whether the millionth digit in the decimal expansion of π belongs to the set of even integers or not. However, it is possible, at least in principle, to determine whether a given object is an even integer or not, and therefore the set of even integers is well defined.

Definition 2.1   **(Subset)**   *If every element of a set X also belongs to a set Y, that is, if $x \in X$ implies that $x \in Y$, then we say that X is a subset of Y and write*

$$X \subset Y.$$

If $X \subset Y$ and $Y \subset X$ then X and Y are said to be equal and we write

$$X = Y.$$

If $X \subset Y$ but $X \neq Y$, we say that X is a proper subset of Y.

Clearly, X is equal to Y if and only if X and Y contain exactly the same elements. It follows from the definition of a subset that, for any set X,

$$\varnothing \subset X \subset X$$

and, in particular, that any two empty sets are equal.

Several remarks about the standard notation for sets are in order. If it is feasible, we denote a set by actually writing out all the elements or all the symbols representing its elements. Thus

$$X = \{a_1, a_2, a_3\}$$

means that X is the set composed of elements a_1, a_2, and a_3. For example, $\{4\}$ denotes the set containing one element, the number 4, while $\{7, 3, -2, 5, 13\}$ is the set consisting of the numbers 7, 3, -2, 5, and 13. We can sometimes define a set by giving a symbolic description of its elements. This is particularly convenient if we define a subset of a previously defined set. For example, if N and Re denote the sets of natural and real numbers respectively, then

$$\{x \in N \mid x = 2y, \, y \in N\}$$

denotes the set of all positive even integers;

$$\{x \in Re \mid 1 < x < 2\}$$

denotes the set of all real numbers between 1 and 2; and

$$\{x \in Re \mid x^2 + 2 = 0\}$$

represents the set of all real solutions of the equation $x^2 + 2 = 0$. This last set happens to be empty and we can write

$$\{x \in Re \mid x^2 + 2 = 0\} = \varnothing.$$

As usual, once new entities are introduced in the study of mathematics we begin to investigate how these entities can be combined to produce other new items. Sets are just collections of objects. Given several sets it is natural to define the set that contains all the elements involved, and the set that contains all the elements common to all the given sets.

Definition 2.2   (Union, intersection) *The union of two sets X and Y is the set containing all elements that belong either to X or to Y (or to both); we denote the union of X and Y by $X \cup Y$. Thus*

$$X \cup Y = \{x \mid x \in X \text{ or } x \in Y\}. \tag{1}$$

The intersection of X and Y is the set of all elements common to X and Y; we denote the intersection of X and Y by $X \cap Y$. Thus

$$X \cap Y = \{x \mid x \in X \text{ and } x \in Y\}. \tag{2}$$

More generally, if $\{X_1, X_2, \dots\}$ is any given collection of sets, then we denote their union and intersection by $\bigcup_i X_i$ and $\bigcap_i X_i$ respectively and define them by

$$\bigcup_i X_i = \{x \mid x \in X_i, \text{ for some } i\}, \tag{3}$$

$$\bigcap_i X_i = \{x \mid x \in X_i, \text{ for all } i\}. \tag{4}$$

If the collection of the sets X_i is finite and contains n sets then we sometimes denote their union and intersection by $\bigcup_{i=1}^n X_i$ and $\bigcap_{i=1}^n X_i$ respectively. If n is small we can write out the union and the intersection of the sets X_i in full. For example, if $n = 4$, we can write $X_1 \cup X_2 \cup X_3 \cup X_4$ and $X_1 \cap X_2 \cap X_3 \cap X_4$.

Examples 2.1

(a) If $X = \{1, 2, 3, 4, 5\}$, $Y = \{1, 3, 5, 7\}$, and $Z = \{2, 4, 6, 8\}$, then

$$X \cup Y = \{1, 2, 3, 4, 5, 7\},$$

$$X \cup Z = \{1, 2, 3, 4, 5, 6, 8\},$$

$$Y \cup Z = \{1, 2, 3, 4, 5, 6, 7, 8\},$$

$$X \cup Y \cup Z = \{1, 2, 3, 4, 5, 6, 7, 8\},$$

$$X \cap Y = \{1, 3, 5\},$$

$$X \cap Z = \{2, 4\},$$

$$Y \cap Z = \varnothing,$$

$$X \cap Y \cap Z = \varnothing.$$

(b) If N is the set of all natural numbers, E is the set of all even positive integers, P the set of all primes (recall that $p \in N$ is a prime if $p \neq 1$ and $p = ab$, $a, b \in N$, implies that either $a = 1$ or $b = 1$; that is, $p \neq 1$ is a prime if it is divisible only by itself and by 1), then

$$N \cup E = N \cup P = N,$$

$$N \cap E = E,$$

$$N \cap P = P,$$

$$P \cap E = \{2\}.$$

(c) For any sets X and Y,

$$\varnothing \subset X \cap Y \subset X \subset X \cup Y.$$

(d) If $X = \{x \in \mathrm{Re} \,|\, 0 \leq x < 1\}$, $Y = \{x \in \mathrm{Re} \,|\, 0 < x < 3\}$, and $Z = \{x \in \mathrm{Re} \,|\, 2 \leq x \leq 4\}$, then

$$X \cup Y = \{x \in \mathrm{Re} \,|\, 0 \leq x < 3\},$$

$$X \cap Y = \{x \in \mathrm{Re} \,|\, 0 < x < 1\},$$

$$X \cup Z = \{x \in \mathrm{Re} \,|\, 0 \leq x < 1 \ or \ 2 \leq x \leq 4\},$$

$$X \cap Z = \varnothing,$$

$$Y \cup Z = \{x \in \mathrm{Re} \,|\, 0 < x \leq 4\},$$

$$Y \cap Z = \{x \in \mathrm{Re} \,|\, 2 \leq x < 3\},$$

$$X \cup Y \cup Z = \{x \in \text{Re} \,|\, 0 \le x \le 4\},$$

$$X \cap Y \cap Z = \varnothing.$$

Definition 2.3 (Cartesian Product) *The Cartesian product of X and Y is the set of all ordered pairs* (x, y), $x \in X$, $y \in Y$. *By an "ordered pair" we mean a set of two elements one of which is designated as the first element of the pair; thus* $(x_1, y_1) = (x_2, y_2)$, *if and only if* $x_1 = x_2$ *and* $y_1 = y_2$. *The Cartesian product of X and Y is denoted by* $X \times Y$.

For example, if $X = \{1, 2\}$ and $Y = \{1, 3, 5\}$, then

$$X \times Y = \{(1, 1), (1, 3), (1, 5), (2, 1), (2, 3), (2, 5)\}.$$

Another important way of making new sets from old ones is given in the following definition.

Definition 2.4 (Power set) *Given a set X, the set of all subsets of X (including the null set and X itself) is called the power set of X and is denoted by* $P(X)$.

For example, if $X = \{a, b, c\}$, then

$$P(X) = \{\varnothing, \{a\}, \{b\}, \{c\}, \{a, b\}, \{a, c\}, \{b, c\}, \{a, b, c\}\}.$$

Note that $P(X)$ is not the union of all subsets of X, which clearly is equal to X, but $P(X)$ is a set whose elements are the subsets of X. Thus subsets of $P(X)$ consist of elements which are themselves subsets of X. Certain subsets of $P(X)$, called partitions of X, are of special interest.

Definition 2.5 (Partition of a set) *Let X be any nonempty set. A subset S of* $P(X)$ *not containing* $\varnothing$ *is called a partition of X if each element of X belongs to one and only one of the subsets in S.*

Definition 2.6 (Binary relation) *A binary relation* R *on a set X is a rule that stipulates for any ordered pair of elements a, b in X (not necessarily distinct) either that they are* R-*related, in which case we write* a R b, *or that they are not* R-*related in which case we write* a Ʀ b.

An alternative definition which is less descriptive, but perhaps more exact, is the following: a binary relation R on a set X is a subset of $X \times X$. Then if $(a, b) \in X \times X$ and $(a, b) \in$ R we say that a is R-related to b and write a R b. If $(a, b) \notin$ R then a is not R-related to b and we write a Ʀ b.

EXAMPLES 2.2

(a) Let $X = \{1, 2, 3, 4\}$ and let R $= \{(1, 2), (2, 3), (3, 4)\}$. Then, for a and b elements of X, a R b if and only if $b - a = 1$.

(b)   Let X be the set in (a) and suppose that $a \mathrel{R} b$ if and only if $a > b$. Then $R = \{(2, 1), (3, 1), (3, 2), (4, 1), (4, 2), (4, 3)\}$.

Definition 2.7   (Equivalence relation)   *A binary relation* R *on a set* X *is called an equivalence relation if, for all a, b, c in* X,
    (i) $a \mathrel{R} a$ (*reflexive property*),
    (ii) $a \mathrel{R} b$ *implies* $b \mathrel{R} a$ (*symmetric property*),
    (iii) $a \mathrel{R} b$ *and* $b \mathrel{R} c$ *imply* $a \mathrel{R} c$ (*transitive property*).
If R *is an equivalence relation we usually write* $a \sim b$ *instead of* $a \mathrel{R} b$, *once the relation is understood.*

EXAMPLES 2.3

(a)   Let R be the relation on the set of real numbers, Re, defined as follows. If x and y are in Re then $x \mathrel{R} y$ if $x - y$ is a rational number. Then R is an equivalence relation. For, if x, y, z are any real numbers then
    (i) $x - x$ is rational,
    (ii)   if $x - y$ is rational then $y - x = -(x - y)$ is rational,
    (iii)   if $x - y$ and $y - z$ are rational then $(x - y) + (y - z) = x - z$ is rational.
(b)   Let R be the relation on the set of integers defined as follows. If x and y are integers then $x \mathrel{R} y$ if $x - y$ is a multiple of a fixed positive integer d. It is easy to see that R is reflexive, symmetric and transitive and is therefore an equivalence relation.

An interesting property of equivalence relations is contained in the following result.

Theorem 2.1   *Let* X *be a set and let* R *be an equivalence relation on* X. *For any* $x \in X$ *let*

$$[x] = \{y \in X \mid y \mathrel{R} x\}.$$

Let S *be the subset of* $P(X)$ *consisting of all* $[x]$, $x \in X$. *Then* S *is a partition of* X.

Proof.   We prove that for any x_1 and x_2 in X either $[x_1] = [x_2]$ or $[x_1] \cap [x_2] = \varnothing$. As before let $x \sim y$ denote $x \mathrel{R} y$. Suppose that $[x_1] \cap [x_2] \neq \varnothing$. Then there exists $y \in X$ such that $y \in [x_1]$ and $y \in [x_2]$. But then $x_1 \sim y \sim x_2$ and therefore, by the transitive property, $x_1 \sim x_2$. Now, let z_1 and z_2 be elements of $[x_1]$ and $[x_2]$ respectively. Then $z_1 \sim x_1 \sim x_2 \sim z_2$ and thus $z_1 \sim x_2$ and $z_2 \sim x_1$. Therefore, $z_1 \in [x_2]$, $z_2 \in [x_1]$. But z_1 and z_2 were arbitrary elements of $[x_1]$ and $[x_2]$ respectively, and hence $[x_1] = [x_2]$.

Definition 2.8   (Equivalence classes)   *Let* R *be an equivalence relation on a set* X *and let* $S = \{X_1, X_2, \ldots\}$ *be the partition of* X *induced by* R (*see the* *proof of Theorem* 2.1). *Then the sets* $X_1, X_2, \ldots$ *are called the equivalence classes relative to* R, *or the* R-*equivalence classes, or simply equivalence classes, once* R *is understood.*

Quiz

Answer **true** or **false**:

(X, Y, and Z denote sets.)

1. $X \times Y = Y \times X$ for any X, Y.

2. $(X \cup Y) \cap Z = X \cup (Y \cap Z)$ for any X, Y, Z.

3. If X contains m elements and Y contains n elements then $X \times Y$ contains mn elements.

4. If X and Y are the sets in Question 3 then $X \cup Y$ contains $m + n$ elements.

5. The set of solutions of the equation $x + 2 = 2$ is $\varnothing$.

6. $P(\varnothing) = \varnothing$.

7. The binary relation $\geq$ on the set $\{3\}$ is an equivalence relation.

8. If $X \cup Y = Y$ then $X \subseteq Y$.

9. The binary relation $\geq$ on the set of integers is an equivalence relation.

10. Let R be the binary relation on the set of real numbers defined by $x \mathbin{R} y$ if and only if $x - y$ is an integer. Then R is an equivalence relation.

Exercises

1. Let Re, Ra, I, N, and E denote the sets of real numbers, rational numbers, integers, natural numbers and even integers respectively. Describe the following sets:

    (a) $N \cup \{0\}$;

    (b) $N \cup \varnothing$;

    (c) $\{x \in I \mid x \in N\}$;

    (d) $N \cap E$;

    (e) $N \cup E$;

    (f) $I \cup E$;

    (g) $\{x \in \text{Re} \mid -2 < x < 5\} \cap N$;

    (h) $\{x \in \text{Re} \mid x^2 + 2 = 0\} \cap \text{Re}$;

    (i) $\{x \in \text{Re} \mid x^2 - 2 = 0\} \cap \text{Ra}$;

    (j) $\{x \in \text{Re} \mid x^2 - 2 = 0\} \cup \text{Ra}$.

2. Let $X = \{1, 2, 3, 4\}$ and let $Y = \{1, 2, 3\}$. How many distinct elements are there in each of the sets $X \times Y$, $Y \times X$, $X \times X$, $Y \times Y$, $(X \times Y) \cap (Y \times X)$?

3.   Write out all the elements of $P(X)$ where $X = \{1, 2, 3, 4\}$. Construct two different partitions of X.

4.   Show that if n is the number of elements in X then the number of elements in $P(X)$ is 2^n.

5.   Let I denote the set of integers and S denote the set of nonzero integers. Define a relation R on $I \times S$: (n_1, s_1) R (n_2, s_2) if and only if $n_1 s_2 = n_2 s_1$, for any (n_1, s_1) and (n_2, s_2) in $I \times S$. Show that R is an equivalence relation on $I \times S$.

6.   Let R be the binary relation on the set of real numbers defined by x R y if for any integer n either both x and y are not less than n, or both x and y are less than n. Is R an equivalence relation? If so, what are the equivalence classes?

7.   Let X be an arbitrary set and S a partition of X. Define a relation R on X as follows: x R y if and only if x and y belong to the same element of S. Show that R is an equivalence relation. (This is the converse of Theorem 2.1.)

8.   Show that if X has n elements, where n is a nonnegative integer, then $P(X)$ has more than n elements. (Do not use Exercise 4).

1.3   Functions

The concept of a function is fundamental in all mathematics. Other names, such as *mapping*, *map*, *many-one correspondence*, *transformation*, and so on, are also used for the same concept.

Definition 3.1   (**Function**)   *A function f defined on a set X with values in a set Y is a rule that prescribes for every element $x \in X$ a unique element $f(x)$ in Y called the value of f at x (or the image of x under f). We say that f is a function on X into Y and denote it by $f : X \to Y$. The set X is called the domain of f. If Z is a subset of X we denote the set $\{y \in Y \mid y = f(z), z \in Z\}$ by $f(Z)$ and call it the image of Z under f. The set $f(X)$ is called the range of f.*

An alternative, somewhat more rigorous, definition of a function can be given: a function f is a subset of $X \times Y$ such that each $x \in X$ occurs in exactly one pair of f.

Examples 3.1

(a)   Let $X = \{x_1, x_2, \ldots\}$, $Y = \{y_1, y_2, \ldots\}$ and define $f : X \to Y$ by $f(x_k) = y_1$, $k = 1, 2, \ldots$. Then, for any nonempty subset Z of X, $f(Z) = \{y_1\}$.

(b)   Let Re denote the set of real numbers. Define $f : \text{Re} \times \text{Re} \to \text{Re}$ by $f((x, y)) = \sqrt{x^2 + y^2}$ for all $(x, y) \in \text{Re} \times \text{Re}$. Here the range consists of all nonnegative real numbers.

(c)   The function $e_X : X \to X$ defined by $e_X(x) = x$, for all $x \in X$, is called the *identity function* on X. We have $e_X(X) = X$.

(d) Let $X = \{1, 2, 3, 4\}$. Define the function $\sigma : X \to X$ by $\sigma(1) = 2$, $\sigma(2) = 3$, $\sigma(3) = 4$, $\sigma(4) = 1$. Here also $\sigma(X) = X$.

(e) Let N be the set of positive integers and $Y = \{0, 1\}$. Define $\delta : N \times N \to Y$ as follows:

$$\delta((m, n)) = \begin{cases} 0, & \text{if } n \neq m, \\ 1, & \text{if } n = m. \end{cases}$$

The function δ is called the *Kronecker delta*; the usual notation for its value at (m, n) is $\delta_{m,n}$.

A function $f : X \to Y$ may have the same value at several elements of X (see Example 3.1(e)) and Y may contain elements that are not values of f at any elements in X (see Example 3.1(b)).

Definition 3.2 **(One-one, onto)** *If $f(X) = Y$, that is, if every element of Y is a value of f at some element of X, then we say that f is a function onto Y (or sometimes we express it in the somewhat ungrammatical form: f is an onto function). If f has distinct values at distinct elements of X, that is, if $f(x_1) = f(x_2)$ implies $x_1 = x_2$ for all x_1, x_2 in X, then f is said to be a one-one (or univalent) function. We also write: f is 1-1. If $f : X \to Y$ is 1-1 onto, we sometimes express this fact by saying that f is a one-one correspondence between X and Y.*

EXAMPLES 3.2

(a) The identity function e_X (see Example 3.1(c)) is both one-one and onto.

(b) The function σ defined in Exercise 3.1(d) is both 1-1 and onto. The function δ of Exercise 3.1(e) is onto but not 1-1.

(c) Let $f : N \to N$, where N is the set of natural numbers, be defined by: $f(n) = n + 1$, $n \in N$. Then f is 1-1 but not onto.

(d) Let X be any set and let f be a function defined on N with values in X. Then for each natural number $n \in N$ there exists an element $x_n \in X$ such that $f(n) = x_n$. The function f is called an *infinite sequence* and $f(n)$ is sometimes called the nth element of the sequence.

(e) Let $f : \text{Re} \to \text{Re}$ be defined by $f(x) = x^3$. Then f is 1-1 and onto. Note that, given any real number y, there exists a unique real number x such that $f(x) = y$, namely $x = y^{1/3}$.

Definition 3.3 **(Inverse function)** *Let $f : X \to Y$ be a one-one function onto Y. Define the function $f^{-1} : Y \to X$ in the following way. Let y be any element in Y. Since f is onto Y and one-one there exists a unique element x in X such that $y = f(x)$. Then define*

$$f^{-1}(y) = f^{-1}(f(x)) = x.$$

The function f^{-1}, whose domain and range are the range and the domain of f respectively, is called the inverse function of f, or briefly, f inverse. In other words, $f^{-1} : Y \to X$ is the 1-1 function onto X whose value at any element y of Y is that element of X at which the value of f is y.

EXAMPLES 3.3

(a)   If σ is the function defined in Example 3.1(d) then $\sigma^{-1}(1) = 4$, $\sigma^{-1}(2) = 1$, $\sigma^{-1}(3) = 2$, $\sigma^{-1}(4) = 3$.

(b)   If $f : \mathrm{Re} \to \mathrm{Re}$ is defined by $f(x) = x^3 - 1$ then f is 1-1 and onto Re. The inverse function $f^{-1} : \mathrm{Re} \to \mathrm{Re}$ is given by $f^{-1}(x) = (x+1)^{1/3}$.

(c)   Let $f : I \to N$ be the function on the set of integers into the set of natural numbers defined thus:

$$f(n) = \begin{cases} 2n, & \text{if } n > 0, \\ 2(-n) + 1, & \text{if } n \le 0. \end{cases}$$

Then f is 1-1 onto N. In fact, if $m \in N$ then

$$f^{-1}(m) = \begin{cases} m/2, & \text{if } m \text{ is even,} \\ -(m - 1)/2, & \text{if } m \text{ is odd.} \end{cases}$$

If $f : X \to Y$ is not 1-1 then we can always define a 1-1 function g on a subset Z of X, such that $g(z) = f(z)$ for all $z \in Z$. For example, if $f : \mathrm{Re} \to \mathrm{Re}$ is the function given by $f(x) = x^2$, $x \in \mathrm{Re}$, then f is not 1-1, of course. However, we can define a 1-1 real-valued function g on the set of nonnegative real numbers, Re^+, by $g(z) = f(z) = z^2$, for all $z \in \mathrm{Re}^+$. For this and other reasons the following definition is useful.

Definition 3.4   (Restricted functions)   Let $Z \subset X$ and let f be a function defined on X, $f : X \to Y$. Define $g : Z \to Y$ by $g(z) = f(z)$ for all $z \in Z$. Then g is said to be the function f restricted to Z; the function g is denoted by $f \,|\, Z$.

It should be noted that not every restriction of f is 1-1 and that even if $f \,|\, Z$ is 1-1 then Z is in no way unique. Of course, if f is 1-1 then $f \,|\, Z$ must be 1-1 as well.

EXAMPLE 3.4

(For the purposes of the example, we assume that the reader is familiar with the elementary properties of the trigonometric function sine. We shall define this function in Chapter 4, Section 3.) Let $Y = \{y \in \mathrm{Re} \,|\, -1 \le y \le 1\}$ and let $f : \mathrm{Re} \to Y$, $f(x) = \sin x$, $x \in \mathrm{Re}$. Then, for any $y \in Y$, there is an infinite number of real numbers x such that $y = f(x)$. If, however, $Z = \{z \in \mathrm{Re} \mid -\pi/2 \leq z \leq \pi/2\}$ then $f \mid Z$ is 1-1. Moreover, $f \mid Z$ is onto. In fact, $(f \mid Z)^{-1}$ is the function usually denoted by $\sin^{-1}$. If $W = \{w \in \mathrm{Re} \mid 0 \leq w \leq \pi/2\}$ then $f \mid W$ is still 1-1, since $W \subset Z$, but it is not onto.

Definition 3.5   (Composition of functions)   *Let $f : X \to Y$ and $g : Y \to Z$. Then the composite function gf is defined on X into Z by $(gf)(x) = g(f(x))$. The function $gf : X \to Z$ is also called the product with respect to composition, or simply the product, of g and f. In other words, the function gf first maps every element x in the domain of f into its value $f(x)$ and then maps $f(x)$ into its image under g.*

EXAMPLES 3.5

(a)   Let $X = \{1, 2, 3, 4\}$ and let $f : X \to X$ and $g : X \to X$ be defined by

$$f(1) = 4, \qquad f(2) = 3, \qquad f(3) = 2, \qquad f(4) = 1;$$

$$g(1) = 1, \qquad g(2) = 3, \qquad g(3) = 4, \qquad g(4) = 2.$$

Then the functions $gf : X \to X$ and $fg : X \to X$ are both defined and

$$gf(1) = 2, \qquad gf(2) = 4, \qquad gf(3) = 3, \qquad gf(4) = 1;$$

$$fg(1) = 4, \qquad fg(2) - 2, \qquad fg(3) = 1, \qquad fg(4) = 3.$$

Hence $fg \neq gf$. Thus composition of function is *noncommutative*.

(b)   Let Re, I and N denote the sets of real numbers, integers, and natural numbers, respectively. Let $f : I \to N$ be the function defined in Example 3.3(c), and let $g : \mathrm{Re} \to I$ be defined by $g(x) = [x]$, where $[x]$ denotes the largest integer not exceeding x. For example, $[3] = 3$, $[\sqrt{5}] = 2$, $[\pi] = 3$, $[-\pi] = -4$, $[-\sqrt{5}] = -3$, $[-3] = -3$, and so on. Then fg is a function on Re with values in N:

$$fg(x) = \begin{cases} 2[x], & \text{if } x \geq 1, \\ -2[x] + 1, & \text{if } x < 1. \end{cases}$$

(c)   Let $X = \{1, 2, 3, 4\}$ and define $f : X \to X$, $g : X \to X$ as follows:

$$f(1) = 2, \qquad f(2) = 3, \qquad f(3) = 4, \qquad f(4) = 1;$$

$$g(1) = 4, \qquad g(2) = 1, \qquad g(3) = 2, \qquad g(4) = 3.$$

Then

$$fg(1) = gf(1) = 1, \qquad fg(2) = gf(2) = 2,$$

$$fg(3) = gf(3) = 3, \qquad fg(4) = gf(4) = 4,$$

that is, $fg = gf = e_X$. In fact, $g = f^{-1}$ and $f = g^{-1}$. This conclusion is quite general. We incorporate it with other simple properties of composite functions and of inverse functions in the following theorem.

Theorem 3.1   (a)   *If* $f : X \to Y$, $g : Y \to Z$ *and* $h : Z \to W$, *then*

$$(hg)f = h(gf).$$

In other words, composition of functions is associative.
    (b)   *If* $f : X \to Y$ *is onto* Y *and* $g : Y \to X$ *is onto* X *and*

$$gf = e_X,$$

then $g = f^{-1}$ *and* $fg = e_Y$.
    (c)   *If* f^{-1} *exists then* $(f^{-1})^{-1} = f$.
    (d)   *If* f^{-1} *and* g^{-1} *exist and* gf *is defined then* $(gf)^{-1}$ *exists and*

$$(gf)^{-1} = f^{-1}g^{-1}.$$

Proof.   (a)   By Definition 3.5,

$$((hg)f)(x) = (hg)(f(x))$$

$$= h(g(f(x))), \qquad \text{for all } x \in X,$$

while

$$(h(gf))(x) = h((gf)(x))$$

$$= h(g(f(x))), \qquad \text{for all } x \in X.$$

Thus

$$(hg)f = h(gf).$$

    (b)   Note that f is 1-1. For, if $f(x_1) = f(x_2)$, then

$$x_1 = gf(x_1) = gf(x_2) = x_2.$$

Thus f^{-1} exists. Now, for any $y \in Y$ there exists $x \in X$ such that $y = f(x)$ and

$$g(y) = g(f(x)) = (gf)(x) = e_X(x) = x = f^{-1}(f(x)) = f^{-1}(y).$$

Therefore $g = f^{-1}$ and clearly $fg = ff^{-1} = e_Y$.
    (c)   If the inverse of $f : X \to Y$ exists then both f and f^{-1} are 1-1 onto. Therefore $(f^{-1})^{-1}$ exists. Also, $ff^{-1} = e_Y$ and therefore, by part (b), $f = (f^{-1})^{-1}$.
    (d)   If f^{-1} and g^{-1} exist and gf is defined, then both $f : X \to Y$ and $g : Y \to Z$ are 1-1 onto, and therefore $gf : X \to Z$ is 1-1 onto as well. Now $(gf)(X) = g(f(X)) = g(Y) = Z$, and thus $(gf)(x_1) = (gf)(x_2)$ implies $g(f(x_1)) = g(f(x_2))$. Therefore $f(x_1) = f(x_2)$ and $x_1 = x_2$. Now

$$(f^{-1}g^{-1})(gf) = f^{-1}(g^{-1}(gf))$$

$$= f^{-1}((g^{-1}g)f),$$

by part (a). Hence

$$(f^{-1}g^{-1})(gf) = f^{-1}(e_Y f)$$

$$= f^{-1}f$$

$$= e_X.$$

Therefore, by part (b),

$$f^{-1}g^{-1} = (gf)^{-1}.$$

Quiz

Answer **true** or **false**:

1. If f and g are both 1-1 and fg exists then fg is 1-1.

2. A function $f : X \to Y$ is onto if and only if $Y \subseteq f(X)$.

3. If $f : X \to X$ is 1-1 then it is onto.

4. If a 1-1 function is onto a finite set then its domain is a finite set.

5. There exists a 1-1 correspondence between the set of integers and the set of natural numbers.

6. If V and W are subsets of the domain of f and $V \cap W \neq \varnothing$ then $f(V \cap W) = f(V) \cap f(W)$.

7. If V and W are nonempty subsets of the domain of f then $f(V \cup W) = f(V) \cup f(W)$.

8. If $[x]$ denotes the largest integer not exceeding the real number x (see Example 3.5(b)), then $[-x] = -[x]$.

9. If $f : X \to Y$ and $g : Y \to X$ is 1-1 onto and $fg = gf$, then f is 1-1.

10. If f is a 1-1 onto function, and g and h are functions such that $fg = fh$, then $g = h$.

Exercises

1. (a) Evaulate $\delta_{0,k}$ where $k = \delta_{3,0}$.
   (b) Evaluate $\delta_{0,t}$ where $t = \delta_{5,5}$.
   (c) Eveluate $\sum\limits_{t=1}^{4} \delta_{1,t} \, \delta_{t,2}$.
   (d) Evaluate $\sum\limits_{t=1}^{4} (\delta_{1,t} + \delta_{t,2})/2$.

2. If $f : \text{Re} \to I$ is defined by $f(x) = [x]$, what is $f \mid N$?

3. Let σ and τ be functions on $X = \{1, 2, 3, 4\}$ defined by

$$\sigma(1) = 4, \qquad \sigma(2) = 1, \qquad \sigma(3) = 2, \qquad \sigma(4) = 3;$$

$$\tau(1) = 2, \qquad \tau(2) = 1, \qquad \tau(3) = 4, \qquad \tau(4) = 3.$$

Find the functions σ^{-1}, $\sigma\tau$, $\tau\sigma$.

4. If σ is the function in the preceding exercise, find the functions σ^3 and σ^4, where $\sigma^3 = \sigma\sigma\sigma$ and $\sigma^4 = \sigma\sigma^3$.

5. Let $f : X \to X$ be a function onto a finite set X. Show that f is 1-1.

6. How many distinct functions can be defined on $X = \{1, 2, \ldots, n\}$ into itself? How many of these are 1-1?

1.4   Cardinality

Although the theory of sets is less than a century old, it has by now permeated every branch of mathematics. Its methods are of particular importance in the mathematics of the infinite.

The number of elements in a finite set can be determined by actually counting them. Clearly, a set X contains n elements if and only if there is a one-one correspondence between X and the set of integers $\{1, 2, \ldots, n\}$. We extend this idea of comparing the elements of a set with the elements of another set to infinite sets. By an infinite set we mean any set which is not finite (and, of course, nonempty).

Definition 4.1   (Equipotent sets)   *Two sets X and Y are said to be equipotent (or equivalent, or of the same cardinality, or of the same power), if there exists a 1-1 correspondence between the elements of X and those of Y, that is, if there exists a one-one function mapping X onto Y. We then write $X \sim Y$.*

EXAMPLES 4.1

(a)   Let N be the set of natural numbers and E its subset of even natural numbers. Then the function $f : N \to E$ defined by $f(n) = 2n, n \in N$, is 1-1 onto, and therefore the sets N and E are equipotent. It is customary to denote the functional relationship $f(n) = 2n$, which establishes the 1-1 correspondence, by $n \leftrightarrow 2n$.

(b)   Let S be the set of distinct elements forming an infinite sequence $\{s_1, s_2, s_3, \ldots\}$. Then S is equipotent to N since there exists the 1-1 correspondence $n \leftrightarrow s_n$.

(c)   Let P be the set of all positive real numbers and let S be the subset $\{x \in P \,|\, 0 < x < 1\}$. We claim that P and S are equipotent. For, if x is any positive real number then $x/(1 + x) \in S$ and

$$x \leftrightarrow \frac{x}{1 + x}$$

is a 1-1 correspondence. To see this, let $f : P \to S$ be defined by

$$f(x) = \frac{x}{1 + x}$$

and let y be any element of S. Then

$$y = f\left(\frac{y}{1 - y}\right)$$

and thus f is onto. Also, if

$$\frac{x_1}{1 + x_1} = \frac{x_2}{1 + x_2},$$

then

$$x_1 + x_1 x_2 = x_2 + x_1 x_2$$

and

$$x_1 = x_2.$$

The function f is therefore 1-1.

Examples 4.1(a) and 4.1(c) demonstrate a remarkable property of infinite sets: they can be equipotent to proper subsets of themselves. This property has been actually used by some mathematicians to "define" an infinite set.

It should be noted that except in trivial cases there is more than one 1-1 correspondence between elements of two equipotent sets. According to Definition 4.1, in order to prove that two sets are equipotent we have to show that there exists at least one such correspondence. However, if we want to prove that two given sets X and Y are not equipotent we must show that no 1-1 correspondence can exist between the elements of X and the elements of Y. Such proofs are, in general, difficult. Before we proceed to exploit the concept of equipotence and to classify infinite sets we shall state and prove a general theorem on sets that are not equipotent.

Theorem 4.1   *No set is equipotent to its power set.*

Proof.   Suppose that there exists a set S equipotent to its power set $P(S)$. Then there exists a 1-1 function f from S onto $P(S)$. We shall show that the assumption that f is onto leads to a contradiction. If s is any element of S, then $f(s) \in P(S)$ and thus is a subset of S. There are two possibilities: either $s \in f(s)$ or $s \notin f(s)$. If $s \in f(s)$, call s an interior element of S, and if $s \notin f(s)$, call s an exterior element. Now, let X be the set of all exterior elements of S. Since $X \in P(S)$ and f is onto, that is, $f(S) = P(S)$, there must be an element x in S such that $f(x) = X$. Then x cannot be an interior element, since this would imply that $x \in f(x) = X$, and thus X would contain an interior element in contradiction to its definition. Therefore x must be an exterior element, that is, $x \notin f(x)$. But all exterior elements belong to X and therefore $x \in X$ while $f(x) = X$. This contradiction implies that no such function f can exist.

Theorem 4.2   *Equipotence is an equivalence relation on any set of sets.*

Proof.   Let X, Y, Z be any three sets. Clearly any set X is equipotent to itself, since e_X is a 1-1 onto function. If there exists a 1-1 onto function $f : X \to Y$, then $f^{-1} : Y \to X$ exists and is 1-1 onto. Thus equipotence is both reflexive and symmetric. Now suppose that the functions $f : X \to Y$ and $g : Y \to Z$ both are 1-1 and onto. Then the function gf is a 1-1 function from X onto Z. Thus if $X \sim Y$ and $Y \sim Z$ then $X \sim Z$ and equipotence is transitive as well.

Definition 4.2   (Denumerable sets)   *A set is called denumerable if it is equipotent to the set of natural numbers N. A set that is either denumerable or finite is sometimes called countable.*

The following important result is intuitively obvious.

Theorem 4.3   *An infinite subset of a denumerable set is denumerable.*

Proof.   Let S be an infinite subset of a denumerable X. Since X is denumerable, there exists a function $f : N \to X$ having the property that, for any element x in X, there exists a unique natural number n such that $f(n) = x$. The set X can be therefore arranged into the sequence $f(1)$, $f(2)$, $f(3), \dots$. Now delete from this sequence all elements that do not belong to S. The remaining subsequence consists of elements of S and is infinite. Let it be $f(i_1)$, $f(i_2)$, $f(i_3), \dots, i_t \in N$, $i_t < i_{t+1}$, $t = 1, 2, 3, \dots$. Define the function $g : N \to S$ by $g(n) = f(i_n)$. The function g is 1-1 and onto S, and thus S is denumerable.

EXAMPLE 4.2

The following sets are denumerable by virtue of Theorem 4.3:
(a)   the set of prime natural numbers,
(b)   the set of positive integral multiples of any fixed natural number.

Theorem 4.3 can also be used to prove the following rather surprising results.

Theorem 4.4   *The set of all integers is denumerable. The set of all rational numbers is denumerable.*

Proof.   The first part of the theorem can be proved by means of the 1-1 onto function f defined in Example 3.3(c) or from the second part of the present theorem using Theorem 4.3. We first prove that the set $N \times N$ is denumerable. Write the elements of $N \times N$ in the form of an array as follows:

$$(1, 1) \quad (1, 2) \quad (1, 3) \quad (1, 4) \quad (1, 5) \quad \cdots$$
$$(2, 1) \quad (2, 2) \quad (2, 3) \quad (2, 4) \quad (2, 5) \quad \cdots$$
$$(3, 1) \quad (3, 2) \quad (3, 3) \quad (3, 4) \quad (3, 5) \quad \cdots$$
$$(4, 1) \quad (4, 2) \quad (4, 3) \quad (4, 4) \quad (4, 5) \quad \cdots$$
$$(5, 1) \quad (5, 2) \quad (5, 3) \quad (5, 4) \quad (5, 5) \quad \cdots$$

$$\cdots \qquad \cdots \qquad \cdots \qquad \cdots \qquad \cdots \qquad \cdots$$

and arrange these into a sequence as indicated by the arrows, namely

$$(1, 1), (2, 1), (1, 2), (3, 1), (2, 2), (1, 3), (4, 1), (3, 2), \ldots . \tag{1}$$

It is easy, of course, to express this 1-1 correspondence between N and $N \times N$ by an algebraic formula. If $(m, n) \in N \times N$, then

$$(m, n) \leftrightarrow \tfrac{1}{2}(m + n - 1)(m + n - 2) + n. \tag{2}$$

The formula (2) is established as follows. The pair (m, n) lies in the $(m + n - 1)$th diagonal "stripe" in the above diagram and is the nth pair up from the left on that stripe; for example, $(2, 4)$ is in the fifth stripe and occupies the fourth position up from the left. In the first stripe there is one pair, in the second there are two pairs, and so on, so that (m, n) occurs in position numbered

$$n + \sum_{j=1}^{m+n-2} j \tag{3}$$

in our counting procedure. An easy application of induction (see Example 1.1) shows that

$$\sum_{j=1}^{m+n-2} j = \tfrac{1}{2}(m + n - 1)(m + n - 2).$$

Thus (2) implies that $N \times N$ is denumerable.

Now, let S be the subset obtained from $N \times N$ by deleting all pairs (m, n) in which m and n are not relatively prime (that is, for which m and n have a positive integer factor greater than 1 in common). Since S contains among its elements all pairs of the form $(m, 1)$, it is infinite and therefore, by Theorem 4.3, it is denumerable. Next, S is clearly equipotent to the set of positive rational numbers, Ra^+:

$$(m, n) \leftrightarrow m/n.$$

Thus Ra^+ is denumerable. It remains to prove that Ra, the set of all rational numbers, can be arranged into a sequence. Since Ra^+ is denumerable, it can be ordered into an infinite sequence $r_1, r_2, r_3, \ldots$, that is, we can find a 1-1 correspondence between N and Ra^+, $n \leftrightarrow r_n$. Then all the rational numbers can be arranged into a sequence

$$0, r_1, -r_1, r_2, -r_2, r_3, -r_3, . \tag{4}$$

The set Ra is therefore denumerable.

It should be noted that although any number of elements of the sequence (4) can actually be written out (thus $0, 1, -1, 2, -2, \frac{1}{2}, -\frac{1}{2}, 3, -3, \frac{1}{3}, -\frac{1}{3}, 4, -4, \frac{3}{2}, -\frac{3}{2}, \frac{2}{3}, -\frac{2}{3}, \frac{1}{4}, -\frac{1}{4}, 5, -5, \ldots$) we cannot produce a formula for the nth element of the sequence, as we did in (2). This is so because in our construction of the sequence (4) we have deleted all pairs (m, n) in $N \times N$ in which m and n are not relatively prime, and there is no known formula giving the positions of such pairs in the sequence (1).

The fact that the set of rational numbers is denumerable is most surprising, since between any two distinct rational numbers, however small their difference, there is an infinite subset of rational numbers. In fact, if s and t are rational numbers and $s < t$ then all the numbers in the infinite set

$$\{r \in \mathrm{Ra} \mid r = \frac{(n-1)s + t}{n}, n \in N\}$$

are contained between s and t.

We know, of course, from Theorem 4.1 that not all sets are denumerable. We shall now state and prove a celebrated result due to the originator of the theory of sets, Georg Cantor.

Theorem 4.5 *The set of real numbers is not denumerable.*

Proof. We prove that the infinite subset $S = \{x \in \mathrm{Re} \mid 0 \le x < 1\}$ is not denumerable. We show that, given any denumerable set X of elements of S, there exists an element $s \in S$ not contained in X and therefore that the set S is not denumerable. Let $X \subset S$ be a denumerable subset of S. Then its elements can be arranged into an infinite sequence $r_1, r_2, r_3, \ldots$. Let $n \in N$ and let the real number r_n be written out as an infinite decimal

$$r_n = 0.\alpha_{n1}\alpha_{n2}\alpha_{n3}\cdots,$$

where $\alpha_{n1}, \alpha_{n2}, \alpha_{n3}, \ldots$ represent the digits in the decimal expansion of r_n. Define the function $f : N \to \{1, 2\}$ by

$$f(n) = \begin{cases} 1 & \text{if } \alpha_{nn} \ne 1, \\ 2 & \text{if } \alpha_{nn} = 1. \end{cases}$$

Let s be the infinite decimal $s = 0.s_1 s_2 s_3 \ldots$ whose digits s_n are given by $s_n = f(n), n = 1, 2, 3, \ldots$. Then $s \ne r_n$ for any $n \in N$. For, the nth digit of s is 1 if the nth digit of r_n differs from 1, and the nth digit of s is equal to 2 if the

nth digit of r_n is 1. Thus $s \notin X$. We conclude that no denumerable set contains all elements of S (certainly not the set $X \cup \{s\}$ which is denumerable). Clearly, the set Re of all real numbers cannot be denumerable; otherwise, by Theorem 4.2, the subset S would be denumerable. In fact, we have

Theorem 4.6   *Let a and b be fixed real numbers, $a < b$. The subset $Y = \{y \in \mathrm{Re} \mid a < y < b\}$ of Re is equipotent to Re.*

Proof.   Let $f : Y \to \mathrm{Re}$ be defined by

$$
f(y) = \begin{cases} \dfrac{b-a}{2(y-a)} - 1, & \text{if } a < y \le \dfrac{a+b}{2}, \\[2ex] \dfrac{b-a}{2(y-b)} + 1, & \text{if } \dfrac{a+b}{2} \le y < b. \end{cases}
$$

Then given any $x \in \mathrm{Re}$ there is exactly one $y \in Y$ such that $f(y) = x$; namely

$$
y = \frac{b-a}{2(x+1)} + a, \qquad \text{if } x \ge 0,
$$

and

$$
y = \frac{b-a}{2(x-1)} + b, \qquad \text{if } x \le 0.
$$

Thus f is 1-1 onto and Y is equipotent to Re.

Quiz

Answer **true** or **false**:

1.   The union of two denumerable sets is denumerable.

2.   No power set $P(X)$ is denumerable.

3.   The set of all finite decimals (that is, all real numbers whose decimal expansions terminate) is denumerable.

4.   Every nondenumerable infinite set is equipotent to the set of real numbers.

5.   The set of all partitions of N, the set of natural numbers, into two subsets, is nondenumerable.

6.   The only element of the set $P(P(\varnothing))$ is $\varnothing$.

7.   The set $S \times S$ is denumerable if and only if S is denumerable.

8.   An infinite set whose elements are real numbers cannot be denumerable.

9.   The set of all points in the Cartesian plane whose coordinates are rational numbers is denumerable.

10.   The set of real solutions of the equation $\sin x = 0$ is denumerable.

Exercises

1. Show that the set of all triples (n_1, n_2, n_3), where $n_i \in N$, $i = 1, 2, 3$, is denumerable.

2. Show that the set of all integers n which yield a remainder of 2 upon division by 3 is denumerable.

3. Prove that any infinite set of disjoint open real intervals is denumerable. (An open interval (a_i, b_i) is the set $\{x \in \text{Re} \,|\, a_i < x < b_i\}$; two intervals (a_i, b_i) and (a_j, b_j) are disjoint if $(a_i, b_i) \cap (a_j, b_j) = \varnothing$.)

4. Let R be the equivalence relation defined in Example 2.3(a). Show that each of the equivalence classes determined by R is denumerable.

5. Show that the set of natural numbers can be partitioned into an infinite set of denumerable sets.

6. Show that the set Y of all first-degree equations is not denumerable, while the subset Z of all first-degree equations with integer coefficients is denumerable.

7. Prove that the set of all finite sequences of elements of N is denumerable.

8. A real number is called *algebraic* if it is a root of an algebraic equation; that is, one of the form

$$x^n + \sum_{t=0}^{n-1} a_t x^t = 0,$$

where $a_0, \ldots, a_{n-1}$ are rational numbers. Prove that the set of all algebraic equations is denumerable, and deduce that the set of algebraic numbers is denumerable. (You may assume that an algebraic equation has a finite number of solutions.)

2

Combinatorial Analysis

2.1 Introduction to Permutations

In this section we shall study a rather special class of functions called permutations. These functions appear in many parts of both pure and applied mathematics. For example, one can ask: in how many ways can a particle travel between n different points and not visit any point more than once? This kind of question can be answered in a very intuitive way as follows. The journey can begin in n ways at any of n different points. The first leg of the journey can go to any one of the $n - 1$ remaining points, the next to any one of the $n - 2$ remaining points, and so on. We can represent this argument diagrammatically. Write $1, \ldots, n$ in a row to represent the successive stages of the journey. Let $p_1, \ldots, p_n$ be designations of the points. If the journey starts at p_{i_1}, $1 \leq i_1 \leq n$, then write i_1 under 1. If the particle goes from p_{i_1} to p_{i_2} on the first leg of the journey then write i_2 under 2. In general, if the particle goes from p_{i_r} to $p_{i_{r+1}}$ at the rth leg of the journey then write i_{r+1} under $r + 1$. The completed symbol can be exhibited as

$$\begin{pmatrix} 1 & 2 & 3 & 4 & \cdots & n \\ i_1 & i_2 & i_3 & i_4 & \cdots & i_n \end{pmatrix}. \tag{1}$$

With any symbol (1) we can construct precisely one path and with any path we can construct precisely one symbol (1). The second row of (1) consists of the integers $1, \ldots, n$ in some order. There is another way we can think of the information contained in (1). Let σ be a function whose domain is the set of integers $1, \ldots, n$ and whose value at t is i_t; that is,

$$\sigma(t) = i_t, \qquad t = 1, \ldots, n. \tag{2}$$

27

The function σ is 1-1 because of the way we constructed (1) and we can write the symbol (1) in terms of σ:

$$\begin{pmatrix} 1 & 2 & 3 & 4 & \cdots & n \\ \sigma(1) & \sigma(2) & \sigma(3) & \sigma(4) & \cdots & \sigma(n) \end{pmatrix}. \tag{3}$$

Clearly the 1-1 function σ completely specifies the symbol (1) and conversely. We still have not answered the original question about the number of paths. We can do this now in terms of σ. The value $\sigma(1)$ can be any of $1, \ldots, n$; the value of $\sigma(2)$ can be any of the remaining integers in $\{1, \ldots, n\}$ after $\sigma(1)$ has been deleted, that is, the values $\sigma(1)$ and $\sigma(2)$ can be chosen in $n(n-1)$ ways. In general, for $1 \leq r \leq n$, the value of $\sigma(r)$ can be any one of the integers left in $1, \ldots, n$ after $\sigma(1), \ldots, \sigma(r-1)$ have been deleted. Thus there are $n(n-1) \cdot (n-2) \cdots 3 \cdot 2 \cdot 1 = n!$ ways in which σ can be defined.

Definition 1.1   (Permutation)   *Let X be a set of objects. If σ is a 1-1 onto function whose domain (and range) is X then σ is called a permutation of X. If X is a finite set consisting of n objects then the totality of permutations of X is denoted by X_n. In particular, if $X = S = \{1, \ldots, n\}$ then S_n is called the symmetric group* of degree n.*

If X is a finite set consisting of n elements $x_1, \ldots, x_n$ and $\sigma \in X_n$ then we shall sometimes write

$$\sigma = \begin{pmatrix} x_1 & x_2 & \cdots & x_n \\ \sigma(x_1) & \sigma(x_2) & \cdots & \sigma(x_n) \end{pmatrix}$$

to mean that σ is the permutation whose value at x_i is $\sigma(x_i)$, $i = 1, \ldots, n$. It is obvious that the order in which we write the x_i in this notation for σ is immaterial. The only thing that matters is that $\sigma(x_i)$ be directly below x_i. In other words, we must properly identify each element of X with the value of σ at this element. The essential elementary facts concerning permutations are contained in the following theorem.

Theorem 1.1   *Let X be a set. If σ and θ are any permutations of X then*
- (i)   *$\sigma\theta$ is a permutation of X;*
- (ii)   *σ^{-1} is a permutation of X;*
- (iii)   *there exists a unique permutation e of X such that*

$$\varphi e = e\varphi = \varphi$$

  for any permutation φ;
- (iv)   *there exist unique permutations α and β of X such that $\sigma\alpha = \theta$ and $\beta\sigma = \theta$.*

---

* A group is a special mathematical concept which we do not define here, and which is not pertinent to our needs.

Proof.

(i)   We know that $\sigma\theta$ is a function whose domain is X. Suppose $x \in X$ and let $y = \theta^{-1}\sigma^{-1}(x)$. Then $\sigma\theta(y) = \sigma\theta(\theta^{-1}\sigma^{-1})(x) = \sigma(\theta(\theta^{-1}(\sigma^{-1}(x)))) = \sigma(\sigma^{-1}(x)) = x$. Hence $\sigma\theta(X) = X$ and $\sigma\theta$ is onto. Also, $\sigma(\theta(x_1)) = \sigma(\theta(x_2))$ implies that $\theta(x_1) = \theta(x_2)$ (since σ is 1-1) and thus that $x_1 = x_2$ (since θ is 1-1). Hence $\sigma\theta$ is a 1-1 function whose domain and range are both X; that is, $\sigma\theta$ is a permutation of X.

(ii)   Since σ is 1-1 and onto X it follows that σ^{-1} is a permutation of X.

(iii)   We define e to be the identity map on X, that is,

$$e(x) = x, \qquad \text{all } x \in X.$$

Obviously e is a permutation of X. Then clearly $\varphi e(x) = \varphi(x) = e\varphi(x)$ for any permutation φ of X. It follows that $e\varphi = \varphi e = \varphi$. Suppose now that e_1 is any permutation such that $e_1\varphi = \varphi e_1 = \varphi$ for all φ. Then, in particular, if we set $\varphi = e$ we have $e_1 = ee_1 = e$.

(iv)   We can define α to be $\sigma^{-1}\theta$. By parts (i) and (ii), α is a permutation of X and clearly $\sigma\alpha = \sigma(\sigma^{-1}\theta) = (\sigma\sigma^{-1})\theta = e\theta = \theta$. Also, if $\sigma\alpha_1 = \theta$ then

$$\alpha = \sigma^{-1}\theta = \sigma^{-1}(\sigma\alpha_1) = (\sigma^{-1}\sigma)(\alpha_1) = e\alpha_1 = \alpha_1.$$

The proof of the existence of β is similar and is left as an exercise for the student (Exercise 1).

EXAMPLE 1.1

Let $n = 4$ and define σ and θ in S_4 by

$$\sigma = \begin{pmatrix} 1 & 2 & 3 & 4 \\ 2 & 3 & 4 & 1 \end{pmatrix},$$

$$\theta = \begin{pmatrix} 1 & 2 & 3 & 4 \\ 2 & 4 & 1 & 3 \end{pmatrix}.$$

Then σ^2 can be computed as follows. The value of $\sigma^2(1)$ is $\sigma(\sigma(1)) = \sigma(2) = 3$. Similarly, $\sigma^2(2) = \sigma(\sigma(2)) = \sigma(3) = 4$, $\sigma^2(3) = \sigma(\sigma(3)) = \sigma(4) = 1$, $\sigma^2(4) = \sigma(\sigma(4)) = \sigma(1) = 2$. Hence

$$\sigma^2 = \begin{pmatrix} 1 & 2 & 3 & 4 \\ 3 & 4 & 1 & 2 \end{pmatrix}.$$

Next note that σ^{-1} maps 2 into 1, 3 into 2, 4 into 3 and 1 into 4. Hence

$$\sigma^{-1} = \begin{pmatrix} 1 & 2 & 3 & 4 \\ 4 & 1 & 2 & 3 \end{pmatrix}.$$

To compute the unique solution α to $\sigma\alpha = \theta$ we must compute $\alpha = \sigma^{-1}\theta$. Then

$$\alpha = \begin{pmatrix} 1 & 2 & 3 & 4 \\ 4 & 1 & 2 & 3 \end{pmatrix}\begin{pmatrix} 1 & 2 & 3 & 4 \\ 2 & 4 & 1 & 3 \end{pmatrix}$$

$$= \begin{pmatrix} 1 & 2 & 3 & 4 \\ 1 & 3 & 4 & 2 \end{pmatrix}.$$

Observe in addition that

$$\sigma\theta = \begin{pmatrix} 1 & 2 & 3 & 4 \\ 2 & 3 & 4 & 1 \end{pmatrix}\begin{pmatrix} 1 & 2 & 3 & 4 \\ 2 & 4 & 1 & 3 \end{pmatrix} = \begin{pmatrix} 1 & 2 & 3 & 4 \\ 3 & 1 & 2 & 4 \end{pmatrix}$$

whereas

$$\theta\sigma = \begin{pmatrix} 1 & 2 & 3 & 4 \\ 2 & 4 & 1 & 3 \end{pmatrix}\begin{pmatrix} 1 & 2 & 3 & 4 \\ 2 & 3 & 4 & 1 \end{pmatrix} = \begin{pmatrix} 1 & 2 & 3 & 4 \\ 4 & 1 & 3 & 2 \end{pmatrix}.$$

Hence $\sigma\theta \neq \theta\sigma$. The permutation α has the property that $\alpha(1) = 1$; that is, 1 is held fixed. Also, the permutation $\theta\sigma$ holds 3 fixed. This leads us to the following definition.

Definition 1.2   (Permutations acting on a subset)   *If σ is a permutation of X, and Y is the subset of X containing all elements y such that $\sigma(y) \neq y$ then σ is said to act on the subset Y. By convention, the identity permutation e is said to act on any subset of X.*

EXAMPLE 1.2

Define $\sigma \in S_{10}$ by

$$\sigma = \begin{pmatrix} 1 & 2 & 3 & 4 & 5 & 6 & 7 & 8 & 9 & 10 \\ 3 & 1 & 2 & 6 & 7 & 4 & 8 & 5 & 9 & 10 \end{pmatrix}.$$

We can discover, in a systematic way, disjoint subsets on which σ acts. First note that $\sigma(1) = 3$, $\sigma^2(1) = \sigma(3) = 2$, $\sigma^3(1) = \sigma(2) = 1$ and hence, for any p, $\sigma^p(1)$ must be 3, 2, or 1. For example, if $p = 17$ then $17 = 3 \cdot 5 + 2$ so that

$$\sigma^{17}(1) = \sigma^{3 \cdot 5 + 2}(1) = \sigma^2\sigma^3\sigma^3\sigma^3\sigma^3\sigma^3(1).$$

Thus if we repeatedly use the fact that $\sigma^3(1) = 1$ we obtain

$$\sigma^{17}(1) = \sigma^2(1) = 2.$$

That is to say, in evaluating $\sigma^p(1)$ the only thing that matters is the remainder obtained upon dividing p by 3. We now define a permutation $\pi_1 \in S_{10}$ by

$$\pi_1 = \begin{pmatrix} 1 & 2 & 3 & 4 & 5 & 6 & 7 & 8 & 9 & 10 \\ 3 & 1 & 2 & 4 & 5 & 6 & 7 & 8 & 9 & 10 \end{pmatrix}.$$

In other words, π_1 acts on the subset $Y_1 = \{1, 2, 3\}$ and agrees with σ on this subset. To go on, we compute that $\sigma(4) = 6$, $\sigma^2(4) = \sigma(6) = 4$ and once again, if we define $\pi_2 \in S_{10}$ by

$$\pi_2 = \begin{pmatrix} 1 & 2 & 3 & 4 & 5 & 6 & 7 & 8 & 9 & 10 \\ 1 & 2 & 3 & 6 & 5 & 4 & 7 & 8 & 9 & 10 \end{pmatrix},$$

then π_2 acts on the subset $Y_2 = \{4, 6\}$ and agrees with σ there. Again, $\sigma(5) = 7$, $\sigma^2(5) = \sigma(7) = 8$, $\sigma^3(5) = \sigma(8) = 5$ and if we define

$$\pi_3 = \begin{pmatrix} 1 & 2 & 3 & 4 & 5 & 6 & 7 & 8 & 9 & 10 \\ 1 & 2 & 3 & 4 & 7 & 6 & 8 & 5 & 9 & 10 \end{pmatrix}$$

then π_3 acts on the subset $Y_3 = \{5, 7, 8\}$. We have accounted for the action of σ on the integers $1, \ldots, 8$ and we can observe now that $\sigma(9) = 9$ and $\sigma(10) = 10$. Thus we can (rather trivially) define $\pi_4 = \pi_5 = e$ and think of π_4 as acting on $Y_4 = \{9\}$ and π_5 acting on $Y_5 = \{10\}$. This latter notational device just allows us to account for all of $X = \{1, \ldots, 10\}$. We also observe here that $\pi_1 \pi_2 = \pi_2 \pi_1$ because π_1 only acts on $Y_1 = \{1, 2, 3\}$ and π_2 only acts on $Y_2 = \{4, 6\}$. That is, anything that π_2 "moves" is left alone by π_1 and conversely. In general, $\pi_i \pi_j = \pi_j \pi_i$ for $i, j = 1, \ldots, 5$.

The ideas that emerged in this last example are of utmost importance in discovering the general structure of permutations. We make a definition that will somewhat simplify the rather awkward notation for the permutations $\pi_1, \ldots, \pi_5$ that appears above.

Definition 1.3   (Cycles)   *Let π be a permutation of X and assume there exists an $x \in X$ and an integer p such that $x, \pi(x), \ldots, \pi^{p-1}(x)$ are distinct whereas $\pi^p(x) = x$ and $\pi(z) = z$ for $z \notin \{x, \pi(x), \ldots, \pi^{p-1}(x)\}$. Then π is called a cycle of length p. We abbreviate the notation for π as follows:*

$$\pi = (x, \pi(x), \ldots, \pi^{p-1}(x)). \tag{4}$$

By convention, the identity permutation e is considered to be a cycle of length 1. Clearly π acts on the subset $\{x, \pi(x), \ldots, \pi^{p-1}(x)\}$. In general, if $\pi_1, \ldots, \pi_r$ are cycles, other than e, acting on disjoint subsets $Y_1, \ldots, Y_r$ then we will say that $\pi_1, \ldots, \pi_r$ are *disjoint* cycles.

We can generalize the techniques that we used in Example 1.2 in the following important result.

Theorem 1.2   *Let X be any set.*
   (i)   *If π and θ are disjoint cycle permutations of X then*

$$\pi\theta = \theta\pi.$$

   (ii)   *If $x \in X$ and $\pi = (x, \pi(x), \ldots, \pi^{p-1}(x))$ is a cycle of length p and $y = \pi^r(x)$ then $\pi = (y, \pi(y), \ldots, \pi^{p-1}(y))$.*

(iii)   *If X is a set consisting of n elements and π is any permutation in X_n then π is a product of disjoint cycles. This factorization of π is unique, except for the order in which the cycles occur (and except for the appearance of cycles of length 1).*

Proof.

(i)   To say that π and θ are disjoint means that they act on disjoint subsets. Let Y be the subset on which π acts and Z be the subset on which θ acts. Then we know that $Y \cap Z = \varnothing$. Let $z \in Z$. Then $\theta(z) \in Z$ and since $\theta(z) \notin Y$ we know that $\pi\theta(z) = \theta(z)$. But $z \notin Y$ so $\pi(z) = z$ and hence $\theta\pi(z) = \theta(z) = \pi\theta(z)$. Similarly, if $y \in Y$ then $\theta\pi(y) = \pi(y) = \pi\theta(y)$. Finally, if $x \notin Y$ and $x \notin Z$, then $\pi(x) = x$ and $\theta(x) = x$, and we have $\theta\pi(x) = \theta(x) = x = \pi(x) = \pi\theta(x)$.

(ii)   To begin with we can assume that $0 \le r < p$. For, we can always write $r = kp + r_1$ where r_1 is the remainder obtained upon dividing r by p, $0 \le r_1 < p$, and $\pi^r(x) = \pi^{kp+r_1}(x) = \pi^{r_1}(\pi^p)^k(x) = \pi^{r_1}(x)$. Now observe that if $\pi^k(y) = \pi^m(y)$, $0 \le k \le m < p$, then since $y = \pi^r(x)$ we have $\pi^{k+r}(x) = \pi^{m+r}(x)$ and hence $\pi^{m-k}(x) = x$. But $m - k < p$ and p is by definition the least integer for which $\pi^p(x) = x$. Thus $k = m$. Moreover, $\pi^p(y) = \pi^{p+r}(x) = \pi^r(\pi^p(x)) = \pi^r(x) = y$. Thus $y, \pi(y), \ldots, \pi^{p-1}(y)$ are distinct, $\pi^p(y) = y$, and it makes sense to speak of the cycle $\theta = (y, \pi(y), \ldots, \pi^{p-1}(y))$. Moreover, as we saw before, $\pi^t(y) = \pi^{t+r}(x) = \pi^m(x)$ where m is the remainder obtained upon dividing $t + r$ by p. Since $y, \pi(y), \ldots, \pi^{p-1}(y)$ are all distinct and are all elements of $\{x, \pi(x), \ldots, \pi^{p-1}(x)\}$, it follows that $\{y, \pi(y), \ldots, \pi^{p-1}(y)\} = \{x, \pi(x), \ldots, \pi^{p-1}(x)\}$ and both θ and π act on this set. Then,

$$\theta(\pi^k(y)) = \pi^{k+1}(y) = \pi(\pi^k(y)).$$

Thus θ and π agree on $\pi^k(y)$, $k = 0, \ldots, p - 1$, and it follows that $\theta = \pi$.

(iii)   The statement is obvious for one-element sets; that is, $n = 1$. The argument will be by induction on n. Thus assume the statement holds for any set consisting of fewer than n elements and any permutation on the set. Let $y \in X$ and let $p > 1$ be the least positive integer for which $\pi^p(y) = y$ (if no such y exists then clearly $\pi = e$). Next define $\pi_1 = (y, \pi(y), \ldots, \pi^{p-1}(y))$, and $Y_1 = \{y, \pi(y), \ldots, \pi^{p-1}(y)\}$. The elements $y, \pi(y), \ldots, \pi^{p-1}(y)$ are distinct because an equality $\pi^k(y) = \pi^r(y)$, $k > r$, would imply that $\pi^{k-r}(y) = y$, $k - r < p$, and this contradicts the fact that p is the least integer for which $\pi^p(y) = y$. Then, by definition, π_1 acts on Y_1 and agrees with π there. Let Z be the $n - p$ element set consisting of the elements of X which are not in Y_1. Since π maps Y_1 onto itself it also maps Z onto itself. Let $\theta = \pi|Z$ so that θ is a permutation in Z_{n-p}. The set Z has $n - p$ elements and $\theta \in Z_{n-p}$ so that by applying the induction hypothesis it follows that θ is a product of disjoint cycles in Z_{n-p}:

$$\theta = \theta_2\theta_3 \cdots \theta_m.$$

Let $Y_2, \ldots, Y_m$ be the subsets of Z on which $\theta_2, \ldots, \theta_m$ act. We define $\pi_2, \ldots,$ π_m in X_n by

$$\pi_j | Z = \theta_j, \tag{5}$$

$$\pi_j(x) = x, \qquad x \in X, x \notin Z, \qquad j = 2, \ldots, m.$$

Then, π_j is a cycle in X_n acting on $Y_j, j = 2, \ldots, m$. Let $\varphi = \pi_2 \cdots \pi_m \in X_n$ and we verify that

$$\pi = \pi_1 \varphi. \tag{6}$$

If $z \in Z$ then $\varphi(z) \in Z$ and hence $\pi_1 \varphi(z) = \varphi(z) = \theta(z) = \pi(z)$. If $z \notin Z$ then $\varphi(z) = z$ and $\pi_1 \varphi(z) = \pi_1(z) = \pi(z)$. Thus the two sides of (6) agree on all elements of X. It follows that

$$\pi = \pi_1 \varphi = \pi_1 \pi_2 \cdots \pi_m, \tag{7}$$

π_i is a cycle, π_i acts on Y_i, and finally $Y_1, \ldots, Y_m$ are disjoint subsets of X whose union is the set on which π acts.

We proceed to prove the uniqueness part of (iii). Suppose then that $\pi = \pi_1 \cdots \pi_m = \sigma_1 \cdots \sigma_k$ are two factorizations of π into a product of disjoint cycles where we can assume (without loss of generality) that $k \leq m$ and all cycles are of length at least 2. Let $\sigma_1 = (y, \pi(y), \ldots, \pi^{h-1}(y))$. Then y must appear in some π_i, say in $\pi_i = (x, \pi(x), \ldots, \pi^{p-1}(x))$, that is, $y = \pi^r(x)$. But then, according to (ii), $(y, \pi(y), \ldots, \pi^{p-1}(y)) = \pi_i$. Since π_i is a cycle of length p, we know that there are precisely p distinct elements $\pi^j(y)$, obtained as j varies over all integers, and these all appear in both the symbols for π_i and σ_1. Thus $h \geq p$ and by interchanging the roles of σ_1 and π_i it follows that $p \geq h$. Hence $h = p$. In other words $\sigma_1 = \pi_i$. Recalling that disjoint cycles commute we have

$$\sigma_1 \sigma_2 \cdots \sigma_k = \pi = \pi_i \pi_1 \cdots \pi_{i-1} \pi_{i+1} \cdots \pi_m$$

and multiplying by $\sigma_1^{-1} = \pi_i^{-1}$ results in

$$\sigma_2 \cdots \sigma_k = \pi_1 \cdots \pi_{i-1} \pi_{i+1} \cdots \pi_m. \tag{8}$$

We repeat this process with σ_2 in (8) to show that it is equal to one of the remaining cycles π_t. We continue in this way until there are no cycles σ_r left. If $k = m$ we are done. Otherwise we would arrive at a situation in which a product of some of the disjoint cycles π_t is the identity e. But one of these remaining π_t, of length at least 2, would have a value y on some x other than x itself. But the remaining cycles involve neither x nor y, and hence the product of all of them could not be the identity.

In view of Theorem 1.2(iii), if $\sigma = \sigma_1 \sigma_2 \cdots \sigma_m$ is the disjoint cycle decomposition of σ then $\sigma^{-1} = \sigma_m^{-1} \sigma_{m-1}^{-1} \cdots \sigma_1^{-1}$. Thus if we knew that each σ_i^{-1} were a cycle we could say something about the cycle factorization of σ^{-1}.

Theorem 1.3   *If $\sigma \in X_n$ and $\sigma = \sigma_1 \cdots \sigma_m$ is the disjoint cycle factorization for σ then $\sigma_1^{-1}, \ldots, \sigma_m^{-1}$ are disjoint cycles and*

$$\sigma^{-1} = \sigma_m^{-1} \sigma_{m-1}^{-1} \cdots \sigma_1^{-1} = \sigma_1^{-1} \cdots \sigma_{m-1}^{-1} \sigma_m^{-1} \tag{9}$$

is the disjoint cycle factorization of σ^{-1}. In fact,

$$(x_1 x_2 \cdots x_{k-1} x_k)^{-1} = (x_k x_{k-1} \cdots x_2 x_1). \tag{11}$$

Proof.   It suffices to verify (10). For, from (10) we see that if $\sigma_1, \ldots, \sigma_m$ are disjoint then so are $\sigma_1^{-1}, \ldots, \sigma_m^{-1}$. To prove (10) we show that

$$(x_1 x_2 \cdots x_k)(x_k \cdots x_2 x_1) = e. \tag{10}$$

The right factor on the left in (11) sends x_1 into x_k and the other factor sends x_k into x_1. Thus x_1 is left fixed. Similarly each $x_j, j = 2, \ldots, k$, is left fixed by the left side of (11) and the equality is proved. The second equality in (9) follows immediately since the σ_i are disjoint and hence commute.

Quiz

Answer **true** or **false**:

1.   If σ is a cycle of length 2 then $\sigma^2 = e$.

2.   If σ_1 and σ_2 are cycles of length 2 then $(\sigma_1 \sigma_2)^2 = e$.

3.   If $S = \{1, 2, 3, 4\}$ and $\sigma = (1\ 2\ 3\ 4) \in S_4$ then $\sigma^{-1} = (3\ 4\ 1\ 2)$.

4.   If σ is the cycle in the preceding question then $\sigma^{257} = \sigma$.

5. $\begin{pmatrix} 1 & 2 & 3 & 4 & 5 \\ 2 & 3 & 5 & 1 & 4 \end{pmatrix}^{-1} = \begin{pmatrix} 2 & 3 & 5 & 1 & 4 \\ 1 & 2 & 3 & 4 & 5 \end{pmatrix}.$

6.   If $\sigma_0 \in S_n$ is a fixed permutation then the function f defined by $f(\sigma) = \sigma_0 \sigma$ for each $\sigma \in S_n$ is a permutation of S_n, that is, a 1-1 onto mapping of S_n.

7.   The inverse of a cycle is a cycle.

8.   Any power of a cycle is a cycle.

9. $(x_1 x_2 x_3 x_4)^{-1} = (x_4 x_3 x_2 x_1)$.

10. $((x_1 x_2 x_3)(x_4 x_5))^{-1} = (x_5 x_4)(x_1 x_3 x_2)$.

Exercises

1.   Prove the existence of the unique permutation β described in Theorem 1.1(iv).

2.   Show that the permutation σ defined in Example 1.1 satisfies $\sigma^4 = e$.

3.   Show that if $n \geq 3$, $\sigma \in S_n$, and σ commutes with every cycle of length 2 in S_n, then $\sigma = e$.

4.   Let $\sigma \in S_m$. Show that the least positive integer p for which $\sigma^p = e$ is the least common multiple of the cycle lengths in the disjoint cycle factorization of σ. The least common multiple of a finite set of positive integers is the smallest positive integer which is a multiple of every integer in the set.

2.2 Parity

As we saw in Theorem 1.2 it is always possible to factor a permutation $\sigma \in X_n$ into a product of disjoint cycles uniquely except for order. We want to consider a somewhat different kind of factorization in this section. We begin by considering an example.

EXAMPLE 2.1

Let $S = \{1, 2, 3, 4, 5\}$ and let $\sigma \in S_5$ be the cycle $\sigma = (1\ 3\ 4\ 5)$. Then

$$\sigma = (1\ 3\ 4\ 5) = (1\ 5)(1\ 4)(1\ 3). \tag{1}$$

In other words, we can write σ as a product of cycles of length 2. To verify the equality (1) we must see what the right-hand side does to each of the elements 1, 2, 3, 4, 5. Since 2 does not appear, it is left fixed. Then 3 is mapped into 1 by (1 3), 1 is mapped into 4 by (1 4) and finally 4 is left alone by (1 5). Thus the value of the right-hand side at 3 is 4. Similarly the value at 4 is 5 and the value at 5 is 1. Finally, (1 3) maps 1 into 3 and thus (1) is established. Notice that the cycles (1 5), (1 4), (1 3) are not disjoint.

Definition 2.1 (Transpositions) *Let X be a set and let σ be a cycle of length 2 defined on X. Then σ is called a transposition.*

Example 2.1 is typical and we can generalize the idea to obtain the following result.

Theorem 2.1 *Let X be an n element set, $n \geq 2$, and let $\sigma \in X_n$. Then σ is a product of transpositions.*

Proof. From Theorem 1.2(iii) we know that any permutation is a product of disjoint cycles. Thus it suffices to prove the result for $\sigma = (x_1\ x_2 \cdots x_k)$. If $k = 1$ then $\sigma = e$ and we write $\sigma = e = (x_1\ x_2)(x_1\ x_2)$. If $k \geq 2$ then we observe that

$$(x_1\ x_2 \cdots x_k) = (x_1\ x_k)(x_1\ x_{k-1})(x_1\ x_{k-2}) \cdots (x_1\ x_2). \tag{2}$$

For, if $k > j \geq 2$ then the action of the right-hand side on x_j can be written schematically as

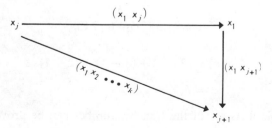

Thus for $k > j \geq 2$, x_j is sent into x_{j+1} by the right side of (2). Also x_1 is obviously sent into x_2 and x_k is sent into x_1. Thus the two sides of (2) agree on each of $x_1, \ldots, x_k$ and therefore are equal.

Note that there is nothing unique about the representation of a permutation σ as a product of transpositions; for example,

$$(1\ 2\ 3) = (1\ 3)(1\ 2),$$

$$(1\ 2\ 3) = (1\ 3)(1\ 2)(2\ 3)(3\ 2)(1\ 3)(3\ 1).$$

We shall soon establish, however, that any two such representations of σ must both involve either an even or an odd number of transpositions. In the equality (2) we see that the number of transpositions used on the right is $k - 1$ where k is the length of the cycle, $(k \geq 2)$.

Definition 2.2 (Cauchy number) *Let X be an n element set and let $\pi \in X_n$. Let $\pi = \pi_1 \pi_2 \cdots \pi_m$ be a representation of π as a product of disjoint cycles in which π_i is of length p_i, $i = 1, \ldots, m$. Then we define the Cauchy number of π, denoted by $N(\pi)$, to be*

$$N(\pi) = (p_1 - 1) + (p_2 - 1) + \cdots + (p_m - 1). \tag{3}$$

By convention, $N(e) = 0$.

Examples 2.2

(a)   If we write $e = (x_1)(x_2) \cdots (x_n)$ where the length p_i of (x_i) is 1, we see that

$$\sum_{i=1}^{n} (p_i - 1) = 0$$

and formula (3) continues to hold even in this trivial situation.

(b) $N((x_1\ x_2 \cdots x_k)) = k - 1$.

(c)   We compute $N(\sigma)$ where $\sigma \in S_8$,

$$\sigma = \begin{pmatrix} 1 & 2 & 3 & 4 & 5 & 6 & 7 & 8 \\ 3 & 5 & 1 & 6 & 4 & 2 & 8 & 7 \end{pmatrix}.$$

Then

$$\sigma = (1\ 3)(2\ 5\ 4\ 6)(7\ 8).$$

Hence

$$N(\sigma) = (2 - 1) + (4 - 1) + (2 - 1)$$

$$= 5.$$

Some simple facts about the Cauchy number can be proved easily.

Theorem 2.2   *Let X be an n element set. Let s, t, $x_1, \ldots, x_m$, $y_1, \ldots, y_r$ be $m + r + 2$ distinct elements of X. Then*

(i) $N((x_1 \, x_2 \cdots x_m)^{-1}) = m - 1$;

(ii) $N((s \, t)(s \, x_1 \, x_2 \cdots x_m \, t \, y_1 \cdots y_r)) = m + r$;

(iii) $N((s \, t)(s \, x_1 \, x_2 \cdots x_m)(t \, y_1 \, y_2 \cdots y_r)) = m + r + 1$;

(iv)   *if $\pi \in X_n$ then $N((s \, t)\pi) = N(\pi) \pm 1$.*

Proof.   To prove (i) we refer to Theorem 1.3 which states that $(x_1 \cdots x_m)^{-1} = (x_m \cdots x_1)$. Thus any cycle and its inverse have the same Cauchy number. To prove (ii) we check that

$$(s \, t)(s \, x_1 \, x_2 \cdots x_m \, t \, y_1 \cdots y_r) = (s \, x_1 \cdots x_m)(t \, y_1 \cdots y_r). \qquad (4)$$

The student should verify (4) by computing what each side of the equality does to the elements s, t, $x_1, \ldots, x_m$, $y_1, \ldots, y_r$. If we multiply (4) on the left by $(s \, t)$ we have

$$(s \, t)(s \, x_1 \cdots x_m)(t \, y_1 \cdots y_r) = (s \, x_1 \cdots x_m \, t \, y_1 \cdots y_r). \qquad (5)$$

The right side of (4) is a product of two disjoint cycles of lengths $m + 1$ and $r + 1$. Hence (ii) follows. Similarly, the right side of (5) is a cycle of length $m + r + 2$ and (iii) follows.

To prove (iv) we must distinguish cases. We first write π as a product of disjoint cycles, $\pi_1, \ldots, \pi_q$. If neither s nor t is involved in any of these disjoint cycles (none of which is the identity), then $(s \, t)\pi$ is the product of disjoint cycles $(s \, t)\pi_1 \cdots \pi_q$. Thus

$$N((s \, t)\pi) = (2 - 1) + (p_1 - 1) + \cdots + (p_q - 1)$$

$$= 1 + N(\pi)$$

where p_i is the length of π_i, $i = 1, \ldots, q$. Next suppose s is involved in one of the π_i and t is not involved in any of them. Since disjoint cycles commute, it follows that we may as well assume that s is involved in π_1; that is, $\pi_1 = (s \, x_2 \cdots x_{p_1})$. Then $(s \, t)(s \, x_2 \cdots x_{p_1}) = (s \, x_2 \cdots x_{p_1} t)$ and

$$(s \, t)\pi = (s \, t)\pi_1 \pi_2 \cdots \pi_q = (s \, x_2 \cdots x_{p_1} t)\pi_2 \cdots \pi_q.$$

Hence $(s \, t)\pi$ is a product of the disjoint cycles $(s \, x_2, \cdots x_{p_1} t)$, $\pi_2 \ldots, \pi_q$:

$$N((s \, t)\pi) = (p_1 + 1 - 1) + (p_2 - 1) + \cdots + (p_m - 1)$$

$$= N(\pi) + 1.$$

If both s and t are involved in the same cycle, π_1, then (4) implies that $N((s \, t)\pi) = N(\pi) - 1$ by reasoning similar to the preceding cases. Also (5) implies that

$$N((s \, t)\pi) = N(\pi) + 1,$$

when s and t are involved in different cycles.

We are now in a position to state and prove the most important facts about factorization of permutations into transpositions.

Theorem 2.3   *Let X be an n element set and assume that $\sigma \in X_n$. Then any factorization of σ into transpositions involves an even or an odd number of transpositions according as $N(\sigma)$ is even or odd. Thus any two factorizations of σ into transpositions must both involve either an even or an odd number of transpositions.*

Proof.   Let $\sigma = \sigma_1 \sigma_2 \cdots \sigma_m$ where σ_i is a transposition. Since $\sigma_i^{-1} = \sigma_i$, $i = 1, \ldots, m$, it follows that $\sigma_m \sigma_{m-1} \cdots \sigma_1 \sigma = e$. By Theorem 2.2(iv) we have

$$
\begin{aligned}
0 = N(e) \\
= N(\sigma_m \sigma_{m-1} \cdots \sigma_1 \sigma) \\
= N(\sigma_{m-1} \cdots \sigma_1 \sigma) \pm 1 \\
= N(\sigma_{m-2} \cdots \sigma_1 \sigma) \pm 1 \pm 1 \\
= \cdots \\
= N(\sigma) + \sum_{i=1}^{m} \varepsilon_i
\end{aligned}
\tag{6}
$$

where ε_i is 1 or -1 for each $i = 1, \ldots, m$. Suppose that p of the ε_i are 1 and q of them are -1. Then $q + p = m$ and

$$
N(\sigma) = q - p
\tag{7}
$$

follows from (6). If $N(\sigma) = q - p$ is even, then $m = q + p = q - p + 2p$ is even. Conversely, if $m = q + p$ is even, then $N(\sigma) = q - p = q + p - 2p$ is even. Hence m is even or odd according as $N(\sigma)$ is even or odd.

Definition 2.3   **(Sign of a permutation)**   *Let X be an n element set and let $\sigma \in X_n$. Then the sign of σ, denoted by $\varepsilon(\sigma)$, is defined by the formula*

$$
\varepsilon(\sigma) = (-1)^{N(\sigma)}.
\tag{8}
$$

In other words, $\varepsilon(\sigma)$ is 1 or -1 according as $N(\sigma)$ is even or odd, that is, according as any factorization of σ into transpositions involves either an even or an odd number of transpositions. We say that σ is even if $\varepsilon(\sigma) = 1$ and σ is odd if $\varepsilon(\sigma) = -1$. The set of even permutations is denoted by A_n and is called the alternating group of degree n.

E XAMPLES 2.3

   (a)   We verify that

$$
\varepsilon(\sigma \mu) = \varepsilon(\sigma)\varepsilon(\mu)
$$

where $\sigma, \mu \in X_n$. For, simply write $\sigma = \sigma_1 \cdots \sigma_m$ and $\mu = \mu_1 \cdots \mu_k$ where the σ_i and μ_j are transpositions. Then $\sigma \mu$ is the product of $m + k$ transpositions.

If both m and k are even, then so is $m + k$. It follows that $\varepsilon(\sigma\mu) = 1$, $\varepsilon(\sigma) = 1$, $\varepsilon(\mu) = 1$, and hence $\varepsilon(\sigma\mu) = \varepsilon(\sigma)\varepsilon(\mu)$. If m is even and k is odd then $m + k$ is odd so $\varepsilon(\sigma\mu) = -1$, $\varepsilon(\sigma) = 1$, $\varepsilon(\mu) = -1$ and $\varepsilon(\sigma\mu) = \varepsilon(\sigma)\varepsilon(\mu)$. A similar argument works when m is odd and k is even. If m and k are both odd then $m + k$ is even, and therefore $\varepsilon(\sigma\mu) = 1$, $\varepsilon(\sigma) = -1$, $\varepsilon(\mu) = -1$ and $\varepsilon(\sigma\mu) = \varepsilon(\sigma)\varepsilon(\mu)$.

(b)   Find $\varepsilon(\sigma)$ for

$$\sigma = \begin{pmatrix} 1 & 2 & 3 & 4 & 6 & 7 & 8 & 9 & 10 \\ 3 & 4 & 6 & 7 & 1 & 9 & 10 & 8 & 2 \end{pmatrix}.$$

We compute that

$$\sigma = (1 \quad 3 \quad 6)(2 \quad 4 \quad 7 \quad 9 \quad 8 \quad 10)$$

and hence $N(\sigma) = 2 + 5 = 7$. Thus $\varepsilon(\sigma) = (-1)^7 = -1$.

(c)   Let $\alpha = (\alpha_1, \ldots, \alpha_m)$ be a sequence of m integers α_i. For any $\sigma \in S_m$ define $\alpha^\sigma = (\alpha_{\sigma(1)}, \alpha_{\sigma(2)}, \ldots, \alpha_{\sigma(m)})$:

(i)   if $\alpha = (3, 3, 4, 3)$ and $\sigma = (1\ 2\ 3\ 4)$ then find α^σ;

(ii)   show that if $\alpha^\sigma = \alpha$ and $\alpha^\mu = \alpha$, σ and μ in S_m, then $\alpha^{\sigma\mu} = \alpha$;

(iii)   if there are k distinct integers in α, find the number of σ in S_m for which $\alpha^\sigma = \alpha$.

In (i), $\alpha_1 = 3$, $\alpha_2 = 3$, $\alpha_3 = 4$, $\alpha_4 = 3$. Then $\alpha_{\sigma(1)} = \alpha_2 = 3$, $\alpha_{\sigma(2)} = \alpha_3 = 4$, $\alpha_{\sigma(3)} = \alpha_4 = 3$, $\alpha_{\sigma(4)} = \alpha_1 = 3$. Thus $\alpha^\sigma = (\alpha_2, \alpha_3, \alpha_4, \alpha_1) = (3, 4, 3, 3)$. To see (ii) observe that $\alpha^\sigma = \alpha = \alpha^\mu$ implies $\alpha_{\sigma(i)} = \alpha_i$, $i = 1, \ldots, m$, $\alpha_{\mu(j)} = \alpha_j$, $j = 1, \ldots, m$. Hence $\alpha_{\sigma\mu(j)} = \alpha_{\sigma(\mu(j))} = \alpha_{\mu(j)} = \alpha_j$, $j = 1, \ldots, m$. In order to answer (iii) suppose that there are k distinct integers $\beta_1, \ldots, \beta_k$ appearing among the integers $\alpha_1, \ldots, \alpha_m$. Assume that β_i appears in positions $p_{i1}, \ldots p_{im_i}$, that is, $\alpha_{p_{ij}} = \beta_i$, $j = 1, \ldots, m_i$, $i = 1, \ldots, k$. Let P_i be the m_i element set consisting of $p_{i1}, \ldots, p_{im_i}$, $i = 1, \ldots, k$. Clearly $\alpha^\sigma = \alpha$ if and only if $\sigma(P_i) = P_i$, $i = 1, \ldots, k$. Now the values of σ on P_i can be specified in $m_i!$ ways to ensure that $\sigma(P_i) = P_i$, $i = 1, \ldots, k$. Thus, altogether there are $m_1! \, m_2! \cdots m_k!$ ways of defining σ in order that it satisfy $\alpha^\sigma = \alpha$.

(d)   For a fixed α, how many different sequences α^σ are obtained as σ varies over S_m? To solve this problem we use the notation of the preceding example. Define a relation $\sim$ on S_m as follows: $\sigma \sim \varphi$ if and only if $\alpha^\sigma = \alpha^\varphi$. Then clearly $\sim$ is an equivalence relation. Let $X_1, \ldots, X_d$ be the equivalence classes induced in S_m. Suppose that $\sigma_i \in X_i$ and $\sigma_j \in X_j$. Then $\alpha^{\sigma_i} \neq \alpha^{\sigma_j}$ if $i \neq j$, and $\alpha^{\sigma_i} = \alpha^{\sigma_j}$ if $i = j$. Thus with each equivalence class we can associate a sequence of the form α^σ in such a way that to different equivalence classes correspond different α^σ and moreover each of the distinct sequences α^σ corresponds to an equivalence class. Let $\alpha^{\sigma_1}, \ldots, \alpha^{\sigma_d}$ denote these d different sequences where $\sigma_j \in X_j$, $j = 1, \ldots, d$. Also let $\beta_1, \ldots, \beta_k$ designate the distinct integers in α (and thus in each of the α^{σ_j}, $j = 1, \ldots, d$). If β_i appears in positions $P_i = \{p_{i1}, \ldots, p_{im_i}\}$ in α then β_i appears in positions $\sigma_j^{-1}(P_i) = \{\sigma_j^{-1}(p_{i1}), \ldots, \sigma_j^{-1}(p_{im_i})\}$ in α^{σ_j}. To see this, note that $\alpha_{\sigma_j(s)} = \beta_i$ if and only if $\sigma_j(s) \in P_i$, that is, if and only if $s \in \sigma_j^{-1}(P_i)$. Now $\sigma \in X_j$ if and only if

$\sigma(\sigma_j^{-1}(P_i)) = \sigma_j^{-1}(P_i)$, $i = 1, \ldots, k$, exactly as we saw in the solution to (c)(iii) above. In other words, $\sigma \in X_j$ if and only if $\sigma_j \sigma \sigma_j^{-1}(P_i) = P_i$, $i = 1, \ldots, k$.

We saw that there are precisely $m_1! \cdots m_k!$ permutations φ for which $\varphi(P_i) = P_i$, $i = 1, \ldots, k$, and thus there are precisely $m_1! \cdots m_k!$ permutations σ such that $\sigma_j \sigma \sigma_j^{-1}(P_i) = P_i$, $i = 1, \ldots, k$. In other words, each X_j contains exactly $m_1! \cdots m_k!$ permutations. Since $\{X_1 \cdots X_d\}$ is a partition of S_m it follows that

$$dm_1! \cdots m_k! = m!.$$

In other words, the number d of distinct sequences of the form α^σ, where σ is in S_m, is given by

$$d = \frac{m!}{m_1! \, m_2! \cdots m_k!}. \tag{9}$$

Quiz

Answer **true** or **false**:

1. $(1 \ 7 \ 9 \ 3) = (1 \ 3)(1 \ 9)(1 \ 7)$.

2. If $\sigma = \begin{pmatrix} 1 & 2 & 3 & 4 & 5 & 6 & 7 & 8 \\ 4 & 5 & 1 & 3 & 8 & 2 & 7 & 6 \end{pmatrix}$ then $\varepsilon(\sigma) = 1$.

3. $\varepsilon(\sigma^2)$ is always 1.

4. $\varepsilon(\sigma^{-1}) = \dfrac{1}{\varepsilon(\sigma)}$.

5. If $\alpha = (3, 7, 10)$ and $\sigma \in S_3$ is the cycle $\sigma = (1 \ 2 \ 3)$ then $\alpha^\sigma = (7, 10, 3)$.

6. If $\sigma \in S_m$ and $\sigma^m = e$ then $\sigma^{-1} = \sigma^{m-1}$.

7. If m is odd then $\varepsilon((1 \ 2 \ 3 \cdots m)) = 1$.

8. If $\alpha = (\alpha_1, \ldots, \alpha_m)$, $\sigma \in S_m$, $\mu \in S_m$ then $\alpha^{\sigma\mu} = (\alpha^\sigma)^\mu$.

9. If $\alpha = (\alpha_1, \ldots, \alpha_m)$, $\sigma \in S_m$, and $\beta = (\beta_1, \ldots, \beta_m) = \alpha^\sigma$ then

$$\sum_{i=1}^{m} \alpha_i = \sum_{i=1}^{m} \beta_i.$$

10. If σ and μ are even and odd permutations in S_m respectively, then $\sigma^5 \mu^{24}$ is even.

Exercises

1. Using 1 twice, 3 five times and 6 eight times, how many 15-digit numbers can be constructed?

2. Let $\alpha_2, \ldots, \alpha_m$ be nonnegative integers for which $2\alpha_2 + \cdots + m\alpha_m = m$. How many permutations $\sigma \in S_m$ are there whose disjoint cycle factorizations have α_i cycles of length i, $i = 2, \ldots, m$?

3. Prove: if $\sigma \in X_m$ and $\sigma = (x_{11} \cdots x_{1m_1}) \cdots (x_{k1} \cdots x_{km_k})$ is the disjoint cycle decomposition of σ, then

$$\varphi \sigma \varphi^{-1} = (\varphi(x_{11}) \cdots \varphi(x_{1m_1})) \cdots (\varphi(x_{k1}) \cdots \varphi(x_{km_k})).$$

4. We use the notation of Example 2.3(c). Let $\sigma = (1\ 2\ 3\ 4\ 5\ 6)$. What is the least positive integer t such that $\alpha^{\sigma^t} = \alpha$ for
    (a) $\alpha = (1, 1, 2, 2, 3, 3)$;
    (b) $\alpha = (1, 1, 2, 1, 1, 2)$;
    (c) $\alpha = (1, 2, 3, 4, 5, 6)$;
    (d) $\alpha = (1, 1, 1, 1, 1, 1)$;
    (e) $\alpha = (1, 2, 3, 3, 2, 1)$?

2.3   Incidence Matrices

In this section we develop the beginnings of a topic of great utility and appeal: incidence matrices. These items are helpful, for example, in dealing with a situation in which we wish to identify the elements belonging to certain subsets. However, we shall begin with a slightly different approach.

EXAMPLE 3.1

Suppose we are given a map showing roads connecting points $x_1, \ldots, x_n$ to points $y_1, \ldots, y_m$. Suppose moreover that between points x_j and y_i there are precisely a_{ij} roads, $i = 1, \ldots, m, j = 1, \ldots, n$. We can tabulate this information as follows. Construct a rectangular $m \times n$ *array* or *matrix* M with m rows and n columns in which a_{ij} appears in row i and column j. Thus

$$M = \begin{array}{c} \\ y_1 \\ y_2 \\ \vdots \\ y_m \end{array} \begin{array}{cccccc} x_1 & x_2 & x_3 & \cdots & x_n \\ \left[\begin{array}{ccccc} a_{11} & a_{12} & a_{13} & \cdots & a_{1n} \\ a_{21} & a_{22} & a_{23} & \cdots & a_{2n} \\ \vdots & & & & \\ a_{m1} & a_{m2} & a_{m3} & \cdots & a_{mn} \end{array} \right] \end{array}. \qquad (1)$$

For example, for $n = 3$, $m = 2$ we could have the map

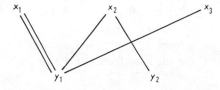

in which there are two roads from x_1 to y_1, one road from x_2 to y_1, one road from x_3 to y_1, no roads from x_1 to y_2, one road from x_2 to y_2 and no roads from x_3 to y_2. This information is neatly summarized by the matrix

$$M = \begin{array}{c} \\ y_1 \\ y_2 \end{array} \begin{array}{ccc} x_1 & x_2 & x_3 \\ \left[\begin{array}{ccc} 2 & 1 & 1 \\ 0 & 1 & 0 \end{array} \right]. \end{array}$$

Suppose now that another map is given in which some points $w_1, \ldots, w_r$ are in turn connected to the points $x_1, \ldots, x_n$. We construct a matrix N of n rows and r columns in which b_{ij}, the number of roads from w_j to x_i, appears in row i and column j:

$$N = \begin{array}{c} \\ x_1 \\ x_2 \\ \vdots \\ x_n \end{array} \begin{array}{cccc} w_1 & w_2 & \cdots & w_r \\ \left[\begin{array}{cccc} b_{11} & b_{12} & \cdots & b_{1r} \\ b_{21} & b_{22} & \cdots & b_{2r} \\ \vdots & & & \\ b_{n1} & b_{n2} & \cdots & b_{nr} \end{array} \right]. \end{array} \qquad (2)$$

For example, for $n = 3$, $r = 4$ we could have

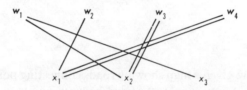

Then

$$N = \begin{array}{c} \\ x_1 \\ x_2 \\ x_3 \end{array} \begin{array}{cccc} w_1 & w_2 & w_3 & w_4 \\ \left[\begin{array}{cccc} 0 & 1 & 0 & 2 \\ 1 & 0 & 2 & 0 \\ 1 & 0 & 0 & 0 \end{array} \right]. \end{array}$$

Now suppose we want to make a trip from point w_j to point y_i through any of the points $x_1, \ldots, x_n$. From w_j we can go to x_1 along any of the b_{1j} paths and from x_1 we can travel to y_i along any of the a_{i1} paths. So altogether we can go from w_j to y_i in $a_{i1}b_{1j}$ ways if we go via x_1. Similarly we can go from w_j to y_i in $a_{ik}b_{kj}$ ways if we go via x_k, $k = 2, \ldots, n$. Hence altogether there are

$$a_{i1}b_{1j} + a_{i2}b_{2j} + a_{i3}b_{3j} + \cdots + a_{in}b_{nj} = \sum_{k=1}^{n} a_{ik}b_{kj} \qquad (3)$$

paths available for going from w_j to y_i, $j = 1, \ldots, r$, $i = 1, \ldots, m$. If we want to make up a matrix C for the map from the w's to the y's we can set

$$c_{ij} = \sum_{k=1}^{n} a_{ik}b_{kj}, \qquad i = 1, \ldots, m, \qquad j = 1, \ldots, r;$$

that is,

$$
C = \begin{array}{c} \\ y_1 \\ \vdots \\ y_m \end{array}
\begin{array}{ccc}
w_1 & w_2 & \cdots \quad w_r \\
\left[\begin{array}{cccc}
\sum\limits_{k=1}^{n} a_{1k}b_{k1} & \sum\limits_{k=1}^{n} a_{1k}b_{k2} & \cdots & \sum\limits_{k=1}^{n} a_{1k}b_{kr} \\
\vdots & \vdots & & \\
\sum\limits_{k=1}^{n} a_{mk}b_{k1} & \sum\limits_{k=1}^{n} a_{mk}b_{k2} & \cdots & \sum\limits_{k=1}^{n} a_{mk}b_{kr}
\end{array}\right].
\end{array}
\tag{4}
$$

To indicate that C is composed of M and N we write $C = MN$ and compute directly from the definition (4) that in our particular example:

$$
C = \begin{bmatrix} 2 & 1 & 1 \\ 0 & 1 & 0 \end{bmatrix}
\begin{bmatrix} 0 & 1 & 0 & 2 \\ 1 & 0 & 2 & 0 \\ 1 & 0 & 0 & 0 \end{bmatrix}
$$

$$
= \begin{bmatrix} 2 & 2 & 2 & 4 \\ 1 & 0 & 2 & 0 \end{bmatrix}.
$$

Thus, for example, there are 2 paths from w_3 to y_2 and 4 paths from w_4 to y_1. Later we shall formally define C to be the product of M and N.

EXAMPLE 3.2

Let X, Y, Z be sets consisting of n, m, and p elements respectively:

$$
X = \{x_1, \ldots, x_n\}; \qquad Y = \{y_1, \ldots, y_m\}; \qquad Z = \{z_1, \ldots, z_p\}.
\tag{5}
$$

Let $f : X \to Y$, $g : Y \to Z$ be functions. Define mn numbers d_{ij} as follows:

$$
d_{ij} = 1 \qquad \text{if } f(x_j) = y_i,
$$

$$
d_{ij} = 0 \qquad \text{if } f(x_j) \neq y_i, \qquad i = 1, \ldots, m, \qquad j = 1, \ldots, n.
$$

We let $A(f)$ denote the matrix or array of these mn numbers:

$$
A(f) = \begin{array}{c} \\ y_1 \\ y_2 \\ \vdots \\ y_m \end{array}
\begin{array}{c}
x_1 \quad x_2 \quad \cdots \quad x_n \\
\left[\begin{array}{cccc}
d_{11} & d_{12} & \cdots & d_{1n} \\
d_{21} & d_{22} & \cdots & d_{2n} \\
\vdots & \vdots & & \\
d_{m1} & d_{m2} & \cdots & d_{mn}
\end{array}\right].
\end{array}
$$

The (i, j) entry is 1 if $f(x_j) = y_i$, otherwise 0. Similarly, construct a matrix $A(g)$ of n columns and p rows where the (i, j) entry of $A(g)$ is defined by

$$
b_{ij} = 1 \qquad \text{if } g(y_j) = z_i,
$$

$$
b_{ij} = 0 \qquad \text{if } g(y_j) \neq z_i, \qquad i = 1, \ldots, p, \quad j = 1, \ldots, m.
$$

Then

$$
A(g) = \begin{array}{c} \\ z_1 \\ z_2 \\ \vdots \\ z_p \end{array}
\overset{\begin{array}{cccc} y_1 & y_2 & \cdots & y_m \end{array}}{
\begin{bmatrix} b_{11} & b_{12} & \cdots & b_{1m} \\ b_{21} & b_{22} & \cdots & b_{2m} \\ \vdots & & & \\ b_{p1} & b_{p2} & \cdots & b_{pm} \end{bmatrix}}.
$$

Suppose we consider the composition of the two functions: $h = gf : X \rightarrow Z$. Let us also construct the corresponding matrix $A(h)$ for the composed function. If we let c_{ij} be the (i, j) entry of $A(h)$ then

$$c_{ij} = 1 \qquad \text{if } h(x_j) = z_i,$$

$$c_{ij} = 0 \qquad \text{if } h(x_j) \neq z_i, \qquad i = 1, \ldots, p, \ j = 1, \ldots, n.$$

Now $c_{ij} = 1$ (that is, $h(x_j) = z_i$) means that $g(f(x_j)) = z_i$. In other words, $f(x_j)$ must be one of those y_t for which $g(y_t) = z_i$. Hence, $c_{ij} = 1$ if and only if there exists an integer t such that both $b_{it} = 1$ and $d_{tj} = 1$. Since f is a function it now follows that if $d_{tj} = 1$, i.e., $f(x_j) = y_t$, then $d_{sj} = 0$; that is $f(x_j) \neq y_s$, for any $s \neq t$. Thus

$$c_{ij} = 1 = b_{it}d_{tj} = \sum_{k=1}^{m} b_{ik}d_{kj}. \tag{6}$$

On the other hand, suppose $c_{ij} = 0$. Then $h(x_j) \neq z_i$, that is, $g(f(x_j)) \neq z_i$. This means that whenever $g(y_t) = z_i$, that is, $b_{it} = 1$, then $f(x_j) \neq y_t$; that is, $d_{tj} = 0$. In other words,

$$c_{ij} = 0 = \sum_{k=1}^{m} b_{ik}d_{kj}. \tag{7}$$

Combining (6) and (7) we see that for all i, j

$$c_{ij} = \sum_{k=1}^{m} b_{ik}d_{kj}. \tag{8}$$

If we use the same notation as in the preceding example we can write

$$A(gf) = A(g)A(f). \tag{9}$$

Definition 3.1 (Matrix product) *Let M and N be $m \times n$ and $n \times r$ matrices respectively*:

$$
M = \begin{bmatrix} a_{11} & a_{12} & \cdots & a_{1n} \\ a_{21} & a_{22} & \cdots & a_{2n} \\ \vdots & & & \\ a_{m1} & a_{m2} & \cdots & a_{mn} \end{bmatrix};
$$

$$
N = \begin{bmatrix} b_{11} & b_{12} & \cdots & b_{1r} \\ b_{21} & b_{22} & \cdots & b_{2r} \\ \vdots & & & \\ b_{n1} & b_{n2} & \cdots & b_{nr} \end{bmatrix}.
$$

Then the product of M and N, written MN, is the $m \times r$ matrix whose (i, j) entry is

$$c_{ij} = \sum_{k=1}^{n} a_{ik}b_{kj}, \qquad i = 1,\dots, m, \qquad j = 1,\dots, r. \tag{10}$$

It is easy to show (see Exercise 2) that the *associative* law for matrix multiplication holds, that is,

$$M(NP) = (MN)P.$$

Definition 3.2   (Incidence matrix for a function) *Let $f: X \to Y$ be a function on an n element set X to an m element set Y:*

$$X = \{x_1, \dots, x_n\}; \qquad Y = \{y_1, \dots, y_m\}.$$

The $m \times n$ array or matrix whose (i, j) entry is 1 if $f(x_j) = y_i$ and 0 if $f(x_j) \neq y_i$ is called the incidence matrix of f. It is denoted by $A(f)$.

We proved the following result in the course of Example 3.2.

Theorem 3.1 *If $f: X \to Y, g: Y \to Z$ are mappings, where $X = \{x_1, \dots, x_n\}$, $Y = \{y_1, \dots, y_m\}, Z = \{z_1, \dots z_p\}$, then*

$$A(gf) = A(g)A(f). \tag{11}$$

EXAMPLE 3.3

Let $X = \{x_1, x_2, x_3\}$. Let $f: X \to X$ be given by $f(x_1) = x_2, f(x_2) = x_3, f(x_3) = x_1$. Find the incidence matrix for f^2 using (11). We compute $A(f)$ and then use (10) to obtain $A(f)A(f) = A(f^2)$. Since $f(x_1) = x_2$, $f(x_2) = x_3$ and $f(x_3) = x_1$ we have

$$A(f) = \begin{bmatrix} 0 & 0 & 1 \\ 1 & 0 & 0 \\ 0 & 1 & 0 \end{bmatrix}.$$

Then

$$A(f^2) = A(f)A(f) = \begin{bmatrix} 0 & 0 & 1 \\ 1 & 0 & 0 \\ 0 & 1 & 0 \end{bmatrix}\begin{bmatrix} 0 & 0 & 1 \\ 1 & 0 & 0 \\ 0 & 1 & 0 \end{bmatrix}$$

$$= \begin{bmatrix} 0 & 1 & 0 \\ 0 & 0 & 1 \\ 1 & 0 & 0 \end{bmatrix}.$$

We can compute directly that $f^2(x_1) = x_3$, $f^2(x_2) = x_1$, $f^2(x_3) = x_2$ and hence

$$A(f^2) = \begin{bmatrix} 0 & 1 & 0 \\ 0 & 0 & 1 \\ 1 & 0 & 0 \end{bmatrix}$$

which agrees with the preceding computation.

EXAMPLE 3.4

If $X = \{x_1, x_2, x_3\}$, can the matrix

$$A = \begin{bmatrix} 1 & 0 & 1 \\ 1 & 0 & 0 \\ 0 & 1 & 0 \end{bmatrix}$$

be an incidence matrix of some function $f : X \to X$? The answer here is "no." For, if the $(1, 1)$ entry and the $(2, 1)$ entry are both 1, this would mean that $f(x_1) = x_1$ and $f(x_1) = x_2$, an impossibility.

EXAMPLE 3.5

If $X = \{x_1, \ldots, x_n\}$ then how do we describe the incidence matrix $A(e)$ where $e : X \to X$ is the identity mapping? To answer this we simply observe that $e(x_j) = x_j$ and hence the (j, j) entry of $A(e)$ is 1 and the (i, j) entry is 0 if $i \neq j$. Thus

$$A(e) = \begin{bmatrix} 1 & 0 & \cdots & 0 \\ 0 & 1 & & \vdots \\ \vdots & & \ddots & \vdots \\ & & & 1 & 0 \\ 0 & \cdots & & 0 & 1 \end{bmatrix}.$$

The matrix $A(e)$ is called the $n \times n$ (or n-square) *identity matrix* and is denoted by I_n.

We distinguish a particular class of incidence matrices.

Definition 3.3 (Permutation matrix) *If* $X = \{x_1, \ldots, x_n\}$ *and* $\sigma \in X_n$, *that is,* σ *is a permutation of X, then the* $n \times n$ *incidence matrix* $A(\sigma)$ *is called a permutation matrix.*

Theorem 3.2 *If* $A(\sigma)$ *is a permutation matrix then* $A(\sigma)$ *has precisely one 1 in each row and each column.*

Proof. Let a_{ij} designate the (i, j) entry of $A(\sigma)$ and suppose $a_{ij} = a_{ik} = 1$. Then $\sigma(x_j) = x_i$, $\sigma(x_k) = x_i$. Since σ is a permutation, it follows that $j = k$. On the other hand, since σ is a function, $a_{ij} = a_{kj} = 1$ implies that $\sigma(x_j) = x_i$ and $\sigma(x_j) = x_k$ and hence that $i = k$. In other words, each row and each column of $A(\sigma)$ possesses exactly one 1.

Theorem 3.3 *The product of two permutation matrices is a permutation matrix.*

Proof. The argument here is quite simple. For, if σ and μ are in X_n then $\sigma\mu$ is in X_n and by (11) we have

$$A(\sigma)A(\mu) = A(\sigma\mu);$$

that is, $A(\sigma)A(\mu)$ is a permutation matrix.

Definition 3.4   (Transpose)   *If A is an m × n matrix then the n × m matrix whose (i, j) entry is the (j, i) entry of A, i = 1, ..., n, j = 1, ..., m, is called the transpose of A and is denoted by A^T.*

Another simple result can be proved by essentially the same techniques.

Theorem 3.4   *If $\sigma \in X_n$ then*

$$A(\sigma)A(\sigma^{-1}) = A(\sigma^{-1})A(\sigma) = I_n. \tag{12}$$

Moreover,

$$A(\sigma^{-1}) = (A(\sigma))^T. \tag{13}$$

Proof.   As we saw in Theorem 3.1,

$$A(\sigma)A(\sigma^{-1}) = A(\sigma\sigma^{-1}) = A(e) = I_n.$$

Similarly,

$$A(\sigma^{-1})A(\sigma) = A(\sigma^{-1}\sigma) = A(e) = I_n.$$

The (i, j) entry of the matrix $A(\sigma^{-1})$ is

$$\begin{cases} 1, & \text{if } \sigma^{-1}(x_j) = x_i, \\ 0, & \text{if } \sigma^{-1}(x_j) \neq x_i; \end{cases}$$

i.e., it is

$$\begin{cases} 1, & \text{if } \sigma(x_i) = x_j, \\ 0, & \text{if } \sigma(x_i) \neq x_j. \end{cases}$$

In other words, the (i, j) entry of $A(\sigma^{-1})$ is 1 or 0 according as $\sigma(x_i) = x_j$ or not. But this is precisely the definition of the (j, i) entry of $A(\sigma)$, that is, the (i, j) entry of $(A(\sigma))^T$. This proves (13).

In our next example we shall motivate another important operation between matrices.

EXAMPLE 3.6

Suppose $X = \{x_1, \ldots, x_n\}$ and $Y = \{y_1, \ldots, y_m\}$ are two sets, and f and g are functions on X to Y. Suppose that we want to write down a matrix that tells us whether y_i appears as the value $f(x_j)$, or the value $g(x_j)$, or appears as both or neither. Let S be an $m \times n$ matrix whose (i, j) entry is the sum of the (i, j) entries of $A(f)$ and $A(g)$. Let s_{ij} denote the (i, j) entry of S. If $s_{ij} = 0$ we know that neither $f(x_j) = y_i$ nor $g(x_j) = y_i$. If $s_{ij} = 1$ then either $f(x_j) = y_i$ or $g(x_j) = y_i$, but not both. If $s_{ij} = 2$ then both $f(x_j) = y_i$ and $g(x_j) = y_i$.

Definition 3.5   (Sum of two matrices)   *If M and N are two m × n matrices then the m × n matrix S whose (i, j) entry is the sum of the (i, j) entries of M and N is called the sum of M and N. The matrix S is written*

$$S = M + N.$$

It is clear from this definition that matrix addition is associative:

$$M + (N + P) = (M + N) + P.$$

We write the common value as $M + N + P$.

EXAMPLES 3.7

(a) If $\sigma \in S_3$ and $\sigma = (1\ 2\ 3)$ then find

$$S = A(\sigma) + A(\sigma^2) + A(\sigma^3).$$

We compute that

$$A(\sigma) = \begin{bmatrix} 0 & 0 & 1 \\ 1 & 0 & 0 \\ 0 & 1 & 0 \end{bmatrix}, \qquad A(\sigma^2) = \begin{bmatrix} 0 & 1 & 0 \\ 0 & 0 & 1 \\ 1 & 0 & 0 \end{bmatrix},$$

$$A(\sigma^3) = \begin{bmatrix} 1 & 0 & 0 \\ 0 & 1 & 0 \\ 0 & 0 & 1 \end{bmatrix}.$$

Then

$$S = \begin{bmatrix} 1 & 1 & 1 \\ 1 & 1 & 1 \\ 1 & 1 & 1 \end{bmatrix}.$$

(b) Can

$$\begin{bmatrix} 1 & 1 & 1 \\ 1 & 1 & 1 \\ 0 & 0 & 0 \end{bmatrix}$$

be a sum of incidence matrices of functions at least one of which is a permutation? The answer is "no" because $A(\sigma)$ must always have a 1 somewhere in every row.

A general question arises: when is a matrix consisting of nonnegative integer entries a sum of incidence matrices at least one of which is a permutation matrix? This question will occupy our attention next.

Definition 3.6   (Diagonals)   *Let A be an $n \times n$ matrix whose (i, j) entry is a_{ij}, $i, j = 1, \ldots, n$. Let $\sigma \in S_n$. Then the diagonal of A corresponding to σ is the following sequence of n entries of A:*

$$\{a_{1\sigma(1)}, a_{2\sigma(2)}, \ldots, a_{n\sigma(n)}\}.$$

EXAMPLE 3.8

If A is a 2×2 matrix of 0's and 1's and every diagonal has a zero in it then what are the possibilities for A? They are

$$\begin{bmatrix} 1 & 0 \\ 0 & 0 \end{bmatrix}, \begin{bmatrix} 1 & 1 \\ 0 & 0 \end{bmatrix}, \begin{bmatrix} 0 & 0 \\ 1 & 0 \end{bmatrix}, \begin{bmatrix} 0 & 0 \\ 1 & 1 \end{bmatrix}, \begin{bmatrix} 1 & 0 \\ 1 & 0 \end{bmatrix}, \begin{bmatrix} 0 & 1 \\ 0 & 1 \end{bmatrix},$$

$$\begin{bmatrix} 0 & 1 \\ 0 & 0 \end{bmatrix}, \begin{bmatrix} 0 & 0 \\ 0 & 1 \end{bmatrix}, \begin{bmatrix} 0 & 0 \\ 0 & 0 \end{bmatrix}.$$

EXAMPLE 3.9

Show by example that if every diagonal of an $n \times n$ matrix A has a 0 in it, it does not follow that A must have a row or column of zeros. To see this, take $n = 3$ and consider the matrix

$$\begin{bmatrix} 0 & 0 & 1 \\ 0 & 0 & 1 \\ 1 & 1 & 1 \end{bmatrix}.$$

We want to find out what happens to the diagonals of a matrix if it is multiplied by a permutation matrix. To answer this we first prove:

Theorem 3.5   *Let P be an $n \times n$ matrix and let σ and φ be in S_n. Then the ith row of P is the row numbered $\sigma(i)$ of $A(\sigma)P$. The jth column of P is the column numbered $\varphi^{-1}(j)$ of $PA(\varphi)$. The (i, j) entry of $A(\sigma)PA(\varphi)$ is p_{st} where $s = \sigma^{-1}(i)$ and $t = \varphi(j)$.*

Proof.   By the Definition 3.1 the ith row of $A(\sigma)P$ is

$$\left(\sum_{j=1}^{n} a_{ij}p_{j1}, \sum_{j=1}^{n} a_{ij}p_{j2}, \ldots, \sum_{j=1}^{n} a_{ij}p_{jn} \right)$$

where a_{ij} and p_{jk} are the (i, j) and (j, k) entries of $A(\sigma)$ and P respectively. Now $a_{ij} = 0$ unless $\sigma(j) = i$ in which case it is 1. That is,

$$a_{ij} = \delta_{i,\sigma(j)}.$$

Hence

$$\sum_{j=1}^{n} a_{ij}p_{jk} = \sum_{j=1}^{n} \delta_{i,\sigma(j)}p_{jk} = P_{\sigma^{-1}(i),k}.$$

Hence the ith row of $A(\sigma)P$ is

$$(p_{\sigma^{-1}(i),1}, p_{\sigma^{-1}(i),2}, \ldots, p_{\sigma^{-1}(i),n}),$$

i.e., it is row numbered $\sigma^{-1}(i)$ of P. Equivalently, the ith row of P is row numbered $\sigma(i)$ of $A(\sigma)P$. Similarly the jth column of $PA(\varphi)$ is

$$(\sum_{k=1}^{n} p_{1k}a_{kj}, \sum_{k=1}^{n} p_{2k}a_{kj}, \ldots, \sum_{k=1}^{n} p_{nk}a_{kj}).$$

But $a_{kj} = \delta_{k,\varphi(j)}$, so

$$\sum_{k=1}^{n} p_{ik}a_{kj} = \sum_{k=1}^{n} p_{ik}\delta_{k,\varphi(j)} = p_{i\varphi(j)}.$$

Thus the jth column of $PA(\varphi)$ is

$$(p_{1\varphi(j)}, p_{2\varphi(j)}, \ldots, p_{n\varphi(j)}),$$

i.e., it is column numbered $\varphi(j)$ of P. Equivalently, the jth column of P is column numbered $\varphi^{-1}(j)$ of $PA(\varphi)$.

The (i, j) entry of $A(\sigma)PA(\varphi)$ must lie in row numbered $\sigma^{-1}(i)$ of P and column numbered $\varphi(j)$ of P; that is, it must be p_{st} where $s = \sigma^{-1}(i)$ and $t = \varphi(j)$.

EXAMPLE 3.10

If

$$P = \begin{bmatrix} p_{11} & p_{12} & p_{13} \\ p_{21} & p_{22} & p_{23} \\ p_{31} & p_{32} & p_{33} \end{bmatrix},$$

what is $A(\sigma)PA(\varphi)$ where $\sigma = (1\ 2)$ and $\varphi = (1\ 2\ 3)$? The answer provided by Theorem 3.5 is obtained by shifting the rows of P according to $\sigma^{-1} = (1\ 2)$ and shifting the columns of the resulting matrix according to φ. Thus

$$A(\sigma)PA(\varphi) = \begin{bmatrix} p_{21} & p_{22} & p_{23} \\ p_{11} & p_{12} & p_{13} \\ p_{31} & p_{32} & p_{33} \end{bmatrix} A(\varphi)$$

$$= \begin{bmatrix} p_{22} & p_{23} & p_{21} \\ p_{12} & p_{13} & p_{11} \\ p_{32} & p_{33} & p_{31} \end{bmatrix}.$$

Theorem 3.6 *If P is an $n \times n$ matrix and σ and φ are in S_n then the diagonals of $B = A(\sigma)PA(\varphi)$ are the same to within order as the diagonals of P.*

Proof. The diagonal of B corresponding to $\theta \in S_n$ is the sequence

$$\{b_{1\theta(1)}, \ldots, b_{n\theta(n)}\}.$$

However, we know from Theorem 3.5 that

$$b_{ij} = p_{\sigma^{-1}(i),\varphi(j)}, \qquad i,j = 1,\ldots,n,$$

and hence

$$b_{i\theta(i)} = p_{\sigma^{-1}(i),\varphi\theta(i)}, \qquad i = 1,\ldots,n.$$

Now, as i runs through $1,\ldots,n$ so does $t = \sigma^{-1}(i)$. Thus the diagonal $\{b_{1\theta(1)},\ldots,b_{n\theta(n)}\}$ is the same to within order as the following diagonal of P:

$$\{p_{1,\varphi\theta\sigma(1)}, p_{2,\varphi\theta\sigma(2)},\ldots, p_{n,\varphi\theta\sigma(n)}\}.$$

Moreover, as θ runs through S_n, $\varphi\theta\sigma$ runs through S_n precisely once. Thus the diagonals of B can be obtained from those of P by a reordering.

We will use Theorem 3.6 in the following way: given that every diagonal of P contains the number 0 then every diagonal of B must contain 0 as well.

Our next result is a very interesting and important combinatorial fact that will allow us to solve a number of difficult problems.

Theorem 3.7   (Frobenius-König theorem)   *Let P be an $n \times n$ matrix whose entries are all 0 or 1. If every diagonal of P contains a 0 then there exist s rows of P and t columns of P such that the st entries lying in the intersection of these rows and columns are all 0, and*

$$s + t = n + 1. \tag{14}$$

Proof.   This proof is by induction on n. For $n = 1$ the matrix P must be the 1×1 matrix $[0]$. Also $1 + 1 = 2$. Assume then that the result is true for all $k \times k$ matrices, $k \le n - 1$. Now if every entry of P is 0 the proof is obviously finished. Thus assume that some entry is 1. By permuting the rows and columns of P we can bring this 1 into the (n,n) position. According to Theorem 3.6 the diagonals of P are merely reordered in this process. Thus we may assume that P looks like

$$P = \begin{bmatrix} * & \cdots & * & * \\ \vdots & & & \vdots \\ * & & & * \\ * & \cdots & * & 1 \end{bmatrix}, \qquad (* \text{ indicates unspecified entries}).$$

Let Q denote the $(n-1) \times (n-1)$ matrix lying in rows and columns $1,\ldots, n-1$ in the above matrix. Any diagonal of Q can be extended to a diagonal of P by adjoining the 1 in the (n,n) position. Thus every diagonal of Q must contain a 0 and, by the induction hypothesis, we can find s_1 rows and t_1 columns of Q such that $s_1 + t_1 = (n-1) + 1$ and the $s_1 t_1$ entries lying in the intersections of these rows and columns are all 0. Once again we can permute the rows and columns of P so that these $s_1 t_1$ zero entries appear in the first s_1 rows and t_1 columns and another application of Theorem 3.6 assures us that every diagonal still contains a zero. Thus we can assume that P looks like this:

$$
\begin{array}{c}
\overbrace{\qquad}^{t_1} \quad \overbrace{\qquad}^{n-t_1} \\
s_1\left\{ \ \ \begin{array}{c} n-s_1\left\{ \ \ \end{array} \right.
\begin{bmatrix}
0 & 0 & \cdots & 0 & & & \\
0 & 0 & \cdots & 0 & & X & \\
\vdots & \vdots & \cdots & \vdots & & & \\
\vdots & \vdots & \cdots & \vdots & & & \\
0 & 0 & \cdots & 0 & & & \\
& & & * & \cdots & * & * \\
& Y & & \vdots & & & \vdots \\
& & & * & & & * \\
& & & * & \cdots & * & 1
\end{bmatrix}
\end{array}
\tag{15}
$$

Now neither $n - s_1$ nor $n - t_1$ can be zero because s_1 and t_1 are positive integers and $s_1 + t_1 = n$. Since $n - s_1 = t_1$ and $n - t_1 = s_1$, it follows that X, the upper right block in (15), is $s_1 \times s_1$ and Y, the lower left block, is $t_1 \times t_1$. Assume for the moment that Y possesses a diagonal consisting of 1's; we can complete it with any diagonal of X to obtain a diagonal of P which must by assumption contain a zero. Thus every diagonal of X must contain a zero and the induction hypothesis tells us that X contains s_2 rows and t_2 columns at whose $s_2 t_2$ intersections zeros appear, and $s_2 + t_2 = s_1 + 1$. Now put these zeros in the first s_2 rows and t_2 columns of X by permuting rows $1, \ldots, s_1$ and columns $t_1 + 1, \ldots, n$ of P. This results in the matrix

$$
\begin{array}{c}
\overbrace{\qquad}^{t_1} \quad \overbrace{\qquad}^{t_2} \\
s_1\left\{ \ \ \begin{array}{c} n-s_1\left\{ \ \ \end{array} \right.
\begin{bmatrix}
0 & 0 & \cdots & 0 & 0 & \cdots & 0 & & * \\
0 & 0 & \cdots & 0 & \cdots & & \cdots & \Big\} s_2 & \vdots \\
\vdots & \vdots & & \vdots & 0 & \cdots & 0 & & \vdots \\
0 & 0 & \cdots & 0 & * & \cdot & \cdot & \cdot & * \\
& & & & * & \cdot & \cdot & \cdot & * \\
& Y & & & \vdots & & & & \vdots \\
& & & & * & \cdot & \cdot & \cdot & *
\end{bmatrix}
\end{array}
\tag{16}
$$

Now consider the elements lying in the first s_2 rows and first $t_1 + t_2$ columns of the matrix in (16). These are clearly all zero. Moreover,

$$
s_2 + (t_1 + t_2) = (s_2 + t_2) + t_1
$$

$$
= s_1 + 1 + t_1
$$

$$
= (s_1 + t_1) + 1
$$

$$
= n + 1.
$$

Thus in the event that Y contains a diagonal of 1's the induction can be completed. If on the other hand every diagonal of Y has a zero in it, then we can apply the induction hypothesis to Y and complete the induction step in precisely the same way.

Quiz

Answer **true** or **false**:

1. The matrix $\begin{bmatrix} 0 & 1 \\ 1 & 1 \end{bmatrix}$ is the incidence matrix of a function.

2. The product of a 3×4 and a 4×3 matrix is not defined.

3. If $A(\sigma)$ is the incidence matrix of the permutation $\sigma \in S_n$ then $(A(\sigma))^n = I_n$.

4. The function $f : S_n \to P_n$, $f(\sigma) = A(\sigma)$, where S_n is the symmetric group of degree n and P_n is the set of all $n \times n$ permutation matrices, is 1-1 and onto.

5. If the first row of a matrix A consists of zeros then the first row of AB consists of zeros.

6. If the first column of a matrix M consists of zeros then the first column of MN consists of zeros.

7. If A is an $n \times n$ matrix in which every entry is 1 or 2 and every diagonal of A contains a 2 then the sum of all the entries of A is at least $n^2 + n$.

8. If $A(\sigma)$ is an $n \times n$ permutation matrix then the sum of the entries in row i of $PA(\sigma)$ is the same as the sum of the entries in row i of P, $i = 1, \ldots, n$. Here P is an $n \times n$ matrix with real entries.

9. Under the same conditions as the preceding question: the sum of the entries in column j of $A(\sigma)P$ is the same as the sum of the entries in column j of P, $j = 1, \ldots, n$.

10. If $A(\sigma)$ is an $n \times n$ permutation matrix $(n \geq 3)$ and $A(\sigma)A(\varphi) = A(\varphi)A(\sigma)$ for all $\varphi \in S_n$ then $\sigma = e$. (*Hint:* See Exercise 3, Section 1.)

Exercises

1. Let A be a 3×3 matrix in which every element is 0 or 1 and the sum of the entries in each row and column is 2. Show that A contains a diagonal consisting of 1's.

2. If A is $m \times n$, B is $n \times p$, and C is $p \times q$, prove the associative law for matrix multiplication:
$$(AB)C = A(BC).$$

(*Hint:* Compare the (i, j) entries of both expressions.)

3. If A is $m \times n$ and B and C are $n \times p$ then prove the left distributive law for matrix multiplication:
$$A(B + C) = AB + AC.$$

4. If B and C are $n \times p$ and A is $p \times q$ prove the right distributive law for matrix multiplication:

$$(B + C)A = BA + CA.$$

5. Can the matrix

$$\begin{bmatrix} 1 & 0 & 1 \\ 1 & 0 & 1 \\ 1 & 1 & 0 \end{bmatrix}$$

be written as a sum of 3×3 permutation matrices? Why?

6. Can the matrix

$$S = \begin{bmatrix} 1 & 1 & 1 \\ 1 & 1 & 1 \\ 0 & 0 & 1 \end{bmatrix}$$

be written as a sum of two incidence matrices for functions f and g, i.e., is $S = A(f) + A(g)$?

7. Compute the entries of AJ where J is the $n \times n$ matrix each of whose entries is 1 and A is an arbitrary $n \times n$ matrix.

8. With the same notation as in the preceding exercise compute the entries in JA.

9. Let f be the function $f(\sigma) = A(\sigma)$ which associates with each permutation σ in S_n the $n \times n$ permutation matrix $A(\sigma)$. Order the elements of S_n in some fashion and do the same for the set of $n \times n$ permutation matrices. How many rows are there in the incidence matrix for f?

10. How many $n \times n$ matrices are there with precisely one 1 and $n - 1$ zeros in each column?

11. If A is an $m \times n$ matrix and c is a number, let $cA\ (= Ac)$ be the matrix obtained from A by multiplying each entry of A by c. Show that

$$(cd)A = c(dA);$$

$$(c + d)A = cA + dA;$$

$$1A = A;$$

$$c(A + B) = cA + cB \quad (B \text{ is } m \times n \text{ also}).$$

12. State and prove the converse of Theorem 3.7.

2.4 Birkhoff's Theorem

In this section we shall study an important class of matrices for which there exists a more or less complete structure theory. We use the following notation (see Exercise 11 in the preceding section): if A is a matrix and c is a number then cA denotes the matrix obtained from A by multiplying each entry of A by c.

Definition 4.1   (Doubly stochastic matrix)   *Let A be an $n \times n$ matrix in which every entry a_{ij} is a nonnegative real number. If the sum of the entries in each row and in each column is 1 then A is said to be doubly stochastic. In other words, a doubly stochastic matrix A satisfies*

$$a_{ij} \geq 0, \qquad i, j = 1, \ldots, n, \tag{1}$$

$$\sum_{j=1}^{n} a_{ij} = 1, \qquad i = 1, \ldots, n, \tag{2}$$

$$\sum_{i=1}^{n} a_{ij} = 1, \qquad j = 1, \ldots, n. \tag{3}$$

EXAMPLE 4.1

Let $X = \{x_1, \ldots, x_n\}$ be an n element set and let $X_1, \ldots, X_n$ be n subsets of X each containing k of the elements of X. Assume also that each x_i belongs to exactly k of the subsets $X_1, \ldots, X_n$. Let A be an $n \times n$ matrix whose (i, j) entry is 1 or 0 according as $x_j \in X_i$ or $x_j \notin X_i$. Then we claim that the matrix $S = (1/k)A$ is doubly stochastic. If we look at the jth column of A, then (since x_j is in precisely k of the sets X_i) it follows that there are k ones and $(n - k)$ zeros in this column. Thus the sum of the entries in the jth column of A is k. Similarly, a given subset X_i contains exactly k of the elements $x_1, \ldots, x_n$ and thus there are precisely k ones and $n - k$ zeros in row i of A. Hence the sum of the entries in the ith row of A is also k. It follows that $S = (1/k)A$ is doubly stochastic.

EXAMPLE 4.2   (Dance problem)

Suppose that at a school dance there are n boys, $b_1, \ldots, b_n$, and n girls, $g_1, \ldots, g_n$. Assume that each boy has previously met exactly k girls and each girl has previously met exactly k boys. Is it possible to pair off the boys and girls into dance partners who were introduced before the dance? To begin this problem let A be an $n \times n$ matrix whose (i, j) entry is 1 if b_j has met g_i and 0 if b_j has not met g_i. Then let $S = (1/k)A$. Once again, each column of A contains precisely k ones because each boy has met k girls. Similarly, each row of A contains k ones because each girl has met k boys. Thus S is doubly stochastic. The question now is whether S (or equivalently A) contains a diagonal of nonzero entries. For suppose $a_{i\sigma(i)} = 1$, $i = 1, \ldots, n$, for some $\sigma \in S_n$. This would mean that $(g_1, b_{\sigma(1)}), (g_2, b_{\sigma(2)}), \ldots, (g_n, b_{\sigma(n)})$ would be a pairing of boys and girls who had met. We shall defer the proof of the existence of such a σ until later in this section.

EXAMPLE 4.3

Each of n cities $c_1, \ldots, c_n$ produces k dollars worth of goods which are sold among the n cities. Moreover, each city in turn buys precisely k dollars worth of the goods produced by the n cities. Does there exist a pairing of the n cities $(c_1, c_{\sigma(1)}), (c_2, c_{\sigma(2)}), \ldots, (c_n, c_{\sigma(n)})$ in which $c_{\sigma(j)}$ sells to $c_j, j = 1, \ldots, n$? Once again the approach to this question is to set up the appropriate incidence matrix. Let A be an $n \times n$ matrix in which a_{ij} is the number of dollars worth of goods that city c_j sells to city c_i. Then

$$\sum_{j=1}^{n} a_{ij}$$

represents the total amount of sales made by cities $c_1, \ldots, c_n$ to city c_i. This is k by assumption. Similarly

$$\sum_{i=1}^{n} a_{ij}$$

is the total amount that city c_j sells to all the cities $c_1, \ldots, c_n$. Again this is k. Thus $S = (1/k)A$ is a doubly stochastic matrix and the problem once more reduces to finding a diagonal of S (or A) which consists of positive elements. We must defer the solution of this problem until later.

Definition 4.2 (Permanent) *Let A be any $n \times n$ matrix. The number*

$$\sum_{\sigma \in S_n} \prod_{i=1}^{n} a_{i\sigma(i)} \tag{4}$$

is called the permanent of A. It is denoted by per (A).

The permanent can thus be thought of as a function whose domain is the set of $n \times n$ real matrices and whose range is the set of real numbers. Notice that per (A) is the sum of all $n!$ products obtained by multiplying together the elements in each of the $n!$ diagonals of A. Also observe that if A is a matrix with nonnegative entries then per (A) is positive if and only if there exists a diagonal of A consisting of positive elements. For if per $(A) > 0$ then some term $\prod_{i=1}^{n} a_{i\sigma(i)}$ in (4) must be positive. This means that $a_{i\sigma(i)}$ is positive for $i = 1, \ldots, n$.

EXAMPLE 4 4

Let J be the $n \times n$ matrix each of whose entries is 1. What is the value of per (J)? To answer this observe that every diagonal product has value 1 and there are $n!$ such products. Thus per (J), which is the sum of all $n!$ of these products, has value $n!$

EXAMPLE 4.5

With reference to the "dance problem" in Example 4.2, give an interpretation to the number per (A). We examine a typical product $\prod_{i=1}^{n} a_{i\sigma(i)}$. It is 1 if and only if $a_{1\sigma(1)} = \cdots = a_{n\sigma(n)} = 1$. This means that $(g_1, b_{\sigma(1)}),\ldots,$ $(g_n, b_{\sigma(n)})$ is a pairing of girls and boys who have met. Hence per (A) is just the total number of such pairings and the question in Example 4.2 is equivalent to asking if per (A) is positive.

Our first result will be an application of the Frobenius-König Theorem (Theorem 3.7), and will answer the question posed in Example 4.2 in the affirmative.

Theorem 4.1 *Let A be an $n \times n$ doubly stochastic matrix. Then there exists a diagonal of A consisting of positive entries.*

Proof. The entries of A are either zero or positive. Let us construct a matrix S whose (i, j) entry is 1 if $a_{ij} > 0$, and 0 if $a_{ij} = 0$. Thus S and A have zero entries and nonzero entries in precisely the same places. Now suppose no diagonal of A consists exclusively of positive entries. Then every diagonal of A (and hence of S) must contain a zero. By Theorem 3.7 this implies that for both A and S there exist s rows and t columns, $s + t = n + 1$, such that the st entries lying in the intersections of these rows and columns are all zero. Hence by suitable permutation of the rows and columns of A we may bring it to the following form:

$$
\begin{array}{c}
 \\
s \left\{ \vphantom{\begin{array}{c} 0 \\ \cdot \\ 0 \end{array}} \right. \\
 \\
n-s \left\{ \vphantom{B} \right.
\end{array}
\overset{\displaystyle \overbrace{}^{t} \quad \overbrace{}^{n-t}}{
\left[
\begin{array}{ccc|c}
0 & \cdots & 0 & \\
\cdot & \cdots & \cdot & D \\
0 & \cdots & 0 & \\
\hline
\multicolumn{3}{c|}{B} & C
\end{array}
\right]}
\tag{5}
$$

Now let b, c, d be the sums of the entries in B, C, and D respectively. We first remark that the matrix in (5) was obtained from A by a permutation of rows and columns and hence its row and column sums must still be 1. Thus, since D has s rows, it follows that $d = s$; and similarly, since B has t columns, that $b = t$. The sum of all the entries in the matrix (5) must be n because every row sum is 1. Thus, $b + d + c = n$. But $b = t$ and $d = s$ and thus, $b + d = s + t = n + 1$. Hence $c = n - (n + 1) = -1$. This is a contradiction because the entries of A and C are nonnegative.

Our next result is a corollary of Theorem 4.1.

Theorem 4.2 (Birkhoff's Theorem) *Let A be an $n \times n$ doubly stochastic matrix. Then there exist $n \times n$ permutation matrices, $P_1,\ldots,P_m$, and positive numbers $c_1,\ldots, c_m$ such that*

$$
\sum_{i=1}^{m} c_i = 1
\tag{6}
$$

and

$$A = \sum_{i=1}^{m} c_i P_i. \tag{7}$$

In other words, any doubly stochastic matrix A is a sum of positive multiples of permutation matrices $c_1 P_1, \ldots, c_m P_m$ in which the numbers $c_1, \ldots, c_m$ add up to 1.

Proof.   The argument is by induction on the number of positive entries in A. Since each row sum of A is 1, it follows that A has at least n positive entries. If it has exactly n positive entries then these must each be 1. Since each column sum is also 1, it follows that in this case A is already a permutation matrix P_1; that is, we can take $A = P_1, c_1 = 1, m = 1$. Now assume that the theorem is true for any doubly stochastic matrix with fewer than q positive entries, $q > n$, and let A be a matrix with q positive entries. By Theorem 4.1 there exists a diagonal of positive entries in A. Let P_1 be an $n \times n$ permutation matrix with 1's in precisely the positions of this positive diagonal and let a be the smallest of the positive entries on this diagonal. We first claim that $a < 1$. For, if $a = 1$, then (because a is the smallest entry on the diagonal and every entry in A is at most 1) we can conclude that the whole diagonal consists of 1's. But then the doubly stochastic property of A would imply that A is a permutation matrix and the number of positive entries in A would be precisely n. However we are assuming that this number is $q > n$. Now define an $n \times n$ matrix A_1 as follows:

$$A_1 = \frac{1}{1-a}(A - aP_1). \tag{8}$$

Let us observe some of the properties of A_1. First, $1 - a > 0$ and since a is the smallest entry in the diagonal of A corresponding to the positions of the 1's in P_1, we can conclude that the entries of A_1 are nonnegative. But more is true. One of the elements in the diagonal of A corresponding to P_1 has value a and thus A_1 has at most $q - 1$ positive entries. Also if the entries of A_1 are designated by b_{ij}, $i, j = 1, \ldots, n$, and the entries of P_1 are denoted by p_{ij} we can conclude that

$$\sum_{j=1}^{n} b_{ij} = \sum_{j=1}^{n} \frac{1}{1-a}(a_{ij} - ap_{ij})$$

$$= \frac{1}{1-a}(\sum_{j=1}^{n} a_{ij} - a \sum_{j=1}^{n} p_{ij})$$

$$= \frac{1}{1-a}(1 - a)$$

$$= 1, \qquad i = 1, \ldots, n.$$

A similar calculation shows that each column sum of A_1 is also 1. At this point we have proved that A_1 is a doubly stochastic matrix with at most $q - 1$

positive entries and hence we can apply the induction hypothesis to A_1. It follows that there exist permutation matrices $P_2, \ldots, P_m$ and positive numbers $d_2, \ldots, d_m$ such that

$$A_1 = \sum_{j=2}^{m} d_j P_j \qquad (9)$$

and

$$\sum_{j=2}^{m} d_j = 1. \qquad (10)$$

If we combine (8) and (9) we obtain

$$\frac{1}{1-a}(A - aP_1) = \sum_{j=2}^{m} d_j P_j$$

or, solving for A,

$$A = aP_1 + \sum_{j=2}^{m} (1-a)d_j P_j. \qquad (11)$$

Set $c_1 = a$, $c_j = (1-a)d_j$, $j = 2, \ldots, m$, and observe from (10) that

$$c_1 + c_2 + \cdots + c_m = a + (1-a)(\sum_{j=2}^{m} d_j)$$
$$= a + 1 - a$$
$$= 1.$$

Hence

$$A = \sum_{j=1}^{m} c_j P_j,$$

and

$$\sum_{j=1}^{m} c_j = 1, \qquad c_j > 0, \qquad j = 1, \ldots, m.$$

The proof is complete.

There are several remarks that we should make here. First, the sum of elements in the kth row of $A + B$ is obviously the sum of the kth row sums of A and B. It follows that any matrix of the form (7) in which the c_i, $i = 1, \ldots, m$, satisfy (6) and are positive must be doubly stochastic. For, the kth row sum of $\sum_{i=1}^{m} c_i P_i$ is just $\sum_{i=1}^{m} c_i = 1$. Similarly for the column sums. Thus we see from Theorem 4.2 that A is doubly stochastic if and only if A has the form given in (7) in which the c_i, $i = 1, \ldots, m$, are positive and satisfy (6).

We also observe that arguments much like those used in Theorem 4.2 will prove an analogous statement for matrices with 0 and 1 as entries. In fact we have

Theorem 4.3 *Let A be an $n \times n$ matrix whose entries are zeros and ones with k ones in each row and each column. Then A is a sum of k permutation matrices*:

$$A = \sum_{i=1}^{k} P_i.$$

Proof. The matrix $(1/k)A$ is doubly stochastic and hence has a diagonal of positive entries by Theorem 4.1. In other words, A has a diagonal of ones. We can thus write $A = P_1 + B$ where B has $k - 1$ ones in each row and column. We now repeat the argument with B, and so on. Of course, we can see how a formal induction on k may be made here.

We next note that Theorem 4.1 can be stated in terms of the permanent; namely, if A is doubly stochastic, then

$$\text{per}\,(A) > 0. \tag{12}$$

One might ask if something better than the inequality (12) is true. For example, in the dance problem (Example 4.2) we can conclude from (12) that there exists at least one pairing of boys and girls who have met. But in Example 4.5 we asked a much more difficult question: how many such pairings are there? We can gain at least some information about such problems after we prove the following result.

Theorem 4.4 *If A and B are $n \times n$ matrices with nonnegative entries then*

$$\text{per}\,(A + B) \geq \text{per}\,(A) + \text{per}\,(B). \tag{13}$$

Proof. The (i, j) entry of $A + B$ is just $a_{ij} + b_{ij}$. Thus a typical term in the sum defining per $(A + B)$ is

$$\prod_{i=1}^{n} (a_{i\sigma(i)} + b_{i\sigma(i)}). \tag{14}$$

Now if we multiply out the product (14) and throw away all terms except $\prod_{i=1}^{n} a_{i\sigma(i)}$ and $\prod_{i=1}^{n} b_{i\sigma(i)}$ we obtain (remember A and B have nonnegative entries)

$$\prod_{i=1}^{n} (a_{i\sigma(i)} + b_{i\sigma(i)}) \geq \prod_{i=1}^{n} a_{i\sigma(i)} + \prod_{i=1}^{n} b_{i\sigma(i)}. \tag{15}$$

If we sum all the inequalities (15) for $\sigma \in S_n$ we get

$$\sum_{\sigma \in S_n} \prod_{i=1}^{n} (a_{i\sigma(i)} + b_{i\sigma(i)}) \geq \sum_{\sigma \in S_n} \prod_{i=1}^{n} a_{i\sigma(i)} + \sum_{\sigma \in S_n} \prod_{i=1}^{n} b_{i\sigma(i)};$$

that is,

$$\text{per}\,(A + B) \geq \text{per}\,(A) + \text{per}\,(B).$$

Now we return to doubly stochastic matrices. If A is doubly stochastic then $A = \sum_{i=1}^{m} c_i P_i$ as in Theorem 4.2. Thus applying (13) we have

$$
\begin{aligned}
\text{per}\,(A) &= \text{per}\,\Big(\sum_{i=1}^{m} c_i P_i\Big) \\
&= \text{per}\,\Big(c_1 P_1 + \sum_{i=2}^{m} c_i P_i\Big) \\
&\geq \text{per}\,(c_1 P_1) + \text{per}\,\Big(\sum_{i=2}^{m} c_i P_i\Big) \\
&\geq \cdots \\
&\geq \sum_{i=1}^{m} \text{per}\,(c_i P_i).
\end{aligned}
\tag{16}
$$

Now each term per $(c_i P_i)$ is just c_i^n because P_i is a permutation matrix. Thus

$$\text{per}\,(A) \geq \sum_{i=1}^{m} c_i^n. \tag{17}$$

EXAMPLE 4.6

Show that in the dance problem of Example 4.2 there are at least k pairings of the boys and girls possible without making further introductions. The incidence matrix A can be written

$$A = \sum_{i=1}^{k} P_i,$$

according to Theorem 4.3. Hence, by (13),

$$\text{per}\,(A) \geq \sum_{i=1}^{k} \text{per}\,(P_i) = k.$$

Quiz

Answer **true** or **false**:

1. If D is an $n \times n$ matrix with c_i as (i, i) entry, 0 as (i, j) entry, $i \neq j$, and P is an $n \times n$ permutation matrix then per $(DP) = c_1 \cdots c_n$.

2. If A is an $n \times n$ doubly stochastic matrix and P is an $n \times n$ permutation matrix then PA is doubly stochastic.

3. With A and P as in the preceding problem, per $(PA) =$ per $(AP) =$ per (A).

4. If

$$A = \begin{bmatrix} 1 & 1 & 0 & 0 \\ 0 & 1 & 1 & 0 \\ 0 & 0 & 1 & 1 \\ 0 & 0 & 0 & 1 \end{bmatrix},$$

   then per $(A) = 2$.

5. The matrix

$$A = \begin{bmatrix} 1 & 0 & 0 & 1 \\ 0 & 1 & 1 & 0 \\ 0 & 1 & 1 & 0 \\ 1 & 0 & 0 & 1 \end{bmatrix}$$

   has four diagonals each of whose elements is positive.

6. The $n \times n$ matrix J with every entry equal to $1/n$ has as permanent $1/n^n$.

7. If A is a 2×2 doubly stochastic matrix then $A^T = A$.

8. If A and B are 2×2 doubly stochastic matrices and

$$AB = \begin{bmatrix} \frac{1}{2} & \frac{1}{2} \\ \frac{1}{2} & \frac{1}{2} \end{bmatrix} \text{ then either } A \text{ or } B \text{ must be } \begin{bmatrix} \frac{1}{2} & \frac{1}{2} \\ \frac{1}{2} & \frac{1}{2} \end{bmatrix}.$$

9. Let A be an $n \times n$ doubly stochastic matrix. If $\sum_{i=1}^{n} a_{ii} = n$ then $A = I_n$, the $n \times n$ identity matrix (see Example 3.5).

10. If P is an $n \times n$ permutation matrix having no 1's in positions (i, i), $i = 1, \ldots, n$, then $I_n + P$ has just two diagonals consisting of positive numbers.

Exercises

1. Show that if A and B are $n \times n$ doubly stochastic matrices and $0 \leq \theta \leq 1$ then $\theta A + (1 - \theta)B$ is doubly stochastic.

2. Show that if A and B are $n \times n$ doubly stochastic matrices then AB is doubly stochastic.

3. Answer the question posed in Example 4.3.

4. Write

$$A = \begin{bmatrix} \frac{2}{3} & \frac{1}{6} & \frac{1}{6} \\ 0 & \frac{1}{6} & \frac{5}{6} \\ \frac{1}{3} & \frac{2}{3} & 0 \end{bmatrix}$$

as a sum of multiples of permutation matrices as in Theorem 4.2. Can this be done in more than one way?

5. Let J be the $n \times n$ matrix with each entry equal to $1/n$. Show that an $n \times n$ matrix A is doubly stochastic if and only if $AJ = JA = J$ and A has nonnegative entries.

6. Let A be a 2×2 doubly stochastic matrix. Show that the roots of the quadratic in x, per $(xI_2 - A)$, cannot exceed 1 in absolute value.

3

Convexity

3.1 Convex Sets

There is very little we can say about a general function f defined on an arbitrary set S. If, however, the function happens to be endowed with special properties and if its domain is of the right type to exploit these properties, then we may obtain significant information concerning the function and the structure of its domain and range. For example, a function f may have any of the following special properties: it may be 1-1 onto; it may be homogeneous of degree k (i.e., $f(tx) = t^k f(x)$); it may be additive (i.e., $f(x + y) = f(x) + f(y)$); it may be monotonically increasing (i.e., $f(x) \geq f(y)$, whenever $x \geq y$); and so on. The domain may be a closed interval $\{x \mid a \leq x \leq b\}$; it may be a Cartesian product of such intervals; or, more generally, it may be a "convex set." A set of points S is convex if S includes all the points on the line segment joining an arbitrary pair of points in S. The purpose of this chapter is to study the properties of convex sets and special types of functions defined on these sets. One of our goals will be to obtain some interesting and important inequalities that find application throughout mathematics.

Before we give any general formal definitions let us investigate convex sets in the plane and obtain an analytical expression equivalent to the geometric definition of a convex figure. Thus let (x_1, y_1) and (x_2, y_2) be the Cartesian coordinates of any two points in a convex figure C. To fix our picture suppose that $x_1 > x_2$ and $y_1 > y_2$. Let (x, y) be any point on the line connecting (x_1, y_1) and (x_2, y_2).

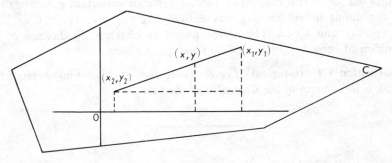

Then let θ be the common value of

$$\frac{y - y_2}{y_1 - y_2} = \frac{x - x_2}{x_1 - x_2}. \tag{1}$$

Clearly, if (x, y) is situated on the segment joining the other two points, then θ is a real number between 0 and 1. We compute that

$$x = \theta x_1 + (1 - \theta)x_2,$$

$$y = \theta y_1 + (1 - \theta)y_2,$$

which can be more compactly written as

$$(x, y) = \theta(x_1, y_1) + (1 - \theta)(x_2, y_2). \tag{2}$$

In fact, a point (x, y) lies on the line segment joining (x_1, y_1) and (x_2, y_2) if and only if there exists a number θ, $0 \le \theta \le 1$, such that (2) holds. Thus we can say that C is convex if and only if for any (x_1, y_1) and (x_2, y_2) in C and any real number θ, $0 \le \theta \le 1$, we have

$$\theta(x_1, y_1) + (1 - \theta)(x_2, y_2) = (\theta x_1 + (1 - \theta)x_2, \theta y_1 + (1 - \theta)y_2) \in C.$$

(Note that $\theta = 0$ gives (x_2, y_2), and $\theta = 1$ gives (x_1, y_1).)

The situation in 3-dimensional space is similar: a set of points C is convex if and only if the following condition holds. Given any pair of points (x_1, y_1, z_1) and (x_2, y_2, z_2) in C, and any real number θ, $0 \le \theta \le 1$, the set C also contains the point

$$\theta(x_1, y_1, z_1) + (1 - \theta)(x_2, y_2, z_2)$$

$$= (\theta x_1 + (1 - \theta)x_2, \theta y_1 + (1 - \theta)y_2, \theta z_1 + (1 - \theta)z_2).$$

If we forget for the moment the geometric meaning of symbols like (x_1, x_2) and (x_1, x_2, x_3), we can observe that

$$\{(x_1, x_2) \mid x_1, x_2 \in R\} = R \times R$$

and

$$\{(x_1, x_2, x_3) \mid x_1, x_2, x_3 \in R\} = R \times R \times R,$$

(see Definition 2.3, Chapter 1). (Here, and throughout this chapter, $R = \text{Re}$ denotes the set of real numbers.) This suggests an important generalization. We can define in an obvious way entities like (x_1, x_2, x_3, x_4), $(x_1, x_2, x_3, x_4, x_5)$, and so on. The philosophical or physical significance of the definition of such "points" is of no consequence here.

Definition 1.1 (*n*-tuples) *Let R denote the set of real numbers. A real n-tuple is an element of the Cartesian product set*

$$\overbrace{R \times R \times \cdots \times R}^{n}.$$

That is, a real n-tuple is a finite sequence of n real numbers $(a_1, \ldots, a_n)$.
The a_i, $i = 1, \ldots, n$, *are called coordinates or components. Two n-tuples* $a = (a_1, \ldots, a_n)$ *and* $b = (b_1, \ldots, b_n)$ *are equal if* $a_i = b_i$, $i = 1, \ldots, n$.

As is commonly the case in algebra, as soon as we define any interesting sets we start thinking about significant ways of combining elements of these sets. We can define *addition* and *scalar multiplication* for *n*-tuples. If $a = (a_1, \ldots, a_n)$, $b = (b_1, \ldots, b_n)$ are real *n*-tuples and $\alpha \in R$, then

$$a + b = (a_1 + b_1, \ldots, a_n + b_n), \tag{3}$$

$$\alpha a = (\alpha a_1, \ldots, \alpha a_n), \tag{4}$$

where the addition and the multiplication on the right-hand side is the ordinary addition and multiplication of real numbers. It is conventional to write $-(a_1, \ldots, a_n)$ for $-1(a_1, \ldots, a_n)$. The set of all real *n*-tuples, together with addition and scalar multiplication, is called the *vector space* of real *n*-tuples and is denoted by R^n. Elements of R are sometimes called *scalars* whereas the elements of R^n are called *vectors*. A subset S of R^n is said to be a *subspace* of R^n if it is *closed* under addition and scalar multiplication; that is, if for any a and b in S and any α in R, the *n*-tuples $a + b$ and αa also belong to S.

EXAMPLES 1.1

(a) If $a = (3, 1, -1, 2)$ and $b = (-1, 0, 2, 1)$ then $a + b = (2, 1, 1, 3)$ and $4a = (12, 4, -4, 8)$.

(b) Let $S = \{(a_1, \ldots, a_n) \in R^n \mid a_1 = a_2\}$. Then S is a subspace of R^n. For, if $a = (a_1, \ldots, a_n) \in S$ and $b = (b_1, \ldots, b_n) \in S$, that is, if $a_1 = a_2$ and $b_1 = b_2$, then $c = (c_1, \ldots, c_n) = a + b \in S$; for, $c_1 = a_1 + b_1 = a_2 + b_2 = c_2$. Also, if α is any real number, then $d = (d_1, \ldots, d_n) = \alpha a \in S$, since $d_1 = \alpha a_1 = \alpha a_2 = d_2$.

(c) Let P^n be the set of nonnegative *n*-tuples; that is,

$$P^n = \{(a_1, \ldots, a_n) \in R^n \mid a_j \geq 0, j = 1, \ldots, n\}.$$

Then P^n is not a subspace although it is closed under addition. For, if $a = (a_1, \ldots, a_n) \in P^n$ and not all a_j are 0, then $(-1)a = (-a_1, \ldots, -a_n) \notin P^n$, and thus P^n is not closed under scalar multiplication.

(d) The one-element set consisting of the *n*-tuple $0_n = (0, \ldots, 0)$ clearly forms a subspace of R^n.

Definition 1.2 (Convex set) *A subset C of R^n is said to be convex if for any a and b in C and any θ in R, $0 \leq \theta \leq 1$, the n-tuple $\theta a + (1 - \theta)b$ also belongs to C; in other words, if a and b are in C then*

$$\{\theta a + (1 - \theta)b \mid 0 \leq \theta \leq 1\} \subset C.$$

EXAMPLES 1.2

(a)   The set P^n defined in Example 1.1(c) is convex.

(b)   Let $D^n = \{(a_1, \ldots, a_n) \in P^n | \sum_{j=1}^n a_j = 1\}$. Then D^n is convex. For, if $a = (a_1, \ldots, a_n)$, $b = (b_1, \ldots, b_n)$ are in D^n and $0 \le \theta \le 1$, and

$$c = (c_1, \ldots, c_n) = \theta a + (1 - \theta)b$$

then

$$\sum_{j=1}^n c_j = \sum_{j=1}^n (\theta a_j + (1 - \theta)b_j)$$

$$= \theta \sum_{j=1}^n a_j + (1 - \theta) \sum_{j=1}^n b_j$$

$$= \theta + (1 - \theta)$$

$$= 1.$$

(c)   Let B^n be the unit ball in R^n, that is,

$$B^n = \{(a_1, \ldots, a_n) \in R^n | \sum_{j=1}^n a_j^2 \le 1\}.$$

Then B^n is convex. To see this let $a = (a_1, \ldots, a_n) \in B^n$, $b = (b_1, \ldots, b_n) \in B^n$, $0 \le \theta \le 1$, and $c = \theta a + (1 - \theta)b$. We compute that

$$\sum_{j=1}^n c_j^2 = \sum_{j=1}^n (\theta a_j + (1 - \theta)b_j)^2$$

$$= \theta^2 \sum_{j=1}^n a_j^2 + (1 - \theta)^2 \sum_{j=1}^n b_j^2 + 2\theta(1 - \theta) \sum_{j=1}^n a_j b_j$$

$$\le \theta^2 + (1 - \theta)^2 + 2\theta(1 - \theta) \sum_{j=1}^n a_j b_j.$$

We next prove that $\sum_{j=1}^n a_j b_j \le 1$. For, we see that

$$0 \le \sum_{j=1}^n (a_j - b_j)^2$$

$$= \sum_{j=1}^n a_j^2 + \sum_{j=1}^n b_j^2 - 2 \sum_{j=1}^n a_j b_j$$

$$\le 2 - 2 \sum_{j=1}^n a_j b_j,$$

and thus

$$1 - \sum_{j=1}^n a_j b_j \ge 0.$$

Hence

$$\sum_{j=1}^{n} c_j^2 \leq \theta^2 + (1 - \theta)^2 + 2\theta(1 - \theta)$$

$$= (\theta + (1 - \theta))^2$$

$$= 1.$$

(d)   Any subspace S of R^n is convex. For, if a and b are in S then by the definition of a subspace, $\theta a \in S$ and $(1 - \theta)b \in S$, and hence $\theta a + (1 - \theta)b \in S$.

(e)   Let $a^1, \ldots, a^p$ be p arbitrary n-tuples in R^n. (We use a superscript to designate these n-tuples in order to avoid confusion with the subscript notation for coordinates.) Define the set

$$H(a^1, \ldots, a^p) = \{\sum_{j=1}^{p} \theta_j a^j \mid \theta_j \geq 0, \quad j = 1, \ldots, p, \quad \sum_{j=1}^{p} \theta_j = 1\}.$$

We prove that $H(a^1, \ldots, a^p)$ is convex. Let

$$\sum_{j=1}^{p} \lambda_j a^j, \qquad \lambda_j \in R, \qquad \lambda_j \geq 0, \qquad \sum_{j=1}^{p} \lambda_j = 1,$$

and

$$\sum_{j=1}^{p} \mu_j a^j, \qquad \mu_j \in R, \qquad \mu_j \geq 0, \qquad \sum_{j=1}^{p} \mu_j = 1,$$

be any two elements of $H(a^1, \ldots, a^p)$ and let $\theta \in R$, $0 \leq \theta \leq 1$. Then

$$\theta \sum_{j=1}^{p} \lambda_j a^j + (1 - \theta) \sum_{j=1}^{p} \mu_j a^j = \sum_{j=1}^{p} v_j a^j$$

where

$$v_j = \theta \lambda_j + (1 - \theta)\mu_j \geq 0, \qquad j = 1, \ldots, p,$$

and

$$\sum_{j=1}^{p} v_j = \theta \sum_{j=1}^{p} \lambda_j + (1 - \theta) \sum_{j=1}^{p} \mu_j = \theta + (1 - \theta) = 1.$$

The result obtained in Example 1.2(e) is of great importance.

Definition 1.3   (Convex polyhedron). *Let* $a^1, \ldots, a^p$ *be* p *points in* R^n. *The n-tuple*

$$\sum_{j=1}^{p} \theta_j a^j, \qquad \theta_j \geq 0, \qquad j = 1, \ldots, p, \qquad \sum_{j=1}^{p} \theta_j = 1,$$

is called a convex combination (or a convex sum) of $a^1, \ldots, a^p$. *If* $X \subset R^n$ *then the set of all (finite) convex combinations of points of* X *is called the convex hull of* X *and is denoted by* $H(X)$. *If* X *is finite,* $X = \{a^1, \ldots, a^p\}$, *then* $H(X)$ *is called the convex polyhedron spanned by* $a^1, \ldots, a^p$ *and is also denoted by* $H(a^1, \ldots, a^p)$.

We illustrate these concepts in the following examples. (The proof that $H(X)$ is a convex set is relegated to the exercises at the end of this section.)

EXAMPLES 1.3

(a)   Let $a^1 = (1, -1)$, $a^2 = (2, 2)$ and $a^3 = (3, 1)$ be points of R^2. Then, by Definition 1.3,

$$H(a^1, a^2, a^3) = \{\theta_1(1, -1) + \theta_2(2, 2) + \theta_3(3, 1) \,|\, \theta_1 + \theta_2 + \theta_3 = 1,$$

$$\theta_j \geq 0, j = 1, 2, 3\}$$

$$= \{(\theta_1 + 2\theta_2 + 3\theta_3, \, -\theta_1 + 2\theta_2 + \theta_3) \,|\, \theta_1 + \theta_2 + \theta_3 = 1,$$

$$\theta_j \geq 0, j = 1, 2, 3\}.$$

Thus the elements of $H(a^1, a^2, a^3)$ are the points (x, y) whose coordinates satisfy

$$x = \theta_1 + 2\theta_2 + 3\theta_3 \quad \text{and} \quad y = -\theta_1 + 2\theta_2 + \theta_3 \tag{5}$$

subject to the conditions

$$\theta_1 + \theta_2 + \theta_3 = 1, \tag{6}$$

$$\theta_1 \geq 0, \quad \theta_2 \geq 0, \quad \theta_3 \geq 0. \tag{7}$$

Eliminate θ_2 and θ_3 between (5) and (6) and obtain

$$x + y = 4(1 - \theta_1). \tag{8}$$

Hence a point (x_0, y_0) of $H(a^1, a^2, a^3)$ must lie on one of the family of parallel lines (8). Since $0 \leq \theta_1 \leq 1$, the point (x_0, y_0) must lie in the strip bounded by the lines $x + y = 0$ and $x + y = 4$; that is,

$$0 \leq x_0 + y_0 \leq 4. \tag{9}$$

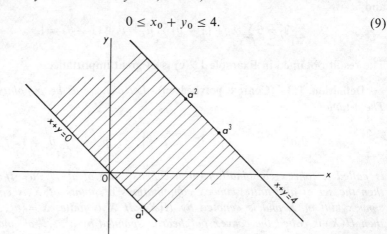

By eliminating θ_1 and θ_3 between (5) and (6) we find similarly that

$$0 \le x_0 - y_0 \le 2; \tag{10}$$

and eliminating θ_1 and θ_2 between (5) and (6) we finally obtain

$$4 \le 3x_0 - y_0 \le 8. \tag{11}$$

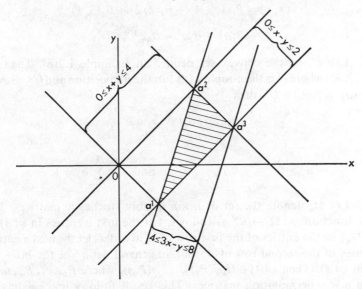

It follows from (9), (10), and (11) that (x_0, y_0) lies inside the triangle with vertices a^1, a^2, a^3. Conversely, the coordinates of any point (x, y) lying inside the triangle or on its boundary must satisfy

$$0 \le x + y \le 4,$$
$$0 \le x - y \le 2,$$
$$4 \le 3x - y \le 8.$$

If we set

$$x - y = 2(1 - \theta_2),$$
$$x + y = 4(1 - \theta_1), \tag{12}$$
$$3x - y = 4 + 4\theta_3$$

where $0 \le \theta_i \le 1$, $i = 1, 2, 3$, we can compute that

$$0 = 2(x - y) + (x + y) - (3x - y)$$
$$= 4(1 - \theta_2) + 4(1 - \theta_1) - 4(1 + \theta_3)$$
$$= 4 - 4(\theta_1 + \theta_2 + \theta_3),$$

that is,

$$\theta_1 + \theta_2 + \theta_3 = 1. \tag{13}$$

Thus from (12) and (13) we have

$$x = 3 - 2\theta_1 - \theta_2 = \theta_1 + 2\theta_2 + 3\theta_3,$$

$$y = 1 - 2\theta_1 + \theta_2 = -\theta_1 + 2\theta_2 + \theta_3,$$

or

$$(x, y) = \theta_1(1, -1) + \theta_2(2, 2) + \theta_3(3, 1)$$

$$= \theta_1 a^1 + \theta_2 a^2 + \theta_3 a^3.$$

(b) Let D^n be the convex set defined in Example 1.2(b). Then $D^n = H(e^1, \ldots, e^n)$ where e^j is the n-tuple with 1 in the jth position and 0's elsewhere. For, if $(a_1, \ldots, a_n) \in D^n$, then

$$(a_1, \ldots, a_n) = \sum_{j=1}^{n} a_j e^j$$

where

$$a_j \geq 0, \qquad j = 1, \ldots, n, \qquad \text{and} \qquad \sum_{j=1}^{n} a_j = 1.$$

(c) Let Ω_n denote the set of $n \times n$ doubly stochastic matrices. Define the 1-1 function $\varphi : \Omega_n \to R^{n^2}$ as follows. Let the first n entries in $\varphi(A)$, $A = (a_{ij}) \in \Omega_n$, be the entries of the first row of A in order; let the next n entries be the entries of the second row of A; and, in general, let a_{ij} be the $n(i-1) + j$ entry in $\varphi(A)$. Then $\varphi(A) \in H(\varphi(P_1), \ldots, \varphi(P_m))$, where $P_1, \ldots, P_m, m = n!$, are the $n \times n$ permutation matrices. This result follows immediately from Birkhoff's Theorem (Theorem 4.2, Chapter 2).

(d) Let P^n be the set of nonnegative n-tuples defined in Example 1.1(c). Let X be the infinite set of n-tuples in P^n that have at most one entry not equal to 0. Then $P^n = H(X)$. We leave the details as an exercise.

(e) Let B^n be the unit ball defined in Example 1.2(c) and let

$$S^n = \{(a_1, \ldots, a_n) \in B^n \mid \sum_{j=1}^{n} a_j^2 = 1\}.$$

Then $B^n = H(S^n)$.

We put together two fairly obvious properties of convex sets that are required later.

Theorem 1.1 (a) *The intersection of convex sets is convex.*

(b) *The Cartesian product $I_1 \times \cdots \times I_n \subset R^n$ of the intervals*

$$I_j = \{x \in R \mid a_j \leq x \leq b_j\}, \qquad j = 1, \ldots, n,$$

is convex.

Proof. (a) Let a and b be in $S \cap T$ where S and T are convex sets. Then, for any $0 \leq \theta \leq 1, \theta a + (1 - \theta)b$ is in S, since S is convex, and $\theta a + (1 - \theta)b$ is in T, since T is convex. Hence $\theta a + (1 - \theta)b \in S \cap T$ and $S \cap T$ is convex.

(b) Let $x = (x_1, \ldots, x_n)$, $y = (y_1, \ldots, y_n)$, $a_j \le x_j \le b_j$, $a_j \le y_j \le b_j$, $j = 1, \ldots, n$, and let $0 \le \theta \le 1$. Then if $z = (z_1, \ldots, z_n) = \theta x + (1 - \theta)y$ we have

$$z_j = \theta x_j + (1 - \theta)y_j \le \theta b_j + (1 - \theta)b_j = b_j, \qquad j = 1, \ldots, n,$$

$$z_j = \theta x_j + (1 - \theta)y_j \ge \theta a_j + (1 - \theta)a_j = a_j, \qquad j = 1, \ldots, n.$$

Hence $a_j \le z_j \le b_j$, $j = 1, \ldots, n$, and $z \in I_1 \times \cdots \times I_n$. Thus $I_1 \times \cdots \times I_n$ is convex.

While we postpone the main application of convex sets to Section 3, we shall now define a special class of functions and prove a remarkable property that such functions have when they are defined on a convex set.

Definition 1.4 **(Linear function)** *A function $f : S \to R$, where $S \subset R^n$, is said to be linear if*

$$f(\alpha x + \beta y) = \alpha f(x) + \beta f(y) \tag{14}$$

for all x and y in S and any pair of real numbers α and β for which $\alpha x + \beta y \in S$.

Theorem 1.2 (a) *Let S be a subspace of R^n. A function $f : S \to R$ is linear if and only if*

$$f\left(\sum_{j=1}^{p} \alpha_j x_j\right) = \sum_{j=1}^{p} \alpha_j f(x_j) \tag{15}$$

for any $x_j \in S$ and $\alpha_j \in R$, $j = 1, \ldots, p$.
   (b) *If a function $f : H(a^1, \ldots, a^p) \to R$ is linear then*

$$f\left(\sum_{j=1}^{p} \theta_j a^j\right) = \sum_{j=1}^{p} \theta_j f(a^j) \tag{16}$$

for any $\theta_j \ge 0$ satisfying $\sum_{j=1}^{p} \theta_j = 1$.
   (c) *A function $f : R^n \to R$ is linear if and only if $f((r_1, \ldots, r_n)) = \sum_{j=1}^{n} \alpha_j r_j$, for all $(r_1, \ldots, r_n) \in R^n$, where $\alpha_1, \ldots, \alpha_n$ are fixed real numbers determined by f.*

Proof. (a) We use induction on p. If $p = 2$, then (15) reduces to (14). Assume that (15) holds for $p - 1$ summands. Then

$$f\left(\sum_{j=1}^{p} \alpha_j x_j\right) = f\left(\alpha_1 x_1 + \sum_{j=2}^{p} \alpha_j x_j\right)$$

$$= \alpha_1 f(x_1) + f\left(\sum_{j=2}^{p} \alpha_j x_j\right)$$

$$= \alpha_1 f(x_1) + \sum_{j=2}^{p} \alpha_j f(x_j)$$

$$= \sum_{j=1}^{p} \alpha_j f(x_j).$$

The converse is proved by taking $p = 2$ in (15).

(b)   The proof is similar to that of part (a). We leave it as an exercise for the student.

(c)   Let e^j, $j = 1, \ldots, n$, be the n-tuple with 1 in the jth position and 0 elsewhere (see Example 1.3(b)). Let $f(e^j) = \alpha_j$. Then, for every $x = (r_1 \ldots, r_n) \in R^n$, we have $x = \sum_{j=1}^n r_j e^j$ and, by part (a),

$$f(x) = \sum_{j=1}^n r_j f(e^j)$$

$$= \sum_{j=1}^n r_j \alpha_j,$$

where $\alpha_j = f(e_j)$, $j = 1, \ldots, n$. Conversely if $f(x) = \sum_{j=1}^n \alpha_j r_j$ and $f(y) = f((s_1, \ldots, s_n)) = \sum_{j=1}^n \alpha_j s_j$, then clearly

$$f(\alpha x + \beta y) = \sum_{j=1}^n \alpha_j (\alpha r_j + \beta s_j)$$

$$= \alpha \sum_{j=1}^n \alpha_j r_j + \beta \sum_{j=1}^n \alpha_j s_j$$

$$= \alpha f(x) + \beta f(y).$$

If $X = \{x_1, x_2, x_3, \cdots\}$ is a set of real numbers then $\max_i (x_i)$ and $\min_i (x_i)$ denote numbers x_n, $x_k \in X$ (if they exist) such that $x_n \geq x_i$ and $x_k \leq x_i$, for all i, respectively. If X is a finite set then both $\max_i (x_i)$ and $\min_i (x_i)$ always exist. We sometimes write $\min_{x \in X} (x)$ and $\max_{x \in X} (x)$.

Theorem 1.3   (a)   *If $\theta_i \geq 0$, $i = 1, \ldots, n$, $\sum_{i=1}^n \theta_i = 1$, and $r_1, \ldots, r_n$ are any real numbers then*

$$\min_i (r_i) \leq \sum_{i=1}^n \theta_i r_i \leq \max_i (r_i).$$

(b)   *Let a^i be points in R^n, $i = 1, \ldots, p$. If $f: H(a^1, \ldots, a^p) \to R$ is linear then, for any $x \in H(a^1, \ldots, a^p)$,*

$$\min_i (f(a^i)) \leq f(x) \leq \max_i (f(a^i)).$$

In other words, a linear function defined on a convex polyhedron takes its maximum (minimum) on an element of the spanning set.

Proof.   (a)

$$\sum_{i=1}^n \theta_i r_i \leq \sum_{i=1}^n \theta_i (\max_i (r_i)) = \max_i (r_i) \sum_{i=1}^n \theta_i = \max_i (r_i)$$

and

$$\sum_{i=1}^n \theta_i r_i \geq \sum_{i=1}^n \theta_i (\min_i (r_i)) = \min_i (r_i) \sum_{i=1}^n \theta_i = \min_i (r_i).$$

(b)   Let x be any element of $H(a^1, \ldots, a^p)$. Then

$$x = \sum_{j=1}^{p} \theta_j a^j, \quad \theta_j \geq 0, \quad j = 1, \ldots, n, \quad \text{and} \quad \sum_{j=1}^{p} \theta_j = 1.$$

Since f is linear,

$$f(x) = f\left(\sum_{j=1}^{p} \theta_j a^j\right)$$

$$= \sum_{j=1}^{p} \theta_j f(a^j)$$

$$\leq \max_{j} (f(a^j)),$$

by part (a). We leave the proof of the other inequality as an exercise for the student.

EXAMPLES 1.4

(a)   Let $D^n \subset R^n$ be the set defined in Example 1.2(b). Let $f : D^n \to R$ be defined by $f((x_1, \ldots, x_n)) = \sum_{j=1}^{n} \alpha_j x_j$, where $\alpha_1, \ldots, \alpha_n$ are fixed real numbers. Find the maximum and the minimum of f. The function f is linear. By Example 1.3(b), $D^n = H(e^1, \ldots, e^n)$, where e^j is the n-tuple with 1 in the jth place and 0's elsewhere. Therefore, by Theorem 1.3(a),

$$\max_{x \in D^n} (f(x)) = \max_{j} (f(e^j)) = \max_{j} (\alpha_j)$$

and

$$\min_{x \in D^n} (f(x)) = \min_{j} (f(e^j)) = \min_{j} (\alpha_j).$$

(b)   Let C be the convex quadrilateral in the Cartesian plane defined by

$$x - 2y \geq -1,$$

$$2x + y \leq 3,$$

$$x - 3y \leq 5,$$

$$x + 2y \geq -5.$$

Find the minimum and the maximum in C of the function $f : C \to R$ defined by

$$f((x, y)) = 4x - 3y.$$

Let v_1, v_2, v_3, v_4 be the vertices of the quadrilateral. Then $C = H(v_1, v_2, v_3, v_4)$. We solve in pairs the equations $x - 2y = -1$, $2x + y = 3$, $x - 3y$

$= 5$, $x + 2y = -5$ and obtain $v_1 = (1, 1)$, $v_2 = (2, -1)$, $v_3 = (-1, -2)$ and $v_4 = (-3, -1)$. We compute $f(v_1) = 1$, $f(v_2) = 11$, $f(v_3) = 2$, $f(v_4) = -9$.

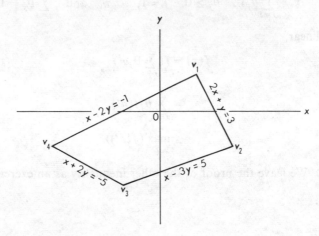

Hence, by Theorem 1.3(b),

$$\max_{p \in C} (f(p)) = \max_i (f(v_i)) = f(v_2) = 11,$$

and

$$\min_{p \in C} (f(p)) = \min_i (f(v_i)) = f(v_4) = -9.$$

(c)   A 30-minute television program consists of a solo recorder performance, a harpsichord performance and commercials. The recorder player
insists on performing at least half as long as the harpsichordist. The sponsor
requires at least 3 minutes of commercials and the station wishes the harpsichord performance to last at least 4 times as long as the commercials. If the
recorder player, the harpsichordist and the commercials cost $250, $180,
$110 per minute respectively, what is the minimal cost of the program?

Let x and y be the number of minutes of the recorder performance and the
harpsichord performance, respectively. The commercials then take $30 - x - y$
minutes. The conditions can be translated into mathematical notation as
follows:

$$x \geq \tfrac{1}{2}y,$$

$$30 - x - y \geq 3,$$

$$y \geq 4(30 - x - y),$$

or

$$2x - y \geq 0,$$

$$x + y \leq 27,$$

$$4x + 5y \geq 120.$$

In the Cartesian plane a point (x, y) satisfies these conditions if and only if it lies inside or on the boundary of the triangle C formed by the lines $2x - y = 0$, $x + y = 27$, $4x + 5y = 120$. We compute the coordinates of the vertices of this triangle: $v_1 = (9, 18)$, $v_2 = (15, 12)$, $v_3 = (\frac{60}{7}, \frac{120}{7})$.

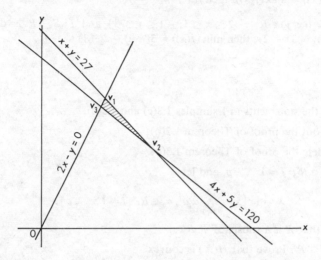

Now, the problem is to minimize the function $f((x, y)) = 250x + 180y + 110(30 - x - y) = 140x + 70y + 3{,}300$ for all permissible values of (x, y). In other words, we want to minimize the linear function $\varphi : H(v_1, v_2, v_3) \to R$ defined by $\varphi((x, y)) = 140x + 70y$. By Theorem 1.3($b$),

$$\min_{p \in H(v_1, v_2, v_3)} \varphi(p) = \min_i (\varphi(v_i)) = \varphi(v_3) = 2{,}400$$

since $\varphi(v_1) = 2{,}520$ and $\varphi(v_2) = 2{,}940$. Thus, the minimum cost of the program is $2{,}400 + 3{,}300 = 5{,}700$ dollars and this minimum can be achieved by allotting $8\frac{4}{7}$ minutes to the recorder player, $17\frac{1}{7}$ minutes to the harpsichord performance, and $4\frac{2}{7}$ minutes to commercials.

Quiz

Answer **true** or **false**:

1. The subset $\{(x_1, \ldots, x_n) \in R^n \mid x_j \geq 0, j = 1, \ldots, n\}$ forms a subspace of R^n.
2. The subset $\{(x_1, \ldots, x_n) \in R^n \mid x_1 \geq x_2 \geq \cdots \geq x_n\}$ forms a subspace of R^n.
3. The subset $\{(x_1, \ldots, x_n) \in R^n \mid x_1 + \cdots + x_n = 0\}$ forms a subspace of R^n.
4. The set $\{(x_1, \ldots, x_n) \in R^n \mid x_1 + \cdots + x_n > 1\}$ is convex.
5. The set $\{(x_1, x_2) \mid x_1^2 + x_2^2 = 1\}$ is convex.
6. If $a \in R^n$ then $H(a) = \{a\}$.

7. If $a = (2, 1)$, $b = (1, 2)$, $c = (1, 1)$ and $d = (2, 2)$, then $H(a, b) = H(c, d)$.

8. If $a = (1, 0)$, $b = (0, 1)$ and $c = (\frac{1}{2}, \frac{1}{2})$, then $H(a, b, c) = H(a, b)$.

9. Let S be the convex polyhedron $H(a^1, \ldots, a^p)$. If $f: S \to R$ is linear and $\min_{x \in S} (f(x)) = \max_{x \in S} (f(x))$, then $f(a^1) = \cdots = f(a^p)$.

10. If $S = \{(x, y) \in R^2 \mid -2 \le x \le 1, -1 \le y \le 3\}$ and $f: S \to R$ is defined by $f((x, y)) = 3x - 2y$, then $\min_{x \in S} (f(x)) = 3(-2) - 2(-1) = -4$.

Exercises

1. Prove the statements in Examples 1.3(c) and 1.3(d).

2. Write out the proof of Theorem 1.2(b).

3. Complete the proof of Theorem 1.3(b).

4. Let $a^j \in R^n$, $j = 1, \ldots, p$, and let

$$X = \{x \mid x = \sum_{j=1}^{p} \alpha_j a^j, \alpha_j \in R, \ j = 1, \ldots, p\}.$$

Show that X is a subspace of R^n.

5. Let $X \subset R^n$. Prove that $H(X)$ is convex.

6. Let a_{ij} and b_i, $i = 1, \ldots, m, j = 1, \ldots, n$, be fixed real numbers. Let S be the set of all real n-tuples $(x_1, \ldots, x_n)$ for which

$$\sum_{j=1}^{n} a_{ij} x_j = b_i, \qquad i = 1, \ldots, m.$$

Show that S is convex.

7. Let a and b be in R, $a < b$, and let $S = \{x \in R \mid a \le x \le b\}$. Show that $S = H(a, b)$.

8. Show that a function $f: R^n \to R$ is linear if and only if it is additive and homogeneous of degree 1; that is,

$$f(x + y) = f(x) + f(y)$$

and

$$f(\alpha x) = \alpha f(x)$$

for all x and y in R^n and all α in R.

9. Let $v_1 = (1, 2)$, $v_2 = (-1, 1)$, $v_3 = (0, -1)$, $v_4 = (2, 2)$ and let $C = H(v_1, v_2, v_3, v_4)$. Let $f: C \to R$ be defined by $f((x, y)) = 2x - y + 3$. Is f linear on C? Find $\max_{a \in C} (f(a))$ and $\min_{a \in C} (f(a))$.

10. Let S be the subset of R^2 containing all pairs (x, y) that satisfy

$$4x - y \le 5,$$

$$5x - 4y \ge -2,$$

$$x - 3y \le 4.$$

Find $\max_{a \in S} (f(a))$ and $\min_{a \in S} (f(a))$ where $f: S \to R$ and $f((x, y)) = 4x - y$. What is the set $\{z \in S \mid f(z) \geq f(a)$ for all $a \in S\}$?

11. A 100-lb. batch of a mixture is to be made of ingredients A, B and C that cost \$5, \$2, and \$3 per pound respectively. What are the largest and least total costs of the mixture if the quantity of A must exceed that of B by at least 10 lb. and must not exceed that of C by more than 40 lb., and if the quantity of B must be at least equal to that of C?

3.2   Elementary Inequalities

Any two given real numbers a and b are either equal, or one of them is greater than the other. We describe this situation by saying that the system of real numbers is ordered. This ordering can be described formally by a system of axioms or it can be based on the simpler concept of positiveness. We have assumed that the student is acquainted with the meaning of "positive (negative) real number" and of "nonnegative (nonpositive) real number." In fact, we used these concepts extensively in Chapter 2. Recall that if a is positive (nonnegative) we write $a > 0$ or $0 < a$ ($a \geq 0$ or $0 \leq a$); if a is negative (nonpositive) we write $a < 0$ or $0 > a$ ($a \leq 0$ or $0 \geq a$). For the sake of completeness we include the following definitions.

Definition 2.1   (Inequality)   *Let a and b be real numbers. Then*
  (i)   *a is greater than b, written $a > b$ or $b < a$, if $a - b > 0$;*
  (ii)   *a is greater than or equal to b, written $a \geq b$ or $b \leq a$, if $a - b \geq 0$.*

We shall state most of our theorems on inequalities in terms of the relation $\geq$; in many cases analogous theorems can be stated in terms of the strict inequality $>$.

In mathematics we often make statements such as

$$\text{"} x^2 + 5x + 5 \geq 1 \qquad \text{for all } x \geq -1\text{,"}$$

or

"$(1 + a)^n \geq 1 + na$ for all nonnegative real numbers a and all positive integers n" (see Example 1.2, Chapter 1),

or

$$\text{"} 5 > 3\text{,"}$$

or we ask questions such as

$$\text{"for what values of } x \text{ is } \frac{4x - 8}{x + 2} \geq x - 3\text{?"}$$

The term "inequality" usually covers any statement or any question of this kind.

Some preliminary elementary properties of inequalities are contained in the following theorem. We shall assume that the reader is acquainted with the various "rules of sign," that is, if $a > 0$, $b > 0$, $c < 0$, $d < 0$, then $ab > 0$, $cd > 0$, and $ad < 0$, etc.

Theorem 2.1

(a)   If $a \geq b$ and $b \geq c$ then $a \geq c$.

(b)   If $a \geq b$ and $c \geq d$ then $a + c \geq b + d$.

(c)   If $a \geq b$ and $c \geq 0$ then $ac \geq bc$.

(d)   If $a \geq b$ and $c \leq 0$ then $ac \leq bc$.

(e)   If $a \geq b \geq 0$ and $c \geq d \geq 0$ then $ac \geq bd$.

(f) $a/b > 0$ if and only if $ab > 0$.

(g)   Let n be a positive integer and let $a \geq 0$ and $b \geq 0$. Then $a \geq b$ if and only if $a^n \geq b^n$.

(h)   If $a \geq b > 0$ then $a^{-1} \leq b^{-1}$.

Proof.   Parts (a) and (b) follow immediately from Definition 2.1. We leave the formal proofs to the student.

(c)   If $a - b \geq 0$ and $c \geq 0$ then $(a - b)c \geq 0$, i.e., $ac - bc \geq 0$ and $ac \geq bc$.

(d)   If $a - b \geq 0$ and $c \leq 0$ then $(a - b)c \leq 0$ and $ac \leq bc$.

(e) $ac - bd = (a - b)c + b(c - d) \geq 0$ since $(a - b)c + b(c - d)$ is a sum of products of nonnegative numbers.

(f)   If $b > 0$ then, by (c), $a = b(a/b) > 0$ and hence $ab > 0$. If $b < 0$ then, by (d), $a = b(a/b) < 0$ and thus $ab > 0$. Conversely, if $ab > 0$ then either $a > 0$ and $b > 0$, or $a < 0$ and $b < 0$. In either case $a/b > 0$.

(g)   To prove that $a \geq b$ implies $a^n \geq b^n$ use induction on n. We assume that $a^{n-1} \geq b^{n-1}$ and $a \geq b$ and the result follows by (e). Conversely, if $a^n \geq b^n$ then $a \geq b$, for $a < b$ would imply, by the first part, that $a^n < b^n$.

(h)   If $a \geq b > 0$ then $b - a \leq 0$ and $ab > 0$. Thus $(b - a)/ab = a^{-1} - b^{-1} \leq 0$ and $a^{-1} \leq b^{-1}$.

EXAMPLE 2.1

Show that if $x \geq y > 0$ and θ is a rational number satisfying $0 \leq \theta \leq 1$, then

$$x + y \geq x^\theta y^{1-\theta} + x^{1-\theta} y^\theta. \tag{1}$$

Let $\theta = p/q$. Then, by Theorem 2.1(g), $x^{1/q} \geq y^{1/q}$ and thus, for the same reason, $x^{p/q} \geq y^{p/q}$, or $x^\theta - y^\theta \geq 0$. Similarly $x^{1-\theta} - y^{1-\theta} \geq 0$. Thus

$$(x^\theta - y^\theta)(x^{1-\theta} - y^{1-\theta}) \geq 0,$$

or, multiplying out,

$$x + y - x^\theta y^{1-\theta} - y^\theta x^{1-\theta} \geq 0,$$

and the result follows.

The results in the remainder of this section are somewhat more sophisticated than Theorem 2.1.

Theorem 2.2   *Let* $q_i > 0$, $i = 1, \ldots, n$. *Then*

$$\min_i \frac{p_i}{q_i} \le \frac{p_1 + \cdots + p_n}{q_1 + \cdots + q_n} \le \max_i \frac{p_i}{q_i} \tag{2}$$

for any real numbers $p_1, \ldots, p_n$.

Proof.   Let $m = \min_i \dfrac{p_i}{q_i}$. Then

$$\frac{p_i}{q_i} \ge m, \qquad i = 1, \ldots, n,$$

and, since $q_i > 0$, we have by Theorem 2.1(c),

$$p_i \ge q_i m, \qquad i = 1, \ldots, n.$$

Therefore, by repeated use of Theorem 2.1(b),

$$p_1 + \cdots + p_n \ge (q_1 + \cdots + q_n)m$$

and, since $1/(q_1 + \cdots + q_n) > 0$,

$$\frac{p_1 + \cdots + p_n}{q_1 + \cdots + q_n} \ge m.$$

The upper bound can be proved similarly.

Definition 2.2   (Arithmetic and geometric means)   *Let* $a_1, \ldots, a_n$ *be nonnegative real numbers. The number*

$$\frac{1}{n} \sum_{j=1}^{n} a_j$$

is called the arithmetic mean of the numbers $a_1, \ldots, a_n$. *The number*

$$\prod_{j=1}^{n} a_j^{1/n}$$

is called the geometric mean of the numbers $a_1, \ldots, a_n$.

Theorem 2.3   (Arithmetic-geometric mean inequality)   *Let* $a_1, \ldots, a_n$ *be nonnegative real numbers. Then*

$$\frac{1}{n} \sum_{j=1}^{n} a_j \ge \prod_{j=1}^{n} a_j^{1/n}. \tag{3}$$

Equality can occur in (3) if and only if $a_1 = \cdots = a_n$.

Proof.   Let

$$A = \frac{1}{n} \sum_{j=1}^{n} a_j \qquad \text{and} \qquad G = \prod_{j=1}^{n} a_j^{1/n}.$$

We first consider the case in which some but not all of the a_j are 0. Then $A > 0$ and $G = 0$ so (3) is an obvious strict inequality. Next assume that every a_j is positive. Set $x_j = a_j/G$. Then

$$x_1 \cdots x_n = \frac{a_1 \cdots a_n}{G^n} = \frac{G^n}{G^n} = 1.$$

In addition,

$$\sum_{j=1}^{n} a_j = G \sum_{j=1}^{n} x_j \, .$$

We are going to prove that if $x_1 \cdots x_n = 1$, $x_j > 0$, then $x_1 + \cdots + x_n \geq n$ with equality if and only if $x_1 = x_2 = \cdots = x_n = 1$. The argument is by induction on n. For $n = 1$ there is nothing to prove. Now suppose we assume the result for any $n - 1$ positive numbers. Not all x_j are less than 1, nor are all of these numbers greater than 1. Thus assume, for example, that $x_1 \geq 1$, $x_2 \leq 1$. Then

$$(x_1 - 1)(x_2 - 1) \leq , 0 \tag{4}$$

so

$$x_1 x_2 + 1 \leq x_1 + x_2 \, . \tag{5}$$

Now consider

$$(x_1 x_2) x_3 \cdots x_n = 1.$$

By applying the induction to the $n - 1$ positive numbers $x_1 x_2, \, x_3, \ldots, x_n$ we have

$$x_1 x_2 + x_3 + \cdots + x_n \geq n - 1. \tag{6}$$

But we have seen in (5) that

$$x_1 x_2 \leq x_1 + x_2 - 1$$

and hence combining with (6) we have

$$x_1 + x_2 + x_3 + \cdots + x_n \geq n. \tag{7}$$

Now suppose that (7) is equality. Then (5) and (6) must be equality. Hence (4) and (6) must be equality. By the induction hypothesis, the equality in (6) tells us that

$$x_1 x_2 = x_3 = \cdots = x_n = 1. \tag{8}$$

The equality in (4) says that either $x_1 = 1$ or $x_2 = 1$. In either case (8) tells us that in fact both $x_1 = 1$ and $x_2 = 1$. In other words, equality in (7) implies that $x_1 = \cdots = x_n = 1$. Returning now to the proof of the original statement (3) we see that

$$\sum_{j=1}^{n} a_j = G \sum_{j=1}^{n} x_j \geq Gn$$

with equality if and only if

$$x_j = \frac{a_j}{G} = 1, \qquad j = 1, \ldots, n.$$

In other words,

$$A \geq G$$

with equality if and only if $a_1 = \cdots = a_n$.

On the basis of this result we can prove a generalized version of the arithmetic-geometric mean inequality.

Theorem 2.4   *Let $b_1, \ldots, b_m$ be nonnegative real numbers and let $r_1, \ldots, r_m$ be positive rational numbers. Set*

$$r = \sum_{j=1}^{m} r_j.$$

Then

$$\frac{1}{r} \sum_{j=1}^{m} r_j b_j \geq (\prod_{j=1}^{m} b_j^{r_j})^{1/r}$$

in which equality holds if and only if $b_1 = \cdots = b_m$.

Proof.   By Theorem 2.3, if $a_1, \ldots, a_n$ are nonnegative numbers then

$$\frac{1}{n} \sum_{j=1}^{n} a_j \geq \prod_{j=1}^{n} a_j^{1/n} \tag{9}$$

with equality if and only if $a_1 = \cdots = a_n$. Now, suppose that k_1 of the a_j's are equal to b_1, k_2 are equal to $b_2, \ldots, k_m$ are equal to b_m. Then (9) becomes

$$\frac{1}{k} \sum_{j=1}^{m} k_j b_j \geq (\prod_{j=1}^{m} b_j^{k_j})^{1/k} \tag{10}$$

where

$$k = \sum_{j=1}^{m} k_j.$$

Equality can hold if and only if $b_1 = \cdots = b_m$. Now, let d be a common denominator of the rational numbers $r_1, \ldots, r_m$. Set

$$dr_j = k_j, \qquad j = 1, \ldots, m,$$

and substitute in (10) to obtain

$$\frac{1}{dr} \sum_{j=1}^{m} dr_j b_j \geq (\prod_{j=1}^{m} b_j^{dr_j})^{1/dr}$$

or

$$\frac{1}{r} \sum_{j=1}^{m} r_j b_j \geq (\prod_{j=1}^{m} b_j^{r_j})^{1/r};$$

equality holds if and only if $b_1 = \cdots = b_m$.

EXAMPLE 2.2

Show that a rectangular box of maximum volume with a fixed surface area must be a cube. To see this, let a_1, a_2, a_3 be the lengths of the sides of the box. Then the surface area is $S = 2(a_1 a_2 + a_1 a_3 + a_2 a_3)$ and the volume is $V = a_1 a_2 a_3$. Now

$$\frac{S}{6} = \frac{2a_1 a_2 + 2a_1 a_3 + 2a_2 a_3}{6}$$

$$\geq (a_1 a_2)^{1/3} (a_1 a_3)^{1/3} (a_2 a_3)^{1/3}$$

$$= (a_1 a_2 a_3)^{2/3}$$

$$= V^{2/3}.$$

In other words,

$$V \leq \left(\frac{S}{6}\right)^{3/2},$$

and moreover the volume is equal to the maximum $\left(\frac{S}{6}\right)^{3/2}$ only if $a_1 a_2 = a_1 a_3 = a_2 a_3$, that is, only if $a_1 = a_2 = a_3$. Thus for maximum volume the box must be a cube.

EXAMPLE 2.3

Show that if n positive numbers add up to no more than 1 then the sum of their reciprocals is always at least n^2. For, if

$$a_1 + \cdots + a_n \leq 1,$$

then by applying Theorem 2.3 to the numbers $1/a_i$, $i = 1, \ldots, n$, we have

$$\frac{1}{a_1} + \cdots + \frac{1}{a_n} \geq n \left(\frac{1}{a_1} \cdots \frac{1}{a_n}\right)^{1/n}.$$

But

$$(a_1 \cdots a_n)^{1/n} \le \frac{a_1 + \cdots + a_n}{n} \le \frac{1}{n}.$$

Hence

$$\frac{1}{a_1} + \cdots + \frac{1}{a_n} \ge n^2.$$

EXAMPLE 2.4

Show that if $x > 0$, then

$$\frac{1}{4} \le \frac{1 + 2x + 3x^2 + 4x^3}{1 + 4x + 9x^2 + 16x^3} \le 1.$$

This is a straightforward application of Theorem 2.2 with

$$p_1 = 1, \qquad p_2 = 2x, \qquad p_3 = 3x^2, \qquad p_4 = 4x^3,$$

and

$$q_1 = 1, \qquad q_2 = 4x, \qquad q_3 = 9x^2, \qquad q_4 = 16x^3.$$

At this juncture we require the following simple theorem on quadratic inequalities.

Theorem 2.5 Let $f(x) = ax^2 + bx + c$, $a \ne 0$, and let $\Delta = b^2 - 4ac$. If $\Delta \le 0$ then $(1/a)f(x) \ge 0$ for all x. If $\Delta \ge 0$ let x_1 and x_2 be respectively the smaller and the larger of the two numbers $(-b - \sqrt{\Delta})/2a$ and $(-b + \sqrt{\Delta})/2a$. Then $(1/a)f(x) \le 0$ if and only if $x_1 \le x \le x_2$.

Proof. We have

$$\frac{1}{a} f(x) = x^2 + \frac{b}{a} x + \frac{c}{a}$$

$$= x^2 + 2\frac{b}{2a} x + \frac{b^2}{4a^2} - \frac{b^2}{4a^2} + \frac{c}{a}$$

$$= \left(x + \frac{b}{2a}\right)^2 - \frac{\Delta}{4a^2}.$$

Thus

$$\frac{1}{a} f(x) \ge -\frac{\Delta}{4a^2}$$

and if $\Delta \le 0$ it follows that $(1/a)f(x) \ge 0$ for all x. If $\Delta \ge 0$ then

$$\frac{1}{a} f(x) = \left(x + \frac{b}{2a} + \frac{\sqrt{\Delta}}{2a}\right)\left(x + \frac{b}{2a} - \frac{\sqrt{\Delta}}{2a}\right)$$

$$= (x - x_1)(x - x_2).$$

Hence for all x satisfying $x_1 \leq x \leq x_2$, we have $x - x_1 \geq 0$ and $x - x_2 \leq 0$. Thus $(1/a)f(x) \leq 0$. Clearly $f(x_1) = f(x_2) = 0$. Conversely, if $(1/a)f(x) \leq 0$ then one of $x - x_1$ and $x - x_2$ must be nonpositive and the other nonnegative. Now $(x - x_1) - (x - x_2) = (x_2 - x_1) \geq 0$ and thus we must have $x - x_1 \geq 0$ and $x - x_2 \leq 0$, i.e., $x_1 \leq x \leq x_2$.

EXAMPLES 2.5

(a) For what values of x is

$$\frac{-2x^2 + x - 1}{2x^2 + x - 1} \geq 0?$$

Let $f_1(x) = -2x^2 + x - 1$ and $f_2(x) = 2x^2 + x - 1$. Then using the notation of Theorem 2.5 we compute that $\Delta_1 = -7$ and hence $f_1(x)/(-2) \geq 0$, i.e., $f_1(x) \leq 0$ for all x. On the other hand, $\Delta_2 = 9$ and therefore $f_2(x) \leq 0$ for all x satisfying $-1 \leq x \leq \frac{1}{2}$. Now $f_1(x)/f_2(x) \geq 0$ if and only if $f_1(x)f_2(x) \geq 0$ and $f_2(x) \neq 0$. Therefore $f_1(x)/f_2(x) \geq 0$ if and only if $-1 < x < \frac{1}{2}$.

(b) For what values of x is

$$\frac{x - 3}{x - 1} \leq 0?$$

By Theorem 2.1(f), the inequality holds if and only if

$$(x - 3)(x - 1) \leq 0 \quad \text{and} \quad x \neq 1;$$

that is, if and only if

$$1 < x \leq 3.$$

(c) For what values of x is

$$(x - 3)(x - 1) \geq (3x + 1)(x + 1)?$$

After simplification the inequality becomes

$$2x^2 + 8x - 2 \leq 0$$

and, by Theorem 2.5, this inequality holds for all x satisfying

$$-2 - \sqrt{5} \leq x \leq -2 + \sqrt{5}.$$

EXAMPLE 2.6

Let $f(x) = \prod_{i=1}^{n}(x - a_i), a_1 \leq \cdots \leq a_n$. Suppose that $a_k \neq a_{k+1}$ for some k, $1 \leq k \leq n$. Then either $f(x) > 0$ for all x satisfying $a_k < x < a_{k+1}$ or $f(x) < 0$ for all x, $a_k < x < a_{k+1}$. For if $a_k < x < a_{k+1}$ then $x > a_i$, $i = 1, \ldots, k$, and

$x < a_i$, $i = k + 1, \ldots, n$. Therefore $f(x) = \prod_{i=1}^{k} (x - a_i) \prod_{i=k+1}^{n} (x - a_i)$ is positive or negative for all x between a_k and a_{k+1} according as $n - k$ is even or odd.

Theorem 2.6   (Cauchy's inequality)   *Let $a_1, \ldots, a_n, b_1, \ldots, b_n$ be any $2n$ real numbers. Then*

$$(\sum_{i=1}^{n} a_i b_i)^2 \le (\sum_{i=1}^{n} a_i^2)(\sum_{i=1}^{n} b_i^2). \tag{11}$$

Equality occurs in (11) if and only if either $a_1 = \cdots = a_n = 0$ or $b_i = c a_i$, $i = 1, \ldots, n$, for some real number c.

Proof.   If $a_1 = \cdots = a_n = 0$ then clearly (11) is an equality. Assume hereafter that not all a_j's are 0. Now, a sum of squares of real numbers is always nonnegative. Therefore,

$$\sum_{i=1}^{n} (x a_i + b_i)^2 \ge 0,$$

or

$$x^2 \sum_{i=1}^{n} a_i^2 + 2x \sum_{i=1}^{n} a_i b_i + \sum_{i=1}^{n} b_i^2 \ge 0, \tag{12}$$

for any real number x. Now, let

$$\Delta = (2 \sum_{i=1}^{n} a_i b_i)^2 - 4(\sum_{i=1}^{n} a_i^2)(\sum_{i=1}^{n} b_i^2).$$

Then $\Delta \le 0$, otherwise the left-hand side of (12) would be negative for some real x. But $\Delta \le 0$ is clearly equivalent to (11). If equality holds in (11) then $\Delta = 0$ and the left-hand side of (12) is equal to

$$(\sum_{i=1}^{n} a_i^2) \left(x - \frac{\sum_{i=1}^{n} ab_{ii}}{\sum_{i=1}^{n} a_i^2} \right)^2,$$

since not all a_i are zero. Thus, for all x,

$$(\sum_{i=1}^{n} a_i^2)(x + c)^2 = \sum_{i=1}^{n} (x a_i + b_i)^2, \tag{13}$$

where

$$c = \frac{\sum_{i=1}^{n} a_i b_i}{\sum_{i=1}^{n} a_i^2}.$$

Putting $x = -c$ we obtain

$$b_i = c a_i, \qquad i = 1, \ldots, n. \tag{14}$$

On the other hand if (14) holds for any real number c, then (11) is obviously equality.

EXAMPLE 2.7

Let $P = (x_1, y_1)$ and $Q = (x_2, y_2)$ be points in the Cartesian plane, distinct from the origin $(0, 0)$. Find an expression for the cosine of the angle QOP and interpret geometrically Cauchy's inequality in R^2. (We assume here that the student is familiar with elementary trigonometry. If not, see Chapter 4, Section 4.3, in particular, Theorem 3.4(b).)

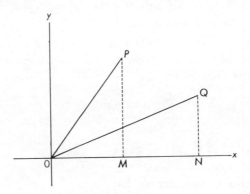

We have

$$\cos(QOP) = \cos(MOP - NOQ)$$

$$= \cos(MOP)\cos(NOQ) + \sin(MOP)\sin(NOQ)$$

$$= \frac{OM}{OP}\frac{ON}{OQ} + \frac{MP}{OP}\frac{NQ}{OQ}$$

$$= \frac{x_1 x_2 + y_1 y_2}{(x_1^2 + y_1^2)^{1/2}(x_2^2 + y_2^2)^{1/2}}.$$

Hence Cauchy's inequality is equivalent to the statement that $(\cos(QOP))^2 \leq 1$.

Theorem 2.7 (Triangle inequality)   *Let $a_1, \ldots, a_n$, $b_1, \ldots, b_n$ be any $2n$ real numbers. Then*

$$\left(\sum_{i=1}^{n}(a_i + b_i)^2\right)^{1/2} \leq \left(\sum_{i=1}^{n}a_i^2\right)^{1/2} + \left(\sum_{i=1}^{n}b_i^2\right)^{1/2}. \tag{15}$$

Equality holds in (15) if and only if either $a_1 = \cdots = a_n = 0$ or $b_i = ca_i$, $i = 1, \ldots, n$, for some $c \geq 0$.

Proof.   We have

$$\sum_{i=1}^{n}(a_i + b_i)^2 = \sum_{i=1}^{n}a_i^2 + 2\sum_{i=1}^{n}a_i b_i + \sum_{i=1}^{n}b_i^2$$

and then, by Theorem 2.6,

$$\sum_{i=1}^{n} a_i b_i \le (\sum_{i=1}^{n} a_i^2)^{1/2} (\sum_{i=1}^{n} b_i^2)^{1/2}. \tag{16}$$

Therefore

$$\sum_{i=1}^{n} (a_i + b_i)^2 \le \sum_{i=1}^{n} a_i^2 + 2(\sum_{i=1}^{n} a_i^2)^{1/2} (\sum_{i=1}^{n} b_i^2)^{1/2} + \sum_{i=1}^{n} b_i^2$$

$$= [(\sum_{i=1}^{n} a_i^2)^{1/2} + (\sum_{i=1}^{n} b_i^2)^{1/2}]^2$$

and (15) follows. Equality in (15) holds if and only if (16) is equality. But (16) is equality if and only if either $a_1 = \cdots = a_n = 0$ or $b_i = ca_i$, $i = 1, \ldots, n$, for an appropriate c. In the latter case (16) becomes

$$c \sum_{i=1}^{n} a_i^2 = (c^2 (\sum_{i=1}^{n} a_i^2)^2)^{1/2}$$

and hence $c \ge 0$.

In case $n = 1$, the inequality (15) reads

$$((a + b)^2)^{1/2} \le (a^2)^{1/2} + (b^2)^{1/2}$$

where $(a^2)^{1/2}$ is nonnegative and equal to a or to $-a$ according as a is nonnegative or negative. This simple notion of a nonnegative "value" of a real number is of importance in the theory of inequalities and in mathematics in general.

Definition 2.3   (Absolute value)   *If x is a real number then the absolute value of x, written $|x|$, is defined as the (nonnegative) square root of x^2, that is,*

$$|x| = \begin{cases} x & \text{if } x \ge 0, \\ -x & \text{if } x \le 0. \end{cases}$$

Theorem 2.8   *If x and y are any real numbers, then*

(a) $|-x| = |x|$;

(b) $-|x| \le x \le |x|$

where exactly one of the inequalities is strict if $x \ne 0$;

(c) $|x + y| \le |x| + |y|$;

(d) $|x - y| \ge ||x| - |y||$;

(e) $|xy| = |x||y|$;

(f) $|x/y| = |x|/|y|$,   *if $y \ne 0$.*

The equality in (c) or (d) occurs if and only if x and y are both nonnegative or both nonpositive.

Proof.   Parts (a), (b), (e), and (f) are immediate consequences of Definition 2.3. Part (c) is a special case of Theorem 2.7. Part (d) follows from part (c). For,

$$|x| = |(x - y) + y|$$

$$\leq |x - y| + |y|,$$

and hence,

$$|x - y| \geq |x| - |y|.$$

Interchanging x and y and noting that $|x - y| = |y - x|$ we have

$$|x - y| \geq |y| - |x|,$$

and the result follows.

E X A M P L E S   2 . 8

   (a)   Show that $|a| \leq b$ if and only if $-b \leq a \leq b$. If $|a| \leq b$ and $a \geq 0$ then $0 \leq a = |a| \leq b$ and therefore $-b \leq a \leq b$. If $|a| \leq b$ and $a \leq 0$, then $-a = |a| \leq b$ and, by Theorem 2.1(d), $0 \geq a \geq -b$ and therefore again $-b \leq a \leq b$. Conversely, if $-b \leq a \leq b$ and $a \geq 0$ then $|a| = a \leq b$. If $-b \leq a \leq b$ and $a \leq 0$, then, by Theorem 2.1(d), $0 \leq -a \leq b$ and $|a| = -a \leq b$.
   (b)   Find all real numbers x for which

$$|x + 2| \leq 1. \tag{17}$$

The inequality (17) holds if and only if

$$-1 \leq x + 2 \leq 1.$$

Thus (17) holds for x if and only if

$$-3 \leq x \leq -1.$$

   We conclude this section with a theorem concerning rearrangements of finite sequences. Let $\{a_1, \ldots, a_n\}$ and $\{b_1, \ldots, b_n\}$ be two sequences of real numbers. The problem is to find the maximum and the minimum of

$$\sum_{i=1}^{n} a_i b_{\sigma(i)}$$

as σ runs over all permutations in S_n. We can give this problem the following equivalent physical interpretation. Given n vertical forces of magnitudes $b_1, \ldots, b_n$ acting at points on the x-axis with x-coordinates $a_1, \ldots, a_n$, what are the arrangements of the forces so that the total moment shall be a maximum or a minimum?

Theorem 2.9 **(Rearrangement theorem)**   *If $a_1 \geq \cdots \geq a_n$, $b_1 \geq \cdots \geq b_n$ and $\sigma \in S_n$ then*

$$\sum_{i=1}^{n} a_i b_{n-i+1} \leq \sum_{i=1}^{n} a_i b_{\sigma(i)} \leq \sum_{i=1}^{n} a_i b_i. \tag{18}$$

Proof.   We prove by using induction on n that

$$\sum_{i=1}^{n} a_i b_{\sigma(i)} \leq \sum_{i=1}^{n} a_i b_i.$$

For $n = 1$ both sides are clearly equal. Thus assume that the inequality holds for sequences of $n - 1$ terms. Let $k = \sigma^{-1}(n)$. If $k = n$ then

$$\sum_{i=1}^{n} a_i b_{\sigma(i)} = \sum_{i=1}^{n-1} a_i b_{\sigma(i)} + a_n b_n$$

and by the induction hypothesis

$$\sum_{i=1}^{n-1} a_i b_{\sigma(i)} \leq \sum_{i=1}^{n-1} a_i b_i.$$

Thus

$$\sum_{i=1}^{n} a_i b_{\sigma(i)} \leq \sum_{i=1}^{n} a_i b_i.$$

Assume then that $k \neq n$. Then since $\sigma(k) = n$ we can separate the kth and nth terms in the sum to obtain

$$\sum_{i=1}^{n} a_i b_{\sigma(i)} = \sum_{\substack{i=1 \\ i \neq k}}^{n-1} a_i b_{\sigma(i)} + a_k b_n + a_n b_{\sigma(n)}. \tag{19}$$

Now $k < n$ and $\sigma(n) < n$. Therefore

$$(a_k b_{\sigma(n)} + a_n b_n) - (a_k b_n + a_n b_{\sigma(n)}) = (a_k - a_n)(b_{\sigma(n)} - b_n) \geq 0.$$

Hence

$$a_k b_{\sigma(n)} + a_n b_n \geq a_k b_n + a_n b_{\sigma(n)}$$

and substituting in (19) we have

$$\sum_{i=1}^{n} a_i b_{\sigma(i)} \leq \sum_{\substack{i=1 \\ i \neq k}}^{n-1} a_i b_{\sigma(i)} + a_k b_{\sigma(n)} + a_n b_n. \tag{20}$$

But now we may apply the induction hypothesis to the numbers $a_1 \geq \cdots \geq a_{n-1}$ to obtain

$$\sum_{\substack{i=1 \\ i \neq k}}^{n-1} a_i b_{\sigma(i)} + a_k b_{\sigma(n)} \leq \sum_{i=1}^{n-1} a_i b_i. \tag{21}$$

Therefore putting (20) and (21) together we have

$$\sum_{i=1}^{n} a_i b_{\sigma(i)} \leq \sum_{i=1}^{n-1} a_i b_i + a_n b_n = \sum_{i=1}^{n} a_i b_i.$$

The left-hand side of the inequality in (18) is proved similarly.

EXAMPLE 2.9

Prove that for any real number x satisfying $|x| \leq 1$ the following inequalities hold:

$$1 + 2\sqrt{1 - x^2} \leq \sqrt{1 - x^2} + \sqrt{1 - x} + \sqrt{1 + x} \leq 3. \qquad (22)$$

If $x \geq 0$ then $\sqrt{1 - x} \leq 1 \geq \sqrt{1 + x}$. Set $a_1 = b_1 = \sqrt{1 - x}$, $a_2 = b_2 = 1$, $a_3 = b_3 = \sqrt{1 + x}$. Then, by the preceding theorem,

$$a_1 b_3 + a_2 b_2 + a_3 b_1 \leq a_1 b_3 + a_2 b_1 + a_3 b_2 \leq a_1 b_1 + a_2 b_2 + a_3 b_3,$$

which is (22). If $x \leq 0$ the inequalities are similarly proved.

Quiz

Answer **true** or **false**:

1. If $a \geq b \geq 0$ and $c \geq d \geq 0$, then $a - c \geq b - d$.
2. If $a/b \geq c/d$ and $a \neq 0$, $c \neq 0$, then $b/a \leq d/c$.
3. If $a + c \geq b + c$ then $a \geq b$.
4. If $|x| > x$, then $|x| = -x$.
5. If x is any real number, then $1 + x^2 + x^4 \geq 3x^2$.
6. If x is any real number, then $|x + 1| > |x|$.
7. If x is any real number, then $|x|^2 = x^2$.
8. If $|x - y| = |y - x|$, then $x = y$.
9. If a and b are any real numbers, then $a + b \leq ((1 + a^2)(1 + b^2))^{1/2}$.
10. If $a > b$ and $c > d > 0$ then $(a + b)/(c + d) > b/c$.

Exercises

1. Prove Theorem 2.1(b).
2. Use Theorem 2.9 to prove that

$$2(\sqrt{40} + \sqrt{42}) \leq \sqrt{30} + \sqrt{42} + \sqrt{56} + \sqrt{40} \leq 26.$$

3. Find all real numbers x for which

$$\frac{x + 2}{x^2 + x + 1} > \frac{x + 1}{x^2 - x + 1}.$$

4. Find all real numbers x and y for which

$$|x| + |y| < 1.$$

5. Prove that $x + y = ((1 + x^2)(1 + y^2))^{1/2}$ if and only if $xy = 1$ and $x > 0$.

6. Prove that

$$\left(\frac{a^2 + b^2}{2}\right)^{1/2} \geq \frac{a + b}{2}$$

for any real numbers a and b. Also, show that equality can hold in the above inequality if and only if $a = b \geq 0$.

7. Prove that if $p_i > 0$ and $q_i > 0$, $i = 1, \ldots, n$, then

$$\min_i \frac{p_i}{q_i} \leq \left(\frac{p_1 p_2 \cdots p_n}{q_1 q_2 \cdots q_n}\right)^{1/n} \leq \max \frac{p_i}{q_i}.$$

8. Show that for any real numbers $a_1, \ldots, a_n$ satisfying $0 \leq a_i \leq 1$, $i = 1, \ldots, n$, the following inequality holds:

$$\prod_{i=1}^{n} (1 - a_i) \geq 1 - \sum_{i=1}^{n} a_i.$$

9. Show that, for any real numbers x, y and z,

$$7x^2 + 5y^2 + 8z^2 \geq 4xy + 10xz + 6yz.$$

10. Show that, for any integer $n > 1$,

$$(n!)^{1/n} < \tfrac{1}{2}(n + 1).$$

3.3 Convex Functions and Inequalities

In this section we will study a large and important class of functions called convex functions. We will see how the study of inequalities is intimately connected with convexity.

Definition 3.1 (Convex function) *Let C be a convex subset of R^n. Let f be a real valued function whose domain is C. If for each x and y in C and each θ, $0 \leq \theta \leq 1$, the inequality*

$$f(\theta x + (1 - \theta)y) \leq \theta f(x) + (1 - \theta)f(y) \tag{1}$$

holds then f is said to be a convex function. If $-f$ is convex then f is called a concave function.

EXAMPLE 3.1

Let C be the interval $a \leq x \leq b$. To say that f is convex is to say that the chord joining any two points on the graph of f is everywhere above the graph of f.

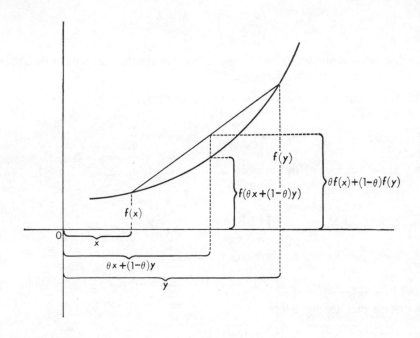

EXAMPLE 3.2

If C is the interval $a \leq x \leq b$ and $f(x) = x^2$ then f is a convex function. To see this we must examine the difference

$$d = \theta f(x) + (1 - \theta)f(y) - f(\theta x + (1 - \theta)y).$$

We want to show that $d \geq 0$ for any x and y in C and any θ, $0 \leq \theta \leq 1$. We compute that

$$
\begin{aligned}
d &= \theta x^2 + (1 - \theta)y^2 - (\theta x + (1 - \theta)y)^2 \\
&= \theta x^2 + (1 - \theta)y^2 - \theta^2 x^2 - (1 - \theta)^2 y^2 - 2\theta(1 - \theta)xy \\
&= x^2(\theta - \theta^2) + y^2[(1 - \theta) - (1 - \theta)^2] - 2\theta(1 - \theta)xy \\
&= x^2\theta(1 - \theta) + y^2\theta(1 - \theta) - 2\theta(1 - \theta)xy \\
&= \theta(1 - \theta)(x^2 + y^2 - 2xy) \\
&= \theta(1 - \theta)(x - y)^2.
\end{aligned}
$$

Now $\theta \geq 0$, $1 - \theta \geq 0$ and $(x - y)^2 \geq 0$. Hence $d \geq 0$.

EXAMPLE 3.3

If $C \subset R^2$ is the unit disk, i.e., C is the set of all (x_1, x_2) satisfying $x_1^2 + x_2^2 \leq 1$, and

$$f(x_1, x_2) = ax_1 + bx_2,$$

where a and b are fixed numbers, then f is a convex function. To see this, let $x = (x_1, x_2) \in C$ and $y = (y_1, y_2) \in C$, $0 \leq \theta \leq 1$. Then

$$
\begin{aligned}
f(\theta x + (1 - \theta)y) &= f(\theta(x_1, x_2) + (1 - \theta)(y_1, y_2)) \\
&= f((\theta x_1 + (1 - \theta)y_1, \theta x_2 + (1 - \theta)y_2)) \\
&= a(\theta x_1 + (1 - \theta)y_1) + b(\theta x_2 + (1 - \theta)y_2) \\
&= \theta(ax_1 + bx_2) + (1 - \theta)(ay_1 + by_2) \\
&= \theta f(x) + (1 - \theta)f(y).
\end{aligned}
$$

In Example 3.3 the inequality in (1) is actually equality. This is in fact a general property of linear functions.

Theorem 3.1 *Let C be a convex subset of R^n. If f is a linear function defined on C then*

$$f(\theta x + (1 - \theta)y) = \theta f(x) + (1 - \theta)f(y) \tag{2}$$

for any $0 \leq \theta \leq 1$, and any points x and y in C. Thus any linear function is convex.

This result follows immediately from Definitions 1.4 and 3.1.

So far we have seen that linear functions are convex and Example 3.2 shows that $f(x) = x^2$ is convex on any interval. Before we can go very far in this subject we must increase our supply of convex functions. One way we can do this is the following. Suppose that we know that $f_1, \ldots, f_n$ are convex functions where f_i is defined on the interval $[a_i, b_i]$ consisting of all real numbers t satisfying $a_i \leq t \leq b_i$. Then we can define a function f on the convex subset C of R^n consisting of all points $x = (x_1, \ldots, x_n)$ for which $a_i \leq x_i \leq b_i$, (see Theorem 1.1(b)) by setting

$$f(x) = \sum_{i=1}^{n} f_i(x_i). \tag{3}$$

Then f is convex on C. For, if x and y are in C and $0 \leq \theta \leq 1$ then

$$
\begin{aligned}
f(\theta x + (1 - \theta)y) &= \sum_{i=1}^{n} f_i(\theta x_i + (1 - \theta)y_i) \\
&\leq \sum_{i=1}^{n} (\theta f_i(x_i) + (1 - \theta)f_i(y_i)) \\
&= \theta \sum_{i=1}^{n} f_i(x_i) + (1 - \theta) \sum_{i=1}^{n} f_i(y_i) \\
&= \theta f(x) + (1 - \theta)f(y).
\end{aligned}
$$

EXAMPLE 3.4

The function $f(x) = x_1^2 + x_2^2$ is convex on $C = \{(x_1, x_2) \in R^2 \mid 0 \le x_1 \le 1, 0 \le x_2 \le 1\}$. Since we know from Example 3.2 that $f_1(t) = t^2$ is convex on $[0, 1]$, we can apply the above argument.

EXAMPLE 3.5

A square is constructed on each of the sides of a triangle in the plane.

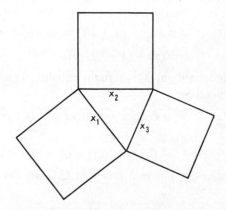

Show that if the perimeter of the triangle is not less than 1 then the sum of the areas of the three squares is at least $\frac{1}{3}$. We already know that the function

$$f(x) = x^2$$

is convex. Therefore

$$f\left(\frac{x_1 + x_2 + x_3}{3}\right) = f\left(\frac{1}{3}x_1 + \frac{2}{3}\left(\frac{x_2 + x_3}{2}\right)\right)$$

$$\le \frac{1}{3}f(x_1) + \frac{2}{3}f\left(\frac{x_2 + x_3}{2}\right)$$

$$\le \frac{1}{3}f(x_1) + \frac{2}{3}\frac{f(x_2) + f(x_3)}{2}$$

$$= \frac{1}{3}f(x_1) + \frac{1}{3}f(x_2) + \frac{1}{3}f(x_3)$$

$$= \frac{x_1^2 + x_2^2 + x_3^2}{3}.$$

In other words,

$$\left(\frac{x_1 + x_2 + x_3}{3}\right)^2 \leq \frac{x_1^2 + x_2^2 + x_3^2}{3}. \tag{4}$$

Now, the perimeter of the triangle is $x_1 + x_2 + x_3 \geq 1$. Hence (4) tells us that

$$\tfrac{1}{3} \leq x_1^2 + x_2^2 + x_3^2.$$

But, $x_1^2 + x_2^2 + x_3^2$ is the sum of the areas of the three squares and the result follows.

The following important inequality will help to widen further our class of examples of convex functions.

Theorem 3.2   *Let n be a positive integer and let x be a nonnegative number. Then*

$$x^n + (n - 1) \geq nx. \tag{5}$$

Proof.   If we multiply out

$$(x - 1)(x^{n-1} + x^{n-2} + \cdots + x - (n - 1)) \tag{6}$$

we obtain

$$x^n - nx + n - 1. \tag{7}$$

Thus it suffices to show that the expression in (6) is nonnegative. Now, if $0 \leq x \leq 1$ then $(x - 1) \leq 0$, and all of the $n - 1$ numbers $x^{n-1}, \ldots, x$ are less than or equal to 1. Hence the sum

$$x^{n-1} + \cdots + x - (n - 1) \tag{8}$$

is also less than or equal to 0. It follows that the product in (6) is nonnegative. If $x \geq 1$ then $(x - 1) \geq 0$ and each of $x^{n-1}, \ldots, x$ is at least 1. Hence the expression (8) is nonnegative and once again (6) is nonnegative.

We can now prove a theorem that will be the fundamental result in our study of convex functions.

Theorem 3.3   *If n is a positive integer and*

$$f(x) = x^n$$

is a function defined on the interval C consisting of all nonnegative real numbers x, then f is convex.

Proof.   Let x and y be two nonnegative numbers and let $0 \leq \theta \leq 1$. Let $z = \theta x + (1 - \theta)y$. We are going to prove that

$$f(x) \geq f(z) + n(x - z)z^{n-1}, \tag{9}$$

and

$$f(y) \geq f(z) + n(y - z)z^{n-1}. \tag{10}$$

Suppose this were done. Then we could multiply both sides of (9) by θ and both sides of (10) by $(1 - \theta)$ and add to obtain

$$\theta f(x) + (1 - \theta)f(y) \geq f(z) + nz^{n-1}[\theta(x - z) + (1 - \theta)(y - z)]$$
$$= f(z) + nz^{n-1}[\theta x + (1 - \theta)y - z]. \tag{11}$$

But $\theta x + (1 - \theta)y = z$ and therefore

$$\theta f(x) + (1 - \theta)f(y) \geq f(\theta x + (1 - \theta)y).$$

Thus we must prove (9) and (10) and our troubles will be over. Since the arguments are virtually the same we will only prove (9). Thus (9) becomes

$$x^n - z^n - nxz^{n-1} + nz^n \geq 0. \tag{12}$$

If $z = 0$ then, of course, (12) holds trivially. Thus assume that $z > 0$ and divide both sides of (12) by z^n to obtain the equivalent inequality

$$\left(\frac{x}{z}\right)^n - 1 - n\frac{x}{z} + n \geq 0$$

or, upon setting $t = \dfrac{x}{z} \geq 0$,

$$t^n + n - 1 \geq nt.$$

This is just the statement (5) with x replaced by t. This completes the proof.

EXAMPLE 3.6

The sum of the cubes of three positive numbers is at most 125. Show that their sum cannot exceed $5 \times 9^{1/3}$.

We know that $f(x) = x^3$ is convex for positive x. It follows that

$$f\left(\frac{x_1 + x_2 + x_3}{3}\right) = f\left(\frac{x_1}{3} + \frac{2}{3}\left(\frac{x_2 + x_3}{2}\right)\right)$$

$$\leq \frac{1}{3}f(x_1) + \frac{2}{3}f\left(\frac{x_2 + x_3}{2}\right)$$

$$\leq \frac{1}{3}f(x_1) + \frac{2}{3}\left(\frac{f(x_2) + f(x_3)}{2}\right)$$

$$= \frac{1}{3}f(x_1) + \frac{1}{3}f(x_2) + \frac{1}{3}f(x_3).$$

In other words,

$$\left(\frac{x_1 + x_2 + x_3}{3}\right)^3 \le \frac{1}{3}(x_1^3 + x_2^3 + x_3^3),$$

or, setting $s = x_1 + x_2 + x_3$,

$$s^3 \le 9(x_1^3 + x_2^3 + x_3^3).$$

If we let x_1, x_2, x_3 be the three positive numbers then

$$x_1^3 + x_2^3 + x_3^3 \le 125.$$

Hence

$$s^3 \le 9 \times 125, \qquad s \le 5 \times 9^{1/3}.$$

Many subsets C of R^n that we have encountered have the property that whenever $x \in C$, then $cx \in C$ for certain scalars c. In Example 1.1(c), if any n-tuple in P^n is multiplied by a positive number we obviously obtain another element of P^n. We have also been dealing with several functions with the property that if each x_i is replaced by cx_i then the function value is multiplied by a power of c; for example, $(cx_1)^2 + (cx_2)^2 = c^2(x_1^2 + x_2^2)$, $(cx_1)^3 + (cx_2)^3 + (cx_3)^3 = c^3(x_1^3 + x_2^3 + x_3^3)$. We formalize these ideas in the following definition.

Definition 3.2   (Cone. Homogeneous function)   *A subset C of R^n having the property that $cx \in C$, whenever $c \ge 0$ and $x \in C$, is called a cone. Let p be a positive integer. A function f defined on a cone C is said to be (positively) homogeneous of degree p if*

$$f(cx) = c^p f(x) \tag{13}$$

for any $x \in C$ and any $c \ge 0$.

Our next result shows how homogeneous functions are related to the idea of convexity.

Theorem 3.4   *Let f be a convex function defined on a convex cone C. If f is homogeneous of degree p and $f(x) > 0$ for all nonzero x in C, then the function g defined on C by*

$$g(x) = (f(x))^{1/p}$$

is convex on C.

Proof.   First observe that if $x \in C$ and $y \in C$ then $\frac{1}{2}x + \frac{1}{2}y \in C$ since C is convex. It follows that $2(x/2 + y/2) = x + y \in C$ because C is a cone. In other words, the sum of two points in C is also in C. Also note that

$$g(0) = (f(0x))^{1/p} = (0f(x))^{1/p} = 0$$

for any $x \in C$. Thus if either x or y is 0 it follows that

$$g(\theta x + (1 - \theta)y) = \theta g(x) + (1 - \theta)g(y), \qquad 0 \le \theta \le 1. \tag{14}$$

For example, if $y = 0$, the left side of (14) is just

$$g(\theta x) = (f(\theta x))^{1/p} = (\theta^p f(x))^{1/p} = \theta(f(x))^{1/p} = \theta g(x).$$

The right side of (14) is also $\theta g(x)$. Now assume that both x and y are in C and are different from 0. Then

$$f\left(\frac{x}{g(x)}\right) = \left(\frac{1}{g(x)}\right)^p f(x) = \frac{1}{f(x)} f(x) = 1, \tag{15}$$

and similarly

$$f\left(\frac{y}{g(y)}\right) = 1. \tag{16}$$

Hence, for any θ, $0 \le \theta \le 1$, we have, by (15) and (16),

$$g\left(\theta \frac{x}{g(x)} + (1 - \theta) \frac{y}{g(y)}\right) = \left(f\left(\theta \frac{x}{g(x)} + (1 - \theta) \frac{y}{g(y)}\right)\right)^{1/p} \tag{17}$$

$$\le \left(\theta f\left(\frac{x}{g(x)}\right) + (1 - \theta) f\left(\frac{y}{g(y)}\right)\right)^{1/p}$$

$$= (\theta + (1 - \theta))^{1/p}$$

$$= 1.$$

Let

$$\theta = \frac{g(x)}{g(x) + g(y)},$$

and observe that since $g(x)$ and $g(y)$ are not 0 and are nonnegative it follows that $0 \le \theta \le 1$. Then

$$1 - \theta = \frac{g(y)}{g(x) + g(y)}$$

and

$$\theta \frac{x}{g(x)} + (1 - \theta) \frac{y}{g(y)} = \frac{x + y}{g(x) + g(y)}.$$

Thus (17) becomes

$$g\left(\frac{x + y}{g(x) + g(y)}\right) \le 1. \tag{18}$$

But $g(cz) = cg(z)$ for any $c > 0$, and any $z \in C$ and hence (18) implies that

$$g(x + y) \le g(x) + g(y). \tag{19}$$

Now let α satisfy $0 \le \alpha \le 1$. Then we have from (19)

$$g(\alpha x + (1 - \alpha)y) \le g(\alpha x) + g((1 - \alpha)y)$$

$$= \alpha g(x) + (1 - \alpha)g(y).$$

In other words, g is convex.

EXAMPLE 3.7

The nonnegative orthant in R^n,

$$C = \{x \mid x \in R^n, x = (x_1, \ldots, x_n), x_i \geq 0\},$$

is a convex cone. In order to check this we must show that $cx \in C$ for any $x \in C$ and any $c \geq 0$ and that $\theta x + (1 - \theta) y \in C$ for any x and y in C and $0 \leq \theta \leq 1$. Both of these facts are trivial to verify.

EXAMPLE 3.8

Let x_1, x_2, y_1, y_2 be nonnegative numbers for which

$$x_1^3 + x_2^3 \leq 27$$

and

$$y_1^3 + y_2^3 \leq 8.$$

Show that

$$(x_1 + y_1)^3 + (x_2 + y_2)^3 < 125.$$

We know from Example 3.7 that the points in the plane with nonnegative coordinates constitute a convex cone C and from Theorem 3.3 we know that the function t^3 is convex for nonnegative t. Hence the function

$$f(x) = x_1^3 + x_2^3, \qquad x = (x_1, x_2) \in C,$$

is convex on C. Also if $c \geq 0$ then

$$f(cx) = (cx_1)^3 + (cx_2)^3$$
$$= c^3(x_1^3 + x_2^3).$$

In other words, f is homogeneous of degree 3. It follows, by direct application of Theorem 3.4, that the function

$$g(x) = (f(x))^{1/3} = (x_1^3 + x_2^3)^{1/3}$$

is convex on C. Thus

$$g\left(\frac{x+y}{2}\right) \leq \frac{g(x) + g(y)}{2} \tag{20}$$

for any x and y in C. But $g(cx) = cg(x)$ and hence (20) becomes

$$g(x+y) \leq g(x) + g(y),$$

or

$$((x_1 + y_1)^3 + (x_2 + y_2)^3)^{1/3} \leq (x_1^3 + x_2^3)^{1/3} + (y_1^3 + y_2^3)^{1/3}.$$

It is given that $x_1^3 + x_2^3 \leq 27$ and $y_1^3 + y_2^3 \leq 8$, and thus

$$(x_1 + y_1)^3 + (x_2 + y_2)^3 \leq 125.$$

We can generalize the idea in this last example to obtain an important inequality.

Theorem 3.5   (Minkowski inequality)   *Let* $x_1, \ldots, x_n, y_1, \ldots, y_n$ *be non-negative numbers. Then, if p is a positive integer,*

$$(\sum_{i=1}^{n} (x_i + y_i)^p)^{1/p} \leq (\sum_{i=1}^{n} x_i^p)^{1/p} + (\sum_{i=1}^{n} y_i^p)^{1/p}.$$

Proof.   From Theorem 3.3 we know that t^p is a convex function for nonnegative t. Hence

$$f(x) = \sum_{i=1}^{n} x_i^p$$

is convex on the cone C consisting of all $x = (x_1, \ldots, x_n)$ for which $x_i \geq 0$, $i = 1, \ldots, n$. Also,

$$f(cx) = \sum_{i=1}^{n} (cx_i)^p = c^p f(x).$$

It follows from Theorem 3.4 that

$$g(x) = (f(x))^{1/p}$$

is convex on C. Now, $g(cx) = cg(x)$ and therefore

$$g(x + y) = 2g\left(\frac{x + y}{2}\right)$$

$$\leq 2 \frac{(g(x) + g(y))}{2}$$

$$= g(x) + g(y).$$

In other words,

$$(\sum_{i=1}^{n} (x_i + y_i)^p)^{1/p} \leq (\sum_{i=1}^{n} x_i^p)^{1/p} + (\sum_{i=1}^{n} y_i^p)^{1/p}.$$

EXAMPLE 3.9

Let P_1, P_2, P_3 be three points in R^3 and let d_{ij} denote the distance from P_i to P_j. Prove the "triangle inequality":

$$d_{13} \leq d_{12} + d_{23}.$$

Let $P_1 = (a_1, a_2, a_3)$, $P_2 = (b_1, b_2, b_3)$ and $P_3 = (c_1, c_2, c_3)$. Then the distance from P_1 to P_2 is given by the Pythagorean theorem as

$$d_{12} = ((a_1 - b_1)^2 + (a_2 - b_2)^2 + (a_3 - b_3)^2)^{1/2}.$$

Similarly,

$$d_{13} = ((a_1 - c_1)^2 + (a_2 - c_2)^2 + (a_3 - c_3)^2)^{1/2},$$

$$d_{23} = ((b_1 - c_1)^2 + (b_2 - c_2)^2 + (b_3 - c_3)^2)^{1/2}.$$

Let $x_i = a_i - b_i$, $y_i = b_i - c_i$, and note that $x_i + y_i = a_i - c_i$, $i = 1, 2, 3$. We know the function t^2 is convex for any t and hence the function

$$f(x) = \sum_{i=1}^{3} x_i^2$$

is convex for all $x \in R^3$. It follows from Theorem 3.4 that

$$g(x) = (f(x))^{1/2}$$

is convex for all $x \in R^3$. Hence

$$d_{13} = (\sum_{i=1}^{3} (a_i - c_i)^2)^{1/2}$$

$$= (\sum_{i=1}^{3} (x_i + y_i)^2)^{1/2}$$

$$= g(x + y)$$

$$\leq g(x) + g(y)$$

$$= (\sum_{i=1}^{3} (a_i - b_i)^2)^{1/2} + (\sum_{i=1}^{3} (b_i - c_i)^2)^{1/2}$$

$$= d_{12} + d_{23}.$$

In our next theorem we assemble a number of easy and interesting results.

Theorem 3.6   (a)   *Let f be a convex function defined on a convex set C and let $x^1, \ldots, x^n$ be n elements of C. If $\theta_i \geq 0$, $i = 1, \ldots, n$, and*

$$\sum_{i=1}^{n} \theta_i = 1$$

then

$$f(\sum_{i=1}^{n} \theta_i x^i) \leq \sum_{i=1}^{n} \theta_i f(x^i). \tag{21}$$

(b)   *If C is a convex set and $f_1, \ldots, f_n$ are convex functions defined on C then their sum,*

$$s(x) = \sum_{i=1}^{n} f_i(x),   \tag{22}$$

and their maximum,

$$m(x) = \max_{i} (f_i(x)),   \tag{23}$$

are both convex functions on C.

(c)   *If f is a convex function defined on the convex polyhedron $H(a^1, \ldots, a^p)$ spanned by $a^1, \ldots, a^p$ in R^n, then the largest value that f assumes on the polyhedron is*

$$\max (f(a^i)).$$

In other words, a convex function defined on a polyhedron assumes its maximum value on an element of the spanning set.

(d)   *Let f be a convex function defined on the convex set C and assume that $a \le f(x) \le b$ for any $x \in C$. Let g be a convex nondecreasing function defined on $[a, b]$; that is, g is convex and if $a \le t_1 < t_2 \le b$ then $g(t_1) \le g(t_2)$. Then the composition of g and f, defined on C by*

$$h(x) = g(f(x)),$$

is also convex.

(e)   *If f is a convex function defined on a convex set C and r is a real number then both*

$$\{x \mid x \in C \text{ and } f(x) \le r\}   \tag{24}$$

and

$$\{x \mid x \in C \text{ and } f(x) < r\}   \tag{25}$$

are convex subsets of C.

Proof.   (a)   We prove (21) by induction on n. If $n = 2$ then (21) is just the definition of convexity. Thus, assume (21) is true for $n - 1$. If θ_1 is 1 or 0 we are reduced to the case of one summand (trivial) or to the case of at most $n - 1$ nonzero summands (the induction hypothesis). Thus assume that $0 < \theta_1 < 1$.   Then

$$f(\sum_{i=1}^{n} \theta_i x^i) = f\left(\theta_1 x^1 + (1 - \theta_1) \sum_{i=2}^{n} \frac{\theta_i}{1 - \theta_1} x^i\right)   \tag{26}$$

$$\le \theta_1 f(x^1) + (1 - \theta_1) f\left(\sum_{i=2}^{n} \frac{\theta_i}{1 - \theta_1} x^i\right).$$

Now

$$\sum_{i=2}^{n} \frac{\theta_i}{1 - \theta_1} = \frac{1}{1 - \theta_1} (\sum_{i=2}^{n} \theta_i)$$

$$= \frac{1}{1 - \theta_1} (1 - \theta_1)$$

$$= 1.$$

Hence, by the induction hypothesis,

$$f\left(\sum_{i=2}^{n} \frac{\theta_i}{1-\theta_1} x^i\right) \le \sum_{i=2}^{n} \frac{\theta_i}{1-\theta_1} f(x^i).$$

Thus from (26) we have

$$f(\sum_{i=1}^{n} \theta_i x^i) \le \theta_1 f(x^1) + (1-\theta_1) \sum_{i=2}^{n} \frac{\theta_i}{1-\theta_1} f(x^i)$$

$$= \theta_1 f(x^1) + \sum_{i=2}^{n} \theta_i f(x^i)$$

$$= \sum_{i=1}^{n} \theta_i f(x^i),$$

which completes the induction.

(b)   We easily compute that

$$s(\theta x + (1-\theta)y) = \sum_{i=1}^{n} f_i(\theta x + (1-\theta)y)$$

$$\le \sum_{i=1}^{n} \theta f_i(x) + (1-\theta)f_i(y)$$

$$= \theta \sum_{i=1}^{n} f_i(x) + (1-\theta) \sum_{i=1}^{n} f_i(y)$$

$$= \theta s(x) + (1-\theta)s(y).$$

Similarly,

$$m(\theta x + (1-\theta)y) = \max_i (f_i(\theta x + (1-\theta)y))$$

$$\le \max_i (\theta f_i(x) + (1-\theta)f_i(y))$$

$$\le \max_i (\theta f_i(x)) + \max_i ((1-\theta)f_i(y))$$

$$= \theta \max_i (f_i(x)) + (1-\theta) \max_i (f_i(y))$$

$$= \theta m(x) + (1-\theta)m(y).$$

In this argument we have used two simple facts about maxima of sets of numbers that are found in Exercise 5.

(c)   Any $x \in H(a^1, \ldots, a^p)$ is of the form

$$x = \sum_{i=1}^{p} \theta_i a^i, \qquad \theta_i \ge 0, \qquad \sum_{i=1}^{p} \theta_i = 1.$$

Therefore we have from (a)

$$f(x) = f(\sum_{i=1}^{p} \theta_i a^i) \le \sum_{i=1}^{p} \theta_i f(a^i).$$

The result then follows from Theorem 1.3(a).

(d)   We have
$$h(\theta x + (1 - \theta)y) = g(f(\theta x + (1 - \theta)y)).$$
Now,
$$f(\theta x + (1 - \theta)y) \le \theta f(x) + (1 - \theta)f(y)$$
and, since $a \le f(x) \le b$ and $a \le f(y) \le b$, it follows that
$$a \le \theta f(x) + (1 - \theta)f(y) \le b.$$

Since g is a nondecreasing convex function defined on the interval $[a, b]$ we have
$$g(f(\theta x + (1 - \theta)y)) \le g(\theta f(x) + (1 - \theta)f(y))$$
$$\le \theta g(f(x)) + (1 - \theta)g(f(y)).$$

(e)   Let S denote the set (24). Then if $x \in S$, $y \in S$ and $0 \le \theta \le 1$ we compute that
$$f(\theta x + (1 - \theta)y) \le \theta f(x) + (1 - \theta)f(y)$$
$$\le \theta r + (1 - \theta)r$$
$$= r.$$

Thus $\theta x + (1 - \theta)y \in S$ and S is convex. The case when the inequality is strict is equally obvious.

EXAMPLES 3.10

(a)   If x_1, x_2 and x_3 are any three numbers then
$$\left(\frac{x_1}{3} + \frac{x_2}{2} + \frac{x_3}{6}\right)^2 \le \tfrac{1}{3}x_1^2 + \tfrac{1}{2}x_2^2 + \tfrac{1}{6}x_3^2.$$

For, $f(x) = x^2$ is a convex function and we may take $\theta_1 = \tfrac{1}{3}$, $\theta_2 = \tfrac{1}{2}$, $\theta_3 = \tfrac{1}{6}$ in (21).

(b)   The function $f(x) = x^2 + 3x^3 + 5x^5$ is convex for $x \ge 0$. This is true because x^2, x^3, and x^5 are all convex for $x \ge 0$. Also $3x^3$ and $5x^5$ are convex and hence we can apply Theorem 3.6(b).

(c)   The function $f(x) = |x|^3$ is convex for all numbers x. We first observe that
$$|x| = \max\,\{x, -x\}$$
and hence, by Theorem 3.6(b), $|x|$ is convex. We know that t^3 is convex and increasing for all $t \ge 0$ and hence, by Theorem 3.6(d), $|x|^3$ is convex.

(d)   The unit ball in R^3 is a convex set. To see this, first note that the function

$$f(x) = x_1^2 + x_2^2 + x_3^2$$

is convex (we have seen this several times). Hence, by Theorem 3.6(e), the set of all $x = (x_1, x_2, x_3)$ for which

$$x_1^2 + x_2^2 + x_3^2 \leq 1,$$

i.e., the unit ball, is a convex set.

(e)   Find the maximum value of the function $f(x) = x_1^2 + x_2^3 + 5x_3^7$ as $x = (x_1, x_2, x_3)$ varies over the triangle C in R^3 whose vertices are $(1, 0, 0)$, $(0, 1, 0)$, $(0, 0, 1)$. The triangle C is, of course, the totality of points

$$x = \theta_1(1, 0, 0) + \theta_2(0, 1, 0) + \theta_3(0, 0, 1),$$

$$\theta_i \geq 0, \qquad \theta_1 + \theta_2 + \theta_3 = 1.$$

Moreover, the function f is convex on C and hence we may apply Theorem 3.6(c) to conclude that the maximum value of f is one of the three numbers

$$f((1, 0, 0)), \quad f((0, 1, 0)), \quad f((0, 0, 1)).$$

The largest of these is 5.

Quiz

Answer **true** or **false**:

1.   If $a \leq x \leq b$ and $a \leq y \leq b$, $0 \leq \theta \leq 1$, then $a \leq \theta x + (1 - \theta)y \leq b$.

2.   If x_1, x_2, y_1 and y_2 are positive numbers then

$$((x_1 + y_1)^5 + (x_2 + y_2)^5)^{1/5} \leq (x_1^5 + x_2^5)^{1/5} + (y_1^5 + y_2^5)^{1/5}.$$

3.   The function $f(x) = (x_1^2 + x_2^2)^3$ is convex for $x_1 \geq 0$, $x_2 \geq 0$.

4.   The function $f((x_1, x_2)) = x_1 x_2$ is convex for nonnegative x_1 and x_2.

5.   The function $f(x) = -|x|$ is concave for all real x.

6.   If f is a convex function defined on a convex set C and r is a positive number, then rf is a convex function defined on C.

7.   Any constant function is convex.

8.   If $t > 0$ then $\dfrac{t^{n-1}}{n} + \dfrac{1}{t} \geq \dfrac{1}{nt}$ whenever n is a positive integer.

9.   If $f(x)$ and $g(x)$ are convex functions defined for $x > 0$ and $g(x) > 0$ then $[f(x)/g(x)]$ is convex.

10.   If $f(x) > 0$ for $x > 0$ and the composite function $f(f)$ is convex for $x > 0$ then f is convex for $x > 0$.

Exercises

1. Prove that the function $f(x) = x^4 + 5|x|$ is convex for all real numbers x.

2. Using Theorem 3.6(d) prove that $f(x) = |x|^p$ is convex for all real numbers x whenever p is a positive integer.

3. Using the preceding exercise and Theorem 3.4, prove that if p is a positive integer and $x_1, \ldots, x_n, y_1, \ldots, y_n$ are any $2n$ real numbers then

    $$\left(\sum_{i=1}^{n} |x_i + y_i|^p\right)^{1/p} \le \left(\sum_{i=1}^{n} |x_i|^p\right)^{1/p} + \left(\sum_{i=1}^{n} |y_i|^p\right)^{1/p}.$$

4. Which is larger:

    $$(3^3 + 7^3 + 11^3 + 15^3 + 19^3)^{1/3}$$

    or

    $$(1^3 + 3^3 + 5^3 + 7^3 + 9^3)^{1/3} + (2^3 + 4^3 + 6^3 + 8^3 + 10^3)^{1/3}?$$

5. Let $a_1, \ldots, a_n, b_1, \ldots, b_n$ be $2n$ real numbers and let $\theta \ge 0$. Prove that

    $$\max_i (a_i + b_i) \le \max_i a_i + \max_i b_i,$$

    and

    $$\max_i \theta a_i = \theta \max_i a_i.$$

6. If n is a positive integer and $r > 0$ then, using the identity

    $$\left(\frac{r^{n+1} - 1}{n+1}\right) - \left(\frac{r^n - 1}{n}\right) = \frac{r - 1}{n(n+1)}(nr^n - r^{n-1} - r^{n-2} - \cdots - r - 1),$$

    show that

    $$\frac{r^{n+1} - 1}{n+1} \ge \frac{r^n - 1}{n}.$$

    (*Hint:*   Check the two cases $r \ge 1$, $r < 1$ separately.)

7. Using Exercise 6, show that if $r > 0$ and n and m are positive integers, $n > m$, then

    $$\frac{r^n - 1}{n} \ge \frac{r^m - 1}{m}.$$

    (*Hint:*   Go from m to n one step at a time using the result in Exercise 6.)

8. From Exercise 7 show that if $\gamma = n/m > 1$ is a rational number and $r > 0$ then

    $$r^\gamma - \gamma r + \gamma - 1 \ge 0.$$

    (*Hint:*   In Exercise 7 replace r by $r^{1/m}$. Compare this result with Theorem 3.2.)

9. Let $f(x) = x^\alpha$, $\alpha > 1$, α rational, $x \ge 0$. Show that if x and y are nonnegative numbers, $0 \le \theta \le 1$, and $z = \theta x + (1 - \theta)y$ then

    $$f(x) \ge f(z) + \alpha(x - z)z^{\alpha - 1}.$$

    Compare this result with (9).

(*Hint:*   The desired inequality is equivalent to

$$x^\alpha - z^\alpha - \alpha x z^{\alpha-1} + \alpha z^\alpha \geq 0.$$

If $z > 0$ divide both sides by z^α, set $r = x/z$, to obtain the equivalent statement

$$r^\alpha + \alpha - 1 \geq \alpha r$$

which is precisely the inequality in Exercise 8.)

10.   By mimicking the proof of Theoerm 3.3 show that if α is a rational number greater than 1 then $f(x) = x^\alpha$ is a convex function for $x \geq 0$.

11.   Generalize the Minkowski inequality to the case in which p is a rational number greater than 1.

4

Rings

4.1 Introduction to Rings

In this chapter we are going to study several mathematical objects that every high school graduate has encountered before. Thus we shall examine properties of integers, some aspects of complex numbers, the structure of polynomials, and the theory of polynomial equations. It is quite probable that most students have studied these items at different times and in separate contexts. However, in this section we shall introduce a very simple and useful mathematical abstraction called a *ring* that will permit us to study seemingly separate mathematical systems all at the same time.

Definition 1.1   (Ring)   *A ring R is a set together with two operations called addition, $+$, and multiplication, $\times$, which obey the following rules. For every a, b, and c in R,*

(i)   *(closure) $a + b$ and $a \times b$ are uniquely determined elements of R,*

(ii)   *(associative laws)*

$$(a + b) + c = a + (b + c),$$

$$(a \times b) \times c = a \times (b \times c),$$

(iii)   *(commutative law of addition) $a + b = b + a$,*

(iv)   *(existence of additive identity) there exists a unique element in R, called zero and denoted by 0, such that $a + 0 = 0 + a = a$,*

(v)   *(existence of additive inverse) there is a unique element denoted by $-a$ satisfying $a + (-a) = (-a) + a = 0$,*

(vi)   *(distributive laws)*

$$a \times (b + c) = (a \times b) + (a \times c),$$

$$(b + c) \times a = (b \times a) + (c \times a).$$

EXAMPLES 1.1

(a)   Let R be the set of ordinary even integers and let " $+$ " and " $\times$ " be the usual operations of addition and multiplication. Then, of course, the rules (i)-(vi) are just the ordinary laws of arithmetic. For example, if a and b are even integers then $a + b$ and $a \times b$ are both even integers and (i) is verified.

(b)   Let R be the set of all real valued functions with domain the closed interval $0 \le x \le 1$ and which satisfy $f(0) = f(1) = 0$. The addition and multiplication of two functions is defined as usual by

$$(f + g)(x) = f(x) + g(x),$$

$$(f \times g)(x) = f(x)g(x).$$

Then clearly $(f + g)(0) = f(0) + g(0) = 0 + 0 = 0 = f(1) + g(1) = (f+g)(1)$. Hence $f + g$, and similarly, $f \times g$, are in R. The zero function is the function whose value for each x is 0. The additive inverse of f is the function $-f$ whose values are given by $(-f)(x) = -(f(x))$. The remaining rules for a ring are easily checked.

(c)   Let R be the set of all 2×2 matrices of the form

$$A = \begin{bmatrix} 0 & a \\ 0 & 0 \end{bmatrix} \tag{1}$$

where a is an integer. Let the addition and multiplication of matrices be the operations in R (see Definitions 3.1 and 3.5 of Chapter 2). Thus,

$$\begin{bmatrix} 0 & a \\ 0 & 0 \end{bmatrix} + \begin{bmatrix} 0 & b \\ 0 & 0 \end{bmatrix} = \begin{bmatrix} 0 & a + b \\ 0 & 0 \end{bmatrix},$$

$$\begin{bmatrix} 0 & a \\ 0 & 0 \end{bmatrix} \begin{bmatrix} 0 & b \\ 0 & 0 \end{bmatrix} = \begin{bmatrix} 0 & 0 \\ 0 & 0 \end{bmatrix}.$$

The zero matrix is

$$0 = \begin{bmatrix} 0 & 0 \\ 0 & 0 \end{bmatrix}$$

and the additive inverse of the matrix A in (1) is

$$-A = \begin{bmatrix} 0 & -a \\ 0 & 0 \end{bmatrix}.$$

Since $A \times B = 0$ for any A and B we can check, for example, that

$$A \times (B + C) = 0 = 0 + 0 = (A \times B) + (A \times C).$$

Similar trivial calculations can be used to verify the rest of the rules in Definition 1.1.

(d)   Let R be the set of all $n \times n$ matrices with real numbers as entries and let $+$ and $\times$ be matrix addition and multiplication. Then R is a ring. The most difficult of the rules to verify is the associative law for multiplication. This was done in Exercise 2, Section 3, Chapter 2. However, we will verify it again here in order to review for the student some of the properties of matrix multiplication. Thus, let A, B and C be $n \times n$ matrices. We wish to verify that

$$A(BC) = (AB)C, \tag{2}$$

where we have dropped the multiplication sign " $\times$ " in conformity with our previous notation for matrix multiplication. The (s, j) entry of (BC) is

$$\sum_{k=1}^{n} b_{sk}c_{kj}$$

and hence the (i, j) entry of $A(BC)$ is

$$\sum_{s=1}^{n} a_{is}\left(\sum_{k=1}^{n} b_{sk}c_{kj}\right),$$

which is equal to

$$\sum_{k=1}^{n} \left(\sum_{s=1}^{n} a_{is}b_{sk}\right)c_{kj}. \tag{3}$$

Now, the (i, k) entry of AB is just

$$\sum_{s=1}^{n} a_{is}b_{sk}$$

and hence (3) is just the formula for the (i, j) entry of $(AB)C$. We have proved that the (i, j) entry of $A(BC)$ is the same as the (i, j) entry of $(AB)C$. The rest of the rules for a ring may be similarly verified.

(e)   Let R be the set of integers 0, 1, 2, 3. Define addition and multiplication as follows: $a \oplus b$ is the remainder obtained upon dividing the ordinary sum of a and b by 4. Similarly, $a \otimes b$ is the remainder obtained upon dividing the ordinary product of a and b by 4. We have circled the operations to distinguish them from the customary operations on integers. The addition and multiplication tables are

$\oplus$	0	1	2	3		$\otimes$	0	1	2	3	
0	0	1	2	3		0	0	0	0	0	
1	1	2	3	0		1	0	1	2	3	(4)
2	2	3	0	1		2	0	2	0	2	
3	3	0	1	2		3	0	3	2	1	

From a look at the tables (4) we see immediately that (i) and (iii) of Definition 1.1 hold. The zero in R is 0 and $-1 = 3$, $-2 = 2$, $-3 = 1$. Thus (v) holds.

Let us examine (ii). By definition,

$$a \oplus b = r_1$$

where

$$a + b = 4q + r_1, \qquad 0 \le r_1 < 4, \tag{5}$$

i.e., q is the quotient and r_1 the remainder that are obtained upon dividing $a + b$ by 4. Then

$$(a \oplus b) \oplus c = r_1 \oplus c = r_2$$

where

$$r_1 + c = 4Q + r_2, \qquad 0 \le r_2 < 4. \tag{6}$$

Again, Q is the quotient and r_2 the remainder obtained upon dividing $r_1 + c$ by 4. Thus, substituting (5) in (6), we have

$$a + b - 4q + c = 4Q + r_2,$$

or

$$a + b + c = 4(q + Q) + r_2.$$

In other words, $r_2 = (a \oplus b) \oplus c$ is the remainder obtained upon dividing the ordinary sum $a + b + c$ by 4. By a similar computation we see that $a \oplus (b \oplus c)$ is also the remainder obtained upon dividing $a + b + c$ by 4. Hence

$$a \oplus (b \oplus c) = (a \oplus b) \oplus c.$$

We can prove in an analogous fashion that

$$a \otimes (b \otimes c) = (a \otimes b) \otimes c.$$

(f) Let $e_1 = (1, 0)$ and $e_2 = (0, 1)$. The ring R will consist of all 2-tuples $(a, b) = ae_1 + be_2$, where a and b are real, and operations $\oplus$ and $\otimes$ are defined as follows:

$$(ae_1 + be_2) \oplus (ce_1 + de_2) = (a + c)e_1 + (b + d)e_2, \tag{7}$$

$$(ae_1 + be_2) \otimes (ce_1 + de_2) = (ac - bd)e_1 + (bc + ad)e_2. \tag{8}$$

The rules (i), (iii), and (v) are easy to verify: in fact,

$$0 = 0e_1 + 0e_2$$

and

$$-(ae_1 + be_2) = (-a)e_1 + (-b)e_2.$$

We check the associative law of multiplication. We have

$$[(ae_1 + be_2) \otimes (ce_1 + de_2)] \otimes (fe_1 + ge_2)$$

$$= [(ac - bd)e_1 + (bc + ad)e_2] \otimes (fe_1 + ge_2)$$

$$= [(ac - bd)f - (bc + ad)g]e_1 + [(ac - bd)g + (bc + ad)f]e_2$$

$$= Ae_1 + Be_2,$$

whereas

$$(ae_1 + be_2) \otimes [(ce_1 + de_2) \otimes (fe_1 + ge_2)]$$

$$= (ae_1 + be_2) \otimes [(cf - dg)e_1 + (cg + df)e_2]$$

$$= [a(cf - dg) - b(cg + df)]e_1 + [b(cf - dg) + a(cg + df)]e_2$$

$$= A_1e_1 + B_1e_2 .$$

Now, if we compare A with A_1 and B and B_1, then we see immediately that $A = A_1$, $B = B_1$, and the associative law is proved. These computations may look familiar. Indeed, the ring R is, in fact, the set of complex numbers. We shall investigate complex numbers in great detail in Section 3 of this chapter.

(g)   Let R consist of all 2×2 matrices of the form $\begin{bmatrix} a & -b \\ b & a \end{bmatrix}$, a and b real numbers, with the usual matrix addition and multiplication as operations. Then R is a ring. To see this we need only verify closure. The rest of the rules follow from the corresponding properties of general $n \times n$ matrices. Observe that

$$\begin{bmatrix} a & -b \\ b & a \end{bmatrix} + \begin{bmatrix} c & -d \\ d & c \end{bmatrix} = \begin{bmatrix} a+c & -(b+d) \\ b+d & a+c \end{bmatrix} \in R.$$

Also

$$\begin{bmatrix} a & -b \\ b & a \end{bmatrix}\begin{bmatrix} c & -d \\ d & c \end{bmatrix} = \begin{bmatrix} ac - bd & -(ad + bc) \\ ad + bc & ac - bd \end{bmatrix} \in R.$$

(h)   If R is any ring then $a \times 0 = 0 \times a = 0$ for any $a \in R$. For,

$$a \times (a + 0) = a \times a + a \times 0,$$

and, since $a + 0 = a$,

$$a \times (a + 0) = a \times a.$$

Thus

$$a \times a = a \times a + a \times 0.$$

Add $-(a \times a)$ to both sides of this last equation to obtain

$$-(a \times a) + a \times a = (-(a \times a) + a \times a) + a \times 0,$$

or

$$0 = 0 + a \times 0,$$

and finally

$$0 = a \times 0.$$

A similar argument shows that $0 \times a = 0$.

Before we go on with our development of rings we want to make a few observations about the preceding examples. Notice that in (a) there is no element $e \in R$ for which $a \times e = e \times a = a$ for any $a \in R$. In other words, the integer 1, which acts as an identity with respect to multiplication, is not an even integer. On the other hand, if in (b) we define a function I by $I(x) = 1$, $0 < x < 1$, and $I(1) = I(0) = 0$ then clearly $I \times f = f \times I = f$ for any $f \in R$. Hence the ring in (b) does possess a multiplicative identity.

The examples (a), (b), (c), (e), and (f) all possess the property that for any two elements r and s in the ring in question, $r \times s = s \times r$. On the other hand, in (d), if we take

$$A = \begin{bmatrix} 0 & 1 \\ 1 & 0 \end{bmatrix}, \qquad B = \begin{bmatrix} 0 & -1 \\ 1 & 0 \end{bmatrix},$$

then

$$AB = \begin{bmatrix} 1 & 0 \\ 0 & -1 \end{bmatrix}$$

whereas

$$BA = \begin{bmatrix} -1 & 0 \\ 0 & 1 \end{bmatrix}.$$

Thus $AB \neq BA$. In other words, not every pair of elements in this ring commutes with respect to multiplication.

In examples (a), (b), and (f), if $r \times s = 0$ then either $r = 0$ or $s = 0$. This is obvious for examples (a) and (b). To verify the assertion for (f) we conclude from (8) that if $(ae_1 + be_2) \otimes (ce_1 + de_2) = 0$ then

$$ac - bd = 0, \qquad bc + ad = 0.$$

Suppose that $ae_1 + be_2 \neq 0$, i.e., not both $a = 0$ and $b = 0$. Then

$$\frac{a}{a^2 + b^2} e_1 - \frac{b}{a^2 + b^2} e_2 \in R$$

and we readily compute that

$$\left(\frac{a}{a^2 + b^2} e_1 - \frac{b}{a^2 + b^2} e_2 \right) \otimes (ae_1 + be_2) = e_1.$$

We have

$$\left(\frac{a}{a^2 + b^2} e_1 - \frac{b}{a^2 + b^2} e_2 \right) \otimes ((ae_1 + be_2) \otimes (ce_1 + de_2)) = 0, \qquad (9)$$

and using the associative law for multiplication in (9) we obtain

$$e_1 \otimes (ce_1 + de_2) = 0,$$

or

$$ce_1 + de_2 = 0.$$

Hence $c = d = 0$. In other words, if $ae_1 + be_2 \neq 0$ then $ce_1 + de_2 = 0$. On the other hand, in example (c) we have

$$\begin{bmatrix} 0 & a \\ 0 & 0 \end{bmatrix}\begin{bmatrix} 0 & b \\ 0 & 0 \end{bmatrix} = \begin{bmatrix} 0 & 0 \\ 0 & 0 \end{bmatrix}$$

for any a and b. Also in (e), $2 \otimes 2 = 0$.

The foregoing observations lead us to make the following definitions for a ring R. (We continue our numbering of ring properties from Definition 1.1.)

Definition 1.2 **(Properties of rings)** *Let R be a ring with the operations $+$ and $\times$. Then*

(vii) *(existence of multiplicative identity) if there exists an element $e \in R$ such that $a \times e = e \times a = a$ for any $a \in R$ then e is called a multiplicative identity for R,*

(viii) *(commutativity of multiplication) if $a \times b = b \times a$ for two elements a and b in R then these elements are said to commute; if every pair of elements commutes then R is called a commutative ring,*

(ix) *(existence of multiplicative inverse) if R has a multiplicative identity e and if for a nonzero $a \in R$ there exists a unique element, denoted by a^{-1}, for which $a \times a^{-1} = a^{-1} \times a = e$ then a is said to have a multiplicative inverse,*

(x) *(zero divisors) if $a \times b = 0$ and neither a nor b is 0 then a and b are called zero divisors.*

Let us return to Example 1.1(d) in which we considered the ring of all $n \times n$ matrices with real number entries. We want to examine a special subset of R, to be denoted by D, consisting of matrices A in which

$$a_{ij} = 0, \quad i \neq j, \quad a_{ii} = \alpha, \quad i, j = 1, \ldots, n. \tag{10}$$

Such matrices are called scalar matrices and, according to (10), all off-diagonal elements in such a matrix are zero while down the main diagonal a single element α appears in every position. We write $A = D(\alpha)$, i.e.,

$$D(\alpha) = \begin{bmatrix} \alpha & 0 & \cdots & 0 \\ 0 & \cdot & & \vdots \\ \vdots & & \cdot & 0 \\ 0 & \cdots & 0 & \alpha \end{bmatrix}.$$

If we multiply two of these scalar matrices together we immediately obtain from the definition of matrix multiplication that

$$D(\alpha)D(\beta) = \begin{bmatrix} \alpha\beta & 0 & \cdots & 0 \\ 0 & \cdot & & \vdots \\ \vdots & & \cdot & 0 \\ 0 & \cdots & 0 & \alpha\beta \end{bmatrix}.$$

In other words,

$$D(\alpha)D(\beta) = D(\alpha\beta). \qquad (11)$$

Similarly, we immediately compute that

$$D(\alpha) + D(\beta) = D(\alpha + \beta). \qquad (12)$$

Thus the set D is closed under addition and multiplication and is itself a ring with respect to the standard matrix operations. We wish to relate the ring of real numbers R to this newly constructed ring D. In order to do this define a function $\varphi : R \to D$ by

$$\varphi(\alpha) = D(\alpha), \qquad \alpha \in R. \qquad (13)$$

Clearly if $\varphi(\alpha) = \varphi(\beta)$, then $D(\alpha) = D(\beta)$ and $\alpha = \beta$. Hence φ is 1-1 and it is obviously onto D. Moreover from (11) and (12) we have

$$\varphi(\alpha\beta) = \varphi(\alpha)\varphi(\beta), \qquad (14)$$

$$\varphi(\alpha + \beta) = \varphi(\alpha) + \varphi(\beta) \qquad (15)$$

for all real numbers α and β. In other words, the operations in R are exactly mirrored in D: for any statement that is true about R there is a corresponding statement that is true about D. For example, R has the number 1 as a multiplicative identity. Thus from (14),

$$\varphi(1)\varphi(\alpha) = \varphi(1\alpha) = \varphi(\alpha) = \varphi(\alpha 1) = \varphi(\alpha)\varphi(1).$$

In other words, $\varphi(1)$ acts as a multiplicative identity in D. Again, the multiplication in R is commutative so that

$$\varphi(\alpha)\varphi(\beta) = \varphi(\alpha\beta) = \varphi(\beta\alpha) = \varphi(\beta)\varphi(\alpha).$$

Hence the multiplication in D is commutative.

We abstract this situation in the following definition.

Definition 1.3   (Isomorphism)   *Two rings R_1 and R_2 are said to be isomorphic if there exists a 1-1 function $\varphi : R_1 \to R_2$ such that φ is onto R_2 and*

$$\varphi(a + b) = \varphi(a) + \varphi(b), \qquad (16)$$

$$\varphi(a \times b) = \varphi(a) \times \varphi(b) \qquad (17)$$

for all a and b in R_1. The function φ is called an isomorphism.

We remark that in (16) and (17) the addition and multiplication signs on the left are the operations in R_1 whereas those on the right are in R_2. We have not distinguished between them notationally in order to avoid clumsy and confusing formulas. There is no chance for error if the student will remember to combine elements according to the operations of the ring in which the elements lie.

The importance of the concept of isomorphism is that it relieves us of the burden of studying a number of outwardly different rings that are in fact identical in form (that is, "isomorphic"!).

EXAMPLE 1.2

Let R_1 be the ring in Example 1.1(f), consisting of all 2-tuples $(a, b) = ae_1 + be_2$, a and b real, with operations $\oplus$ and $\otimes$ given as before by the formulas

$$(ae_1 + be_2) \oplus (ce_1 + de_2) = (a + c)e_1 + (b + d)e_2,$$

$$(ae_1 + be_2) \otimes (ce_1 + de_2) = (ac - bd)e_1 + (bc + ad)e_2.$$

Let R_2 be the ring in Example 1.1(g) consisting of all 2×2 matrices of the form

$$\begin{bmatrix} a & -b \\ b & a \end{bmatrix},$$

a and b real. Define a function $\varphi : R_1 \to R_2$ by the formula

$$\varphi(ae_1 + be_2) = \begin{bmatrix} a & -b \\ b & a \end{bmatrix}.$$

Clearly φ is 1-1 and onto R_2. Next we compute that

$$\varphi((ae_1 + be_2) \oplus (ce_1 + de_2)) = \varphi((a + c)e_1 + (b + d)e_2)$$

$$= \begin{bmatrix} a + c & -(b + d) \\ b + d & a + c \end{bmatrix}$$

$$= \begin{bmatrix} a & -b \\ b & a \end{bmatrix} + \begin{bmatrix} c & -d \\ d & c \end{bmatrix}$$

$$= \varphi(ae_1 + be_2) + \varphi(ce_1 + de_2).$$

Also,

$$\varphi((ae_1 + be_2) \otimes (ce_1 + de_2)) = \varphi((ac - bd)e_1 + (bc + ad)e_2)$$

$$= \begin{bmatrix} ac - bd & -(ad + bc) \\ ad + bc & ac - bd \end{bmatrix}$$

$$= \begin{bmatrix} a & -b \\ b & a \end{bmatrix}\begin{bmatrix} c & -d \\ d & c \end{bmatrix}$$

$$= \varphi(ae_1 + be_2)\varphi(ce_1 + de_2).$$

We have verified the two properties (16) and (17) that φ must have in order to be an isomorphism. It follows that the rings R_1 and R_2 are isomorphic.

As an example of the use of this information recall that if not both a and b are zero then $z = ae_1 + be_2$ has an inverse, namely

$$z^{-1} = \frac{a}{a^2 + b^2} e_1 - \frac{b}{a^2 + b^2} e_2.$$

Then

$$\varphi(z^{-1}) = \begin{bmatrix} \dfrac{a}{a^2 + b^2} & \dfrac{b}{a^2 + b^2} \\ -\dfrac{b}{a^2 + b^2} & \dfrac{a}{a^2 + b^2} \end{bmatrix}$$

is the inverse of $\varphi(z)$. For, $zz^{-1} = z^{-1}z = e_1$ and

$$\varphi(e_1) = \begin{bmatrix} 1 & 0 \\ 0 & 1 \end{bmatrix},$$

the multiplicative identity in R_2. Then

$$\varphi(z)\varphi(z^{-1}) = \varphi(zz^{-1}) = \varphi(e_1),$$

$$\varphi(z^{-1})\varphi(z) = \varphi(z^{-1}z) = \varphi(e_1).$$

Hence $\varphi(z^{-1})$ satisfies the definition of an inverse of $\varphi(z)$. As a check we can directly verify that

$$\begin{bmatrix} a & -b \\ b & a \end{bmatrix} \begin{bmatrix} \dfrac{a}{a^2 + b^2} & \dfrac{b}{a^2 + b^2} \\ -\dfrac{b}{a^2 + b^2} & \dfrac{a}{a^2 + b^2} \end{bmatrix} = \begin{bmatrix} 1 & 0 \\ 0 & 1 \end{bmatrix},$$

and similarly for the product in the other order.

In the preceding example we saw that the nonzero elements in the rings R_1 and R_2 had inverses. On the other hand, the ring in Example 1.1(e) does not have this property since $2 \neq 0$ and yet there is no element b such that $2 \otimes b = 1$ (see the table for $\otimes$ in (4)). This important property of having an inverse merits a definition of its own.

Definition 1.4   (Units in a ring)   *If R is a ring with a multiplicative identity, denoted here by e, and a nonzero element $c \in R$ has an inverse, then c is called a unit in R.*

EXAMPLES 1.3

(a)   The units in the ring R of integers (using ordinary addition and multiplication) are the integers 1 and -1.

(b)   The units in the ring R of real numbers are just all the nonzero real numbers.

(c)   The units in the ring R of Example 1.1(e) are 1 and 3.

Quiz

Answer **true** or **false**:

1.   The ring in Example 1.1(e) has no multiplicative identity.

2.   The multiplicative identity of the ring in Example 1.1(f) is (1, 0).

3.   The ring in Example 1.1(g) contains no zero divisors.

4.   The ring in Example 1.1(g) is commutative.

5.   The only zero divisor in the ring in Example 1.1(e) is 2.

6.   The multiplicative inverse of 3 is 3 in the ring in Example 1.1(e).

7.   If R_1 and R_2 are isomorphic and R_1 has zero divisors then so does R_2.

8.   Every nonzero element in the ring in Example 1.1(g) is a unit.

9.   There are always at least two distinct units in a ring with a multiplicative identity 1, namely 1 and -1.

10.   The following tables for $+$ and $\times$ using the integers 0, 1 define a ring:

+	0	1		×	0	1
0	0	1		0	0	0
1	1	0		1	0	1

Exercises

1.   Prove the associative law for multiplication in the ring in Example 1.1(e).

2.   Let R be a ring and let R_1 be a nonempty subset of R which is closed under the operations in R. Assume also that $a - b \in R_1$, whenever a and $b \in R_1$. Show that R_1 is a ring with the same operations as those in R.

3.   Show that the set of 2×2 matrices of the form $\begin{bmatrix} a & -b \\ b & a \end{bmatrix}$, where a and b are integers, constitute a ring using the operations of Example 1.1(g). What are the units in this ring?

4.   Prove that if $\varphi : R_1 \to R_2$ is an isomorphism then $\varphi^{-1} : R_2 \to R_1$ is an isomorphism. (R_1 and R_2 are rings.)

5.   Let $\mathfrak{a}$ be a set of rings. Define a relation $\sim$ among the rings in $\mathfrak{a}$: $R \sim S$ if and only if R and S are isomorphic. Prove that $\sim$ is an equivalence relation.

6.   The following problems refer to the ring R of Example 1.1(f).
   (a)   Find the multiplicative inverse of $3e_1 + 4e_2$.

    (b) Find $z \in R$ such that $(3e_1 + 4e_2) \otimes z = e_1$.

    (c) Find $z \in R$ such that $(3e_1 + 4e_2) \otimes z = 2e_1 - 4e_2$.

    (d) Find all $z \in R$ for which $z^2 = z \otimes z = z$.

7. Using the results of Exercise 6(c) find a 2×2 matrix A such that

$$\begin{bmatrix} 3 & -4 \\ 4 & 3 \end{bmatrix} A = \begin{bmatrix} 2 & 4 \\ -4 & 2 \end{bmatrix}.$$

8. Find all 2×2 matrices A in the ring of Example 1.1(g) for which

$$A^2 = AA = A.$$

(*Hint*: Use Exercise 6(d) and the isomorphism φ of Example 1.2.)

    In the following exercises let R be the set $\{0, 1, 2, 3, 4, 5\}$. Define addition and multiplication as follows: $a \oplus b$ is the remainder obtained upon dividing the ordinary sum of a and b by 6; similarly, $a \otimes b$ is the remainder obtained upon dividing the ordinary product of a and b by 6.

9. Construct the tables for $\oplus$ and $\otimes$ analogous to (4).

10. Show that R is a ring.

11. Find the units in R.

12. Find the zero divisors in R.

4.2 Integers

    Let I denote the ring of integers together with operations of ordinary addition and multiplication.

    The ring I is a very "well-behaved" ring: it is denumerable; it is commutative; it has a (multiplicative) identity, 1; and it has no zero divisors. The only flaw in this otherwise excellent character is the failure of the elements of I, other than 1 and -1, to have multiplicative inverses which are integers; that is, I has only 1 and -1 as units. Indeed, this failure causes a lot of algebraic complications. For example, an equation $ax = b$, where a and b are integers ($a \neq 0$), may have no solutions x which are integers. On the other hand, this initially awkward attribute of I enriches its structure and makes its study more interesting. Much of the present section is devoted essentially to the study of the solvability in integers of the equation $ax = b$, and to a development of the resulting concepts.

    Definition 2.1 (Divisor, prime) *If a and b are integers, $b \neq 0$, and $a = bc$ for some $c \in I$, then b is called a divisor of a, and a is said to be divisible by b. If b divides a, we write $b \mid a$; if b does not divide a, we write $b \nmid a$. A divisor of 1 is called a unit (see* Definition 1.4). *If $a = ub$, where u is a unit, then a and b are said to be associates. If $b \mid a$ and b is neither a unit nor an associate of a then b is* *said to be a proper divisor of a. An integer is called a prime if it is not a unit and has no proper divisors. A nonzero integer is called composite if it has proper divisors.*

Clearly, the only units of I are 1 and -1 (see Example 1.3(a)) and the only associates of an integer a are $-a$ and a itself. In other words, u is a unit if and only if its absolute value is 1, and a and b are associates if and only if their absolute values are equal. Also, an integer p is a prime if p is neither 1 nor -1 and if $p = ab$ implies that either a or b is a unit.

After a preliminary theorem we shall state and prove a basic result, dating back to Euclid (ca. 300 B.C.) and probably to a century before Euclid, called the *Division Algorithm*. The term "algorithm" means a mathematical procedure for obtaining a definite answer after a finite number of steps. The word "algorithm" is a corruption of the Arabic word *al-khuwārizmi* derived from the name of a ninth-century mathematician.

Theorem 2.1
(a) *If a, b, c are integers, $a \neq 0$, and $ab = ac$, then $b = c$.*
(b) *If $a \mid b$ and $b \mid c$ then $a \mid c$.*
(c) *If $a \mid b$ and $a \mid c$ then $a \mid (mb + nc)$, for any integers m and n.*

Proof.
(a) If $ab = ac$ then $a(b - c) = 0$ and, since $a \neq 0$, we must have $b - c = 0$, i.e., $b = c$.

(b) If $a \mid b$ and $b \mid c$ then $b = ha$ and $c = kb$ for some integers h and k. But then $c = kha$ and $a \mid c$.

(c) If $a \mid b$ and $a \mid c$ then $b = sa$ and $c = ta$ for some integers s and t. Thus $mb + nc = msa + nta = (ms + nt)a$ and $a \mid (mb + nc)$.

EXAMPLE 2.1

Show that a and b are associates if and only if $a \mid b$ and $b \mid a$. If a and b are associates then $a = ub$, for some unit u, and thus $b \mid a$. But $b = u^{-1}a$, since u is a unit, and therefore $a \mid b$. Conversely, if $a \mid b$ and $b \mid a$ then $b = ha$ and $a = kb$ for some integers h and k. Combining the two equalities we obtain $b = hkb$ or $1b = hkb$ and, by Theorem 2.1(a), $hk = 1$, and both h and k are units. Thus a and b are associates. It should be noted that the above proof can be used to establish a similar result for any ring. It is perhaps a bit too elaborate for the simple case of the ring of integers where, after all, two integers a and b are associates if and only if either $a = b$ or $a = -b$.

Theorem 2.2 (**Division Algorithm**) *If a and b are integers, $b \neq 0$, then there exist unique integers q and r such that*

$$a = bq + r, \qquad 0 \leq r < |b|. \tag{1}$$

Proof.   We first prove the existence of integers r and q satisfying (1).
If $a = 0$ we can choose $q = r = 0$. Assume first that $a > 0$ and $b > 0$. Let q
be such a nonnegative integer that

$$bq \le a < b(q + 1).$$

The number q can be determined in a finite number of steps since $0 < a \le ab$
and therefore q must be one of the numbers $0, 1, \dots, a$. Set $r = a - bq$.
Then $a = bq + r$ and $0 \le r < b$. (This shows the existence of q and r when a
and b are both positive. We proceed to show that the other alternatives
depend on this case.) If $a > 0$ and $b < 0$, then $-b > 0$ and hence there exist
integers q and r such that $a = (-b)q + r$, and $0 \le r < |b|$. Rewriting we have
$a = b(-q) + r$. If $a < 0$ and $b > 0$ then $-a > 0$, and again there exist integers
q and r such that $-a = bq + r$ where $0 \le r < b$. Now, if $r = 0$ then $a = b(-q)$,
and if $0 < r < b$ then $a = b(-q - 1) + (b - r)$ where $0 < (b - r) < b$. Lastly,
if $a < 0$ and $b < 0$ then q and r can be found such that $-a = (-b)q + r$ and
$0 \le r < |b|$. Thus if $r = 0$ then $a = bq$, and if $0 < r < -b$ then $a = b(q + 1) +$
$(-b - r)$, where $0 < (-b - r) < |b|$. To prove uniqueness, suppose that

$$a = bq + r = bq' + r', \qquad 0 \le r < |b|, \qquad 0 \le r' < |b|.$$

Then $b(q - q') = r' - r$, and thus

$$|b|\,|q - q'| = |r' - r|. \tag{2}$$

Now, $|r' - r| \le r' < |b|$ while the left-hand side of (2) is a nonnegative
integral multiple of $|b|$. Thus both sides of (2) are zero and $q = q'$, $r = r'$.

Definition 2.2   (Greatest common divisor)   *If $\{a_1, \dots, a_n\}$ is a nonempty
set of integers not all of which are 0 and $d \mid a_j, j = 1, \dots, n$, then d is called a
common divisor of $a_1, \dots, a_n$. Let d be a positive common divisor of $a_1, \dots,
a_n$ with the property that whenever $c \mid a_j, j = 1, \dots, n$, then $c \mid d$. Then d is called
the greatest common divisor, abbreviated g.c.d., of $a_1, \dots, a_n$. We write
$d = \text{g.c.d.}(a_1, \dots, a_n)$ or, if a confusion with elements of R^n is not likely, we
denote the g.c.d. of $a_1, \dots, a_n$ by $(a_1, \dots, a_n)$. If a and b are integers such that
$(a, b) = 1$, then a and b are said to be relatively prime.*

Theorem 2.3   *If a and b are integers then*

$$(a, b) = (b, a) = (|a|, |b|); \tag{3}$$

$$(a, 0) = |a|, \qquad \text{if } a \ne 0; \tag{4}$$

$$(a, 1) = 1; \tag{5}$$

$$(a, b) = |a|, \qquad \text{if and only if } a \mid b. \tag{6}$$

These statements follow immediately from Definitions 2.1 and 2.2.
Our next theorem, the celebrated *Euclidean Algorithm*, gives a procedure
for computing the g.c.d. of two integers.

Theorem 2.4 **(Euclidean Algorithm)** *Let a and b be integers, $b \neq 0$,* and let

$$a = bq_1 + r_1, \qquad 0 < r_1 < |b|,$$

$$b = r_1 q_2 + r_2, \qquad 0 < r_2 < r_1,$$

$$r_1 = r_2 q_3 + r_3, \qquad 0 < r_3 < r_2,$$

$$\vdots$$

$$r_{k-1} = r_k q_{k+1} + r_{k+1}, \qquad 0 < r_{k+1} < r_k, \tag{7}$$

$$r_k = r_{k+1} q_{k+2}.$$

Then $(a, b) = r_{k+1}$.

Proof. We note that, since $0 < r_{k+1} < \cdots < r_1 < |b|$, the procedure described in the statement of the theorem must terminate after at most $|b|$ steps. We first prove that $r_{k+1} \,|\, a$ and $r_{k+1} \,|\, b$. We have from the last line of (7) that $r_{k+1} \,|\, r_k$. Therefore, by successive applications of Theorem 2.1(c),

$$r_{k+1} \,|\, r_{k-1} \qquad \text{because} \qquad r_k q_{k+1} + r_{k+1} = r_{k-1};$$

$$r_{k+1} \,|\, r_{k-2} \qquad \text{because} \qquad r_{k-1} q_k + r_k = r_{k-2};$$

$$\vdots$$

$$r_{k+1} \,|\, r_1 \qquad \text{because} \qquad r_2 q_3 + r_3 = r_1;$$

$$r_{k+1} \,|\, b \qquad \text{because} \qquad r_1 q_2 + r_2 = b;$$

and finally $r_{k+1} \,|\, a$ because $bq_1 + r_1 = a$. Hence r_{k+1} is a common divisor of a and b. Actually we could rephrase our argument in terms of a formal induction. In this situation we feel that the preceding discussion is clearer. We next use a more formally organized induction to prove that

$$r_s = m_s a + n_s b, \qquad s = 1, \ldots, k+1, \tag{8}$$

where m_s and n_s are integers. In the cases $s = 1$ and $s = 2$ we have $r_1 = a - q_1 b$ and $r_2 = b - r_1 q_2 = b - (a - q_1 b)q_2 = -q_2 a + (1 + q_1 q_2)b$. Assume now that s is a fixed integer, $2 < s \leq k+1$ and suppose that $r_t = m_t a + n_t b$ whenever $t < s$. We have

$$r_s = r_{s-2} - r_{s-1} q_s$$

$$= m_{s-2} a + n_{s-2} b - (m_{s-1} a + n_{s-1} b)q_s$$

$$= (m_{s-2} - m_{s-1} q_s)a + (n_{s-2} - n_{s-1} q_s)b$$

$$= m_s a + n_s b.$$

Thus (8) is established for $s = 1, \ldots, k + 1$. In particular, for $s = k + 1$,

$$r_{k+1} = ma + nb, \tag{9}$$

where m and n are written for m_{k+1} and n_{k+1}. Now, suppose that c is a common divisor of a and b. Then, by (9) and Theorem 2.1(c), $c \mid (ma + nb)$ and thus $c \mid r_{k+1}$. Hence r_{k+1} is the g.c.d. of a and b.

EXAMPLE 2.2

Find the g.c.d. of 590,121 and 120,802.
We compute

$$590{,}121 = 120{,}802 \times 4 + 106{,}913,$$

$$120{,}802 = 106{,}913 \times 1 + 13{,}889,$$

$$106{,}913 = 13{,}889 \times 7 + 9{,}690,$$

$$13{,}889 = 9{,}690 \times 1 + 4{,}199,$$

$$9{,}690 = 4{,}199 \times 2 + 1{,}292,$$

$$4{,}199 = 1{,}292 \times 3 + 323,$$

$$1{,}292 = 323 \times 4.$$

Hence $(590{,}121 \, , 120{,}802) = 323$.

The following result is a consequence of (9) and Theorem 2.4.

Theorem 2.5   *If a and b are integers, not both 0, then there exist integers m and n such that*

$$(a, b) = ma + nb.$$

We show in the following example how to evaluate the numbers m and n using the Euclidean Algorithm.

EXAMPLE 2.3

Find integers m and n such that

$$(1{,}820 \, , 1{,}287) = 1{,}820m + 1{,}287n.$$

We first use the Euclidean Algorithm to evaluate the g.c.d. of 1,820 and 1,287:

$$1,820 = 1,287 \times 1 + 533,$$
$$1,287 = 533 \times 2 + 221,$$
$$533 = 221 \times 2 + 91,$$
$$221 = 91 \times 2 + 39,$$
$$91 = 39 \times 2 + 13,$$
$$39 = 13 \times 3.$$

Hence $(1,820, 1,287) = 13$. Next, using the above equalities, we obtain

$$13 = 91 - 39 \times 2$$
$$= 91 - (221 - 91 \times 2) \times 2 = 91 \times 5 - 221 \times 2$$
$$= (533 - 221 \times 2) \times 5 - 221 \times 2 = 533 \times 5 - 221 \times 12$$
$$= 533 \times 5 - (1,287 - 533 \times 2) \times 12 = -1,287 \times 12 + 533 \times 29$$
$$= -1,287 \times 12 + (1,820 - 1,287 \times 1) \times 29 = 1,820 \times 29 - 1,287 \times 41.$$

Thus

$$(1,820, 1,287) = 1,820 \times 29 + 1,287 \times (-41).$$

The next result is sometimes called the "*Fundamental Theorem of Arithmetic*."

Theorem 2.6   *If* $a \mid bc$ *and* $(a, b) = 1$ *then* $a \mid c$. *In words, if a divides the product of two integers and is relatively prime to one of them, it must divide the other.*

Proof.   The g.c.d. of a and b is 1 and therefore, by Theorem 2.5, there exist integers m and n such that $ma + nb = 1$. Thus $mac + nbc = c$. Now, $a \mid mac$ and $a \mid bc$ and therefore, by Theorem 2.1(c), $a \mid (mac + nbc)$, i.e., $a \mid c$.

Theorem 2.7
(a)   *If p is a prime and $p \mid \prod_{i=1}^{n} a_i$ then $p \mid a_k$ for some k.*
(b)   *If $(a, b) = d$ and $a = a'd$, $b = b'd$ then $(a', b') = 1$.*
(c)   *If $c \mid a$ and $c \mid b$ and $c \neq (a, b)$ then $c < (a, b)$. In other words, the* g.c.d. *is the greatest of the common divisors.*

Proof.   (a)   We use induction on n. If $n = 2$, the result follows by Theorem 2.6. For, p is a prime dividing $a_1 a_2$ and therefore either $p \mid a_1$ or $(p, a_1) = 1$ and then $p \mid a_2$. Now assume that the result holds for products of fewer than n factors. Then, by Theorem 2.6, if

$$p \mid a_1 \left(\prod_{i=2}^{n} a_i \right)$$

then either $p \mid a_1$ or

$$p \mid \prod_{i=2}^{n} a_i.$$

But in the latter case $p \mid a_k$ for some k, $2 \le k \le n$, by the induction hypothesis.

(b)   By Theorem 2.1(c), there exist integers m and n such that $ma + nb = d$. Therefore $ma'd + nb'd = d$ or $ma' + nb' = 1$. Again, by Theorem 2.1(c), $(a', b') \mid (ma' + nb')$; that is, $(a', b') \mid 1$, and therefore $(a', b') = 1$.

(c)   This is virtually a restatement of the definition of (a, b) since the g.c.d. of a and b is a positive number and a multiple of any common divisor of a and b.

We are now in a position to prove the main theorem on factorization of integers into primes.

Theorem 2.8   *Every nonzero nonunit integer a is a prime or a product of primes. Moreover this factorization of a is unique, up to associates and order, in the following sense: if*

$$a = \prod_{i=1}^{r} p_i = \prod_{j=1}^{s} q_j,$$

where $p_1, \ldots, p_r$, $q_1, \ldots, q_s$ are primes, then $r = s$ and $|p_i| = |q_{\sigma(i)}|$ for some permutation $\sigma \in S_r$.

Proof.   Let a be an integer different from 0, -1, and 1. Assume first that $a > 1$ and use induction on a to establish the existence of a factorization into primes. If $a = 2$ then it is prime. Suppose $a > 2$ and assume that every integer smaller than a and greater than 1 is either a prime or a product of primes. If a is a prime there is nothing to prove. If a is composite then $a = bc$ where neither b nor c are units. But then $a = |a| = |b||c|$ and both $|b|$ and $|c|$ are smaller than a. Thus, by the induction hypothesis, both $|b|$ and $|c|$ are primes or products of primes and therefore a is a product of primes. If $a < -1$ then $|a| > 1$ and $|a| = \prod_{i=1}^{r} p_i$, where p_i is a prime, $i = 1, \ldots, r$. But then $-p_1$ is a prime and either $a = -p_1$, if $r = 1$, or $a = (-p_1) \prod_{i=2}^{r} p_i$ which is a product of primes. We shall now prove the uniqueness of this factorization, up to associates and order. Let

$$\prod_{i=1}^{r} |p_i| = \prod_{j=1}^{s} |q_j| \tag{10}$$

where $p_1, \ldots, p_r$, $q_1, \ldots, q_s$ are primes. We can assume without loss of generality that $r \le s$ and we use induction on r. If $r = 1$ then the left side of (10) is a prime; therefore, the right side must also be a prime and $|p_1| = |q_1|$. Suppose now that $r > 1$ and that the theorem holds for products of fewer than r primes. We see from (10) that the prime $|p_1|$ divides

$$\prod_{j=1}^{s} |q_j|.$$

Hence, by Theorem 2.7(a), $|p_1|$ divides $|q_k|$ for some k. But both $|p_1|$ and $|q_k|$

are primes and therefore $|p_1| = |q_k|$. Thus, by Theorem 2.1(a), we may cancel $|p_1| = |q_k|$ from both sides of (10) to obtain

$$\prod_{i=2}^{r} |p_i| = \prod_{\substack{j=1 \\ j \neq k}}^{s} |q_j|.$$

By the induction hypothesis, $r - 1 = s - 1$ (hence $r = s$) and $|p_i| = |q_{\tau(i)}|$, $i = 2, \ldots, r$, where τ is a 1-1 function from $\{2, \ldots, r\}$ onto $\{1, \ldots, k-1, k+1, \ldots, r\}$. Define $\sigma \in S_r$, by $\sigma(1) = k$, $\sigma(i) = \tau(i)$ for $i \neq 1$. Then $|p_i| = |q_{\sigma(i)}|$, $i = 1, \ldots, r$.

We conclude the first part of our study of integers by proving, as an example, a special case of the famous *Fermat's Last Theorem*. Fermat, a French mathematician of the seventeenth century, noted on the margin of his copy of the book "Diophantus" by Bachet that the equation $x^n + y^n = z^n$ has no solution in positive integers for $n > 2$ and added: "For this I have discovered a truly wonderful proof, but the margin is too small to contain it." To this day, in spite of efforts by many great mathematicians, Fermat's conjecture remains unproved in its general form. It is regarded as doubtful whether Fermat indeed had a correct proof of his conjecture.

EXAMPLE 2.4

Prove that $p_1^n + p_2^n \neq p_3^n$ for any positive primes p_1, p_2, p_3 and any integer $n > 1$. Suppose that

$$p_1^n + p_2^n = p_3^n. \tag{11}$$

We shall use the following obvious fact repeatedly: a power of an integer is even or odd according as the integer itself is even or odd and conversely. If both p_1 and p_2 are even or both are odd, then $p_1^n + p_2^n = p_3^n$ is even and therefore $p_3 = 2$ since 2 is the only positive even prime. But, since $p_1 \geq 2$ and $p_2 \geq 2$, we would then have $2^n + 2^n \leq p_1^n + p_2^n = 2^n$, an obvious impossibility. Thus if (11) holds, one of p_1 and p_2 is even and one odd, say, $p_1 = 2$ and p_2 is odd. Then p_3 is odd and

$$p_1^n = 2^n = p_3^n - p_2^n = (p_3 - p_2)(p_3^{n-1} + p_3^{n-2}p_2 + \cdots + p_3 p_2^{n-2} + p_2^{n-1}). \tag{12}$$

By Theorem 2.8, $p_3 - p_2$ divides 2^n and hence must itself be a nonnegative power of 2, say 2^k. Now k must be a positive integer, since both p_3 and p_2 are odd and therefore $p_3 - p_2 \neq 1$. We know that p_2 and p_3 are odd primes and hence $p_2 > 2$ and $p_3 > 2$. Hence after cancelling $2^k = p_3 - p_2$ from both sides, the equation (12) yields

$$\begin{aligned}
2^{n-k} &= p_3^{n-1} + p_3^{n-2}p_2 + \cdots + p_3 p_2^{n-2} + p_2^{n-1} \\
&\geq p_3^{n-1} + p_2^{n-1} \\
&> 2^{n-1} + 2^{n-1} \\
&= 2^n
\end{aligned}$$

which is a contradiction. It follows that (11) cannot hold.

We now define a certain equivalence relation on integers and study the resulting equivalence classes. There is a deep connection between this study and the preceding material in the present section.

Definition 2.3   (Congruence) *Let m be a positive integer. Two integers a and b are said to be congruent modulo m if $m \mid (a - b)$. This is written*

$$a \equiv b \bmod m.$$

EXAMPLE 2.5

Let a, b, and m be integers, $m > 0$, and let $a = mq_1 + r_1$, $b = mq_2 + r_2$, where q_1, q_2, r_1, r_2 are integers and $0 \leq r_1 < m$, $0 \leq r_2 < m$. Show that $a \equiv b$ mod m if and only if $r_1 = r_2$. To see this observe that if $r_1 = r_2$ then $a - mq_1 = b - mq_2$ and $a - b = m(q_1 - q_2)$, that is, $m \mid (a - b)$ and $a \equiv b$ mod m. Conversely, if $a \equiv b$ mod m then $a - b = km$ for some integer k. Then

$$(mq_1 + r_1) - (mq_2 + r_2) = km,$$

and

$$m(q_1 - q_2 - k) = r_2 - r_1. \tag{13}$$

But $m > |r_2 - r_1|$ and therefore both sides of (13) are 0 and $r_1 = r_2$.

Theorem 2.9

(a)   *Congruence modulo m is an equivalence relation.*

(b)   *If $a \equiv b$ mod m and $c \equiv d$ mod m then $a + c \equiv b + d$ mod m and $ab \equiv cd$ mod m.*

Proof.   (a)   First, $m \mid (a - a)$ and therefore $a \equiv a$ mod m. Second, if $a \equiv b$ mod m then $m \mid (a - b)$ and therefore $m \mid (b - a)$, i.e., $b \equiv a$ mod m. Last, if $a \equiv b$ mod m and $b \equiv c$ mod m, that is, if $m \mid a - b$ and $m \mid b - c$, then, by Theorem 2.1(c), $m \mid ((a - b) + (b - c))$, and since $a - c = (a - b) + (b - c)$, it follows that $a \equiv c$ mod m.

(b)   The congruences $a \equiv b$ mod m and $c \equiv d$ mod m imply that $m \mid (a - b)$ and $m \mid (c - d)$. Therefore, by Theorem 2.1(c), $m \mid ((a - b) + (c - d))$ and since $(a - b) + (c - d) = (a + c) - (b + d)$ we have $m \mid ((a + c) - (b + d))$. Hence $a + c \equiv b + d$ mod m. Also, by the same theorem, $m \mid (c(a - b) + b(c - d))$, that is, $m \mid (ac - bd)$ and therefore $ac \equiv bd$ mod m.

Definition 2.4   (Residue classes) *Let a and m be integers, $m > 0$. The equivalence class consisting of all integers congruent to a, modulo m, is called the residue class of a, modulo m, and is denoted by $[a]_m$ or simply by $[a]$, once m is understood. We define two operations between residue classes, $[a]_m$ and $[b]_m$, called addition and multiplication modulo m:*

$$[a] + [b] = [a + b], \tag{14}$$

$$[a][b] = [ab]. \tag{15}$$

These definitions require some justification. We have defined operations on sets by means of operations on arbitrarily chosen representative elements of the sets. We must show that the definitions do not really depend on the actual choice of the representative elements; in other words, we must show that if $[a] = [a']$ and $[b] = [b']$ then $[a+b] = [a' + b']$ and $[ab] = [a'b']$. Now, $[a] = [a']$ and $[b] = [b']$ if and only if $m \mid (a - a')$ and $m \mid (b - b')$. But then, by Theorem 2.1(c), $m \mid ((a - a') + (b - b'))$, and $(a - a') + (b - b') = (a + b) - (a' + b')$. Thus $m \mid ((a + b) - (a' + b'))$; that is, $[a + b] = [a' + b']$. Similarly, $m \mid ((a - a')b + a'(b - b'))$ and $(a - a')b + a'(b - b') = ab - a'b'$. Thus $m \mid (ab - a'b')$ and therefore $[ab] = [a'b']$.

EXAMPLE 2.6

Find all residue classes $[x]_6$ satisfying

$$[4][x] + [2] = [0], \qquad \text{(all residue classes taken mod 6).} \qquad (16)$$

Example 2.5 tells us that $[0], [1], [2], [3], [4], [5]$ are all the residue classes mod 6 and substituting these in succession for $[x]$ we find that equation (16) is satisfied only by $[x] = [1]$ and $[x] = [4]$.

EXAMPLE 2.7

Let a be a positive integer written in the decimal notation; that is, $a = a_n 10^n + \cdots + a_1 10 + a_0$. Show that a is divisible by 11 if and only if the number $(a_0 + a_2 + \cdots) - (a_1 + a_3 + \cdots)$ is divisible by 11. In the following argument all the residue classes will be modulo 11. Thus $[10] = [-1]$ and $[10^t] = [10]^t = [-1]^t = [(-1)^t]$. It follows that $[10^t] = [1]$ or $[10^t] = [-1]$ according as t is even or odd. Hence

$$[a] = [a_n][10^n] + [a_{n-1}][10^{n-1}] + \cdots + [a_1][10] + [a_0]$$

$$= [a_n][(-1)^n] + [a_{n-1}][(-1)^{n-1}] + \cdots + [a_1][-1] + [a_0][1]$$

$$= [1]([a_0] + [a_2] + [a_4] + \cdots) + [-1]([a_1] + [a_3] + [a_5] + \cdots)$$

$$= [(a_0 + a_2 + a_4 + \cdots) - (a_1 + a_3 + a_5 + \cdots)].$$

Therefore, a is divisible by 11, i.e., $[a] = [0]$, if and only if $[(a_0 + a_2 + a_4 + \cdots) - (a_1 + a_3 + a_5 + \cdots)] = [0]$; in other words, if and only if $(a_0 + a_2 + a_4 + \cdots) - (a_1 + a_3 + a_5 + \cdots)$ is divisible by 11.

For example, the integer 70,549,281 is divisible by 11, since $(1 + 2 + 4 + 0) - (8 + 9 + 5 + 7) = -22$ is divisible by 11. On the other hand, the integer 261,509,713 is not divisible by 11 since $(3 + 7 + 0 + 1 + 2) - (1 + 9 + 5 + 6) = -8$ is not divisible by 11.

Theorem 2.10

(a) *Residue classes modulo m form a commutative ring with an identity; this ring is denoted by I_m.*

(b) *The ring I_m, $m \geq 2$, has zero divisors if and only if m is composite.*

Proof. (a) By the discussion following Definition 2.4, the set of residue classes modulo m is closed under addition and multiplication. It is a simple matter to check that all the other ring postulates are satisfied.

(b) Suppose that $[a][b] = [0]$, and that $[a] \neq [0]$, $[b] \neq [0]$. Then $[ab] = [0]$, that is, $m \mid ab$ while $m \nmid a$ and $m \nmid b$. Hence, by Theorem 2.7(a), m cannot be a prime. Conversely, let m be composite, i.e., $m = pq$ where $1 < p \leq q < m$. Then $[p][q] = [pq] = [m] = [0]$ and both $[p]$ and $[q]$ are zero divisors.

Example 2.8

Show that $31 \mid (5^{2n} + 5^n + 1)$ if n is a positive integer and $3 \nmid n$. We compute modulo 31:

$$[5^n - 1][5^{2n} + 5^n + 1] = [5^{3n} - 1]$$
$$= [125]^n + [-1]$$
$$= [1]^n + [-1]$$
$$= [0].$$

Now, 31 is prime and therefore, by Theorem 2.10(b), I_{31} has no zero divisors. Thus either $[5^n - 1] = [0]$ or $[5^{2n} + 5^n + 1] = [0]$. But if $3 \nmid n$ then $n = 3m + 1$ or $n = 3m + 2$ for some nonnegative integer m. In the first case we compute that

$$[5^n - 1] = [5^{3m+1} - 1]$$
$$= [5][125]^m + [-1]$$
$$= [5][1]^m + [-1]$$
$$= [4]$$
$$\neq [0],$$

while if $n - 3m + 2$ we have

$$[5^n - 1] = [5^{3m+2} - 1]$$
$$= [25][125]^m + [-1]$$
$$= [25][1]^m + [-1]$$
$$= [24]$$
$$\neq [0].$$

Thus, in either case, if $3 \nmid n$ then $[5^{2n} + 5^n + 1] = [0]$, i.e., $31 \mid (5^{2n} + 5^n + 1)$.

We conclude this section with a theorem on solutions of linear equations in I_m.

Theorem 2.11   *The equation*

$$[a][x] = [b], \tag{17}$$

all residue classes taken in I_m, has a solution $[x]$ if and only if $(a, m) \mid b$. If $(a, m) \mid b$ then the equation is satisfied by exactly (a, m) of the residue classes in I_m.

Proof.   If $[a][x] = [b]$ then $ax + km = b$ for some integer k and, by Theorem 2.1(c), we have $(a, m) \mid b$. Conversely, assume $(a, m) \mid b$ and let $b = n(a, m)$. By Theorem 2.5, there exist integers s and t such that $as + mt = (a, m)$. Then $asn + mtn = b$, that is, $[a][sn] = [b]$. Hence $[sn]$ is a solution of equation (17). Let $d = (a, m)$, $m = kd$ and $a = hd$. Then, if $[x_0]$ is a solution of (17), we assert that the residue classes,

$$[x_0 + kt], \qquad t = 0, \ldots, d - 1, \tag{18}$$

are also solutions. To see this, observe that $m = kd$, $kd \mid ka$, and hence $m \mid akt$, that is, $[akt] = [0]$. Therefore,

$$\begin{aligned} [a][x_0 + kt] &= [a][x_0] + [akt] \\ &= [a][x_0] \\ &= [b]. \end{aligned}$$

Also the d residue classes (18) are distinct. For, if $0 \le t_1 < t_2 \le d - 1$ then $t_2 - t_1 < d$ and $m \nmid k(t_2 - t_1)$ because $m = kd > k(t_2 - t_1)$. Thus $[x_0 + kt_1] \ne [x_0 + kt_2]$. It remains to be shown that all solutions of (17) are included among the residue classes (18). Suppose that $[a][y_0] = [b]$. Then $[a]([x_0] - [y_0]) = [0]$ or $m \mid a(x_0 - y_0)$. Now $m = kd$ and $a = hd$ and therefore $k \mid h(x_0 - y_0)$. By Theorem 2.7(b), $(k, h) = 1$ and, by Theorem 2.6, it follows that $k \mid (x_0 - y_0)$, that is, $y_0 = x_0 + kt$ for some integer t.

EXAMPLE 2.9

Find all the solutions in I_{93} of the equation

$$[36][x] = [15]. \tag{19}$$

We use the Euclidean Algorithm to find integers s and t such that $36s + 93t = (36, 93)$:

$$93 = 36 \times 2 + 21,$$

$$36 = 21 \times 1 + 15,$$

$$21 = 15 \times 1 + 6,$$

$$15 = 6 \times 2 + 3,$$

$$6 = 3 \times 2.$$

Hence
$$d = (36, 93)$$
$$= 3$$
$$= 15 - 6 \times 2$$
$$= 15 - (21 - 15 \times 1) \times 2 = 15 \times 3 - 21 \times 2$$
$$= (36 - 21 \times 1) \times 3 - 21 \times 2 = 36 \times 3 - 21 \times 5$$
$$= 36 \times 3 - (93 - 36 \times 2) \times 5 = 36 \times 13 - 93 \times 5.$$

Therefore $[36][13] = [3]$ (since $[93 \times 5] = [0]$) and thus $[36][65] = [15]$. Hence $[65]$ is a solution of equation (19). The other two solutions are $[65 + 31]$ $= [3]$ and $[65 + 31 \times 2] = [34]$. For, according to (18), $k = \dfrac{m}{(a, m)} = \dfrac{93}{3}$ $= 31$ and the solutions are

$$[65 + 31t], \qquad t = 0, 1, 2.$$

Quiz

Answer **true** or **false**:

1. If a, b, c are nonzero integers then $(a, b, c) \mid (a, b)$.

2. If $p_1, \ldots, p_r, q_1, \ldots, q_s$ are primes, $0 < p_1 \leq \cdots \leq p_r, 0 < q_1 \leq \cdots \leq q_s$, and if $p_1 \cdots p_r = q_1 \cdots q_s$, then $r = s$ and $p_i = q_i, i = 1, \ldots, r$.

3. The residue class $[777]$ is a solution of $[372][x] = [999]$ in $I_{1,072}$.

4. The numbers m and n are relatively prime if and only if $mx \equiv 1 \bmod n$ for some integer x.

5. If $[a]_m[c]_m = [b]_m[c]_m$ and $[c]_m \neq [0]_m$ then $[a]_m = [b]_m$.

6. If $a \mid m$ and $b \mid n$ then $(a + b) \mid (m + n)$.

7. If p is a prime and $p \nmid a$ then the congruence $ax \equiv b \bmod p$ has a solution

8. If $a^2 \equiv a \bmod m$ and $m \nmid a$, then $a \equiv 1 \bmod m$.

9. If a, b, m, n are integers, c is a positive integer and $ma + nb = c$, then $c = (a, b)$.

10. If $a \mid bc$ then either $a \mid b$ or $a \mid c$.

Exercises

1. Find the g.c.d. of 3,451 and 1,411.

2. Find two integers m and n such that $3,451m + 1,411n = (3,451, 1,411)$.

3. Show that the ring in Example 1.1(e) is isomorphic to I_4.

4. Prove that $a_n 10^n + \cdots + a_1 10 + a_0$, where $a_n, \ldots, a_0$ are integers, is divisible by 3, if and only if $a_n + \cdots + a_0$ is divisible by 3.

5. Show that $3^{2n} + 3^n + 1 \equiv 0 \bmod 13$ if $3 \nmid n$ and n is a positive integer.

6. Find all the solutions of
$$[28][x] = [16],$$
    where the residue classes are in I_{64}.

7. Prove that if a, b, c are integers and $(a, c) = 1$, $(b, c) = 1$ then $(ab, c) = 1$.

4.3   Complex Numbers

A characteristic property of real numbers is that given any pair of real numbers a and b, $a \neq 0$, there exists a real number x such that $ax + b = 0$. On the other hand, there are no real numbers x for which $x^2 + 1 = 0$ or $x^4 + 3x^2 + 2 = 0$. We are going to construct a ring which contains an element i such that $i^2 + 1 = 0$ and which contains a ring isomorphic to the ring of real numbers. This ring has the remarkable and somewhat surprising property that given $a_0, \ldots, a_n$ in the ring there always exists an element x in the ring for which
$$a_n x^n + a_{n-1} x^{n-1} + \cdots + a_1 x + a_0 = 0.$$

Definition 3.1   (Complex numbers)   *Let R be the set of real numbers. Define operations of addition and multiplication on $R \times R$ by:*
$$(x_1, y_1) + (x_2, y_2) = (x_1 + x_2, y_1 + y_2),$$
$$(x_1, y_1)(x_2, y_2) = (x_1 x_2 - y_1 y_2, x_1 y_2 + y_1 x_2)$$
for all (x_1, y_1) and (x_2, y_2) in $R \times R$. The elements of $R \times R$ together with the above operations are called complex numbers. If $z = (x, y)$ is a complex number then x is called the real part of z, and is denoted by $\mathrm{Re}\,(z)$, while y is called the imaginary part of z and is denoted by $\mathrm{Im}\,(z)$. The modulus or absolute value of $z = (x, y)$, denoted by $|z|$, is the real number $\sqrt{x^2 + y^2}$.

The term "modulus" is not to be confused with "modulo" as used in Section 4.2. The words "real" and "imaginary" are used for historical reasons and do not, of course, imply in any way that x is a more "concrete" number than y.

The complex numbers constitute precisely the ring that we discussed in Example 1.1(f). We will recapitulate some of the calculations done there in our next theorem.

Theorem 3.1
(a)   *The complex numbers form a ring C.*
(b)   *Multiplication of complex numbers is commutative.*
(c)   *The complex number $(1, 0)$ is the multiplicative identity in C.*
(d)   *Every nonzero complex number has a multiplicative inverse.*

Proof. (a) Closure under addition and multiplication follows from Definition 3.1. Further, addition is associative:

$$((x_1, y_1) + (x_2, y_2)) + (x_3, y_3) = (x_1 + x_2 + x_3, y_1 + y_2 + y_3)$$

$$= (x_1, y_1) + ((x_2, y_2) + (x_3, y_3));$$

the complex number $(0, 0)$ is the additive identity:

$$(x, y) + (0, 0) = (x + 0, y + 0)$$

$$= (x, y);$$

an additive inverse exists:

$$(x, y) + (-x, -y) = (x - x, y - y) = (0, 0);$$

addition is commutative:

$$(x_1, y_1) + (x_2, y_2) = (x_1 + x_2, y_1 + y_2) = (x_2, y_2) + (x_1, y_1);$$

multiplication is associative:

$$((x_1, y_1)(x_2, y_2))(x_3, y_3) = (x_1 x_2 - y_1 y_2, x_1 y_2 + y_1 x_2)(x_3, y_3)$$

$$= (x_1 x_2 x_3 - y_1 y_2 x_3 - x_1 y_2 y_3 - y_1 x_2 y_3,$$

$$x_1 x_2 y_3 - y_1 y_2 y_3 + x_1 y_2 y_3 + y_1 x_2 x_3)$$

$$= (x_1, y_1)(x_2 x_3 - y_2 y_3, x_2 y_3 + y_2 x_3)$$

$$= (x_1, y_1)((x_2, y_2)(x_3, y_3));$$

the distributive laws hold:

$$(x_1, y_1)((x_2, y_2) + (x_3, y_3))$$

$$= (x_1, y_1)(x_2 + x_3, y_2 + y_3)$$

$$= (x_1 x_2 + x_1 x_3 - y_1 y_2 - y_1 y_3, x_1 y_2 + x_1 y_3 + y_1 x_2 + y_1 x_3)$$

$$= (x_1 x_2 - y_1 y_2, x_1 y_2 + y_1 x_2) + (x_1 x_3 - y_1 y_3, x_1 y_3 + y_1 x_3)$$

$$= (x_1, y_1)(x_2, y_2) + (x_1, y_1)(x_3, y_3),$$

and similarly

$$((x_2, y_2) + (x_3, y_3))(x_1, y_1) = (x_2, y_2)(x_1, y_1) + (x_3, y_3)(x_1, y_1).$$

Hence C is a ring.

(b) We have

$$(x_1, y_1)(x_2, y_2) = (x_1 x_2 - y_1 y_2, x_1 y_2 + y_1 x_2)$$

$$= (x_2, y_2)(x_1, y_1).$$

(c) Finally,

$$(1, 0)(x, y) = (1x - 0y, 1y + 0x)$$

$$= (x, y)$$

$$= (x1 - y0, x0 + y1)$$

$$= (x, y)(1, 0).$$

(d) If $(x, y) \neq (0, 0)$ then not both of x and y are 0, hence $x^2 + y^2 > 0$, and we compute that

$$(x, y)\left(\frac{x}{x^2 + y^2}, \frac{-y}{x^2 + y^2}\right) = \left(\frac{x^2 + y^2}{x^2 + y^2}, \frac{-xy + yx}{x^2 + y^2}\right)$$

$$= (1, 0).$$

If z_1 and z_2 are any complex numbers and $z_2 \neq (0, 0)$ then we will write z_1/z_2 for the complex number $z_1 z_2^{-1}$.

Theorem 3.2 *The ring of real numbers is isomorphic to the ring R' in C consisting of all complex numbers of the form $(x, 0)$; the operations in R' are the same as those in C.*

Proof. Let R denote the ring of real numbers. The mapping $\varphi \colon R \to C$ defined by $\varphi(x) = (x, 0)$, for all $x \in R$, is clearly 1-1 and onto R'. Now,

$$\varphi(x + y) = (x + y, 0) = (x, 0) + (y, 0) = \varphi(x) + \varphi(y),$$

and

$$\varphi(xy) = (xy, 0) = (x, 0)(y, 0) = \varphi(x)\varphi(y).$$

Hence φ is an isomorphism and R and R' are isomorphic.

It is conventional to use an abbreviated notation for elements of the ring R': instead of $(x, 0)$ we write simply x and call $(x, 0)$ a real number. The identity $(1, 0)$ is then written as 1. The number $(0, 0)$ is denoted by 0. We introduce a further notational abbreviation: we denote the complex number $(0, 1)$ by i. Observe that any complex number (x, y) can be written uniquely in the form $x(1, 0) + y(0, 1) = x + yi = x + iy$. Thus the addition and multiplication formulas in Definition 3.1 take the following form:

$$(x_1 + iy_1) + (x_2 + iy_2) = (x_1 + x_2) + i(y_1 + y_2);$$

$$(x_1 + iy_1)(x_2 + iy_2) = x_1 x_2 - y_1 y_2 + i(x_1 y_2 + y_1 x_2).$$

Observe that the last formula can be obtained by just using the ring axioms for C together with the fact that

$$i^2 = (0, 1)(0, 1) = (-1, 0),$$

or, using the above abbreviation,

$$i^2 = -1.$$

EXAMPLE 3.1

Let $z_1 = x_1 + iy_1$ be a nonzero complex number. Find all complex numbers $z_2 = x_2 + iy_2$ such that $z_1 z_2$ is real. To solve this problem observe that $x_1 y_2 + x_2 y_1 = 0$. If $y_1 = 0$ (z_1 is real) then, since $z_1 \neq 0$, we must have $y_2 = 0$ and hence z_2 must be real. Similarly, if $x_1 = 0$ then x_2 must be 0 and $z_2 = iy_2$. Suppose neither x_1 nor y_1 is 0. Then

$$\frac{x_2}{x_1} = -\frac{y_2}{y_1},$$

or $x_2 = tx_1$ and $y_2 = -ty_1$ for some real number t. Hence it is always true that $z_2 = t(x_1 - iy_1)$ for some real number t.

Definition 3.2   (Imaginary number, conjugate)   *A complex number of the form $iy = (0, y)$, where y is real, is called (pure) imaginary. If $z = x + iy$, where x and y are real, then the number $x - iy$ is said to be conjugate to z, or the conjugate of z, and is denoted by $\bar{z} = \overline{x + iy}$.*

As we stated before, the word "imaginary" is used here for historical reasons and has no connection whatsoever with any metaphysical problem concerning the existence of numbers. It should be noted that the imaginary part of a complex number (see Definition 3.1) is a real number and, in particular, the imaginary part of iy is y. Thus every number is a sum of a unique real number and a unique imaginary number.

Theorem 3.3   *If z, z_1, z_2 are complex numbers then*

(a) $\bar{\bar{z}} = z$;

(b) $\operatorname{Re}(z) = (z + \bar{z})/2$;

(c) $\operatorname{Im}(z) = (z - \bar{z})/2i$;

(d) $|z|^2 = z\bar{z}$;

(e) $\overline{z_1 + z_2} = \bar{z}_1 + \bar{z}_2$;

(f) $\overline{z_1 z_2} = \bar{z}_1 \bar{z}_2$;

(g) $|z_1 z_2| = |z_1||z_2|$;

(h) $|z_1 + z_2| \leq |z_1| + |z_2|$ *(Triangle inequality)*;

(k) $|z_1 - z_2| \geq ||z_1| - |z_2||$.

Proof.   Let $z = x + iy$, $z_1 = x_1 + iy_1$, and $z_2 = x_2 + iy_2$, where x, y, x_1, y_1, x_2, y_2 are real. Then

(a) $\bar{\bar{z}} = \overline{x - iy} = x + iy = z$;

(b) $(z + \bar{z})/2 = ((x + iy) + (x - iy))/2 = x = \operatorname{Re}(z)$;

(c) $(z - \bar{z})/2i = ((x + iy) - (x - iy))/2i = y = \mathrm{Im}\,(z)$;

(d) $z\bar{z} = (x + iy)(x - iy) = x^2 + y^2 = |z|^2$;

(e) $\overline{z_1 + z_2} = (x_1 + x_2) - i(y_1 + y_2) = (x_1 - iy_1) + (x_2 - iy_2) = \bar{z}_1 + \bar{z}_2$;

(f) $\overline{z_1 z_2} = (x_1 x_2 - y_1 y_2) - i(x_1 y_2 + x_2 y_1) = (x_1 - iy_1)(x_2 - iy_2) = \bar{z}_1 \bar{z}_2$;

(g) $|z_1 z_2|^2 = (z_1 z_2)(\overline{z_1 z_2}) = z_1 z_2 \bar{z}_1 \bar{z}_2 = (z_1 \bar{z}_1)(z_2 \bar{z}_2) = |z_1|^2 |z_2|^2$;

(h) $|z_1 + z_2|^2 = (z_1 + z_2)(\overline{z_1 + z_2})$

$$= (z_1 + z_2)(\bar{z}_1 + \bar{z}_2)$$

$$= z_1 \bar{z}_1 + z_1 \bar{z}_2 + z_2 \bar{z}_1 + z_2 \bar{z}_2$$

$$= |z_1|^2 + z_1 \bar{z}_2 + (\overline{z_1 \bar{z}_2}) + |z_2|^2$$

$$= |z_1|^2 + 2\,\mathrm{Re}\,(z_1 \bar{z}_2) + |z_2|^2.$$

But, for any $z = x + iy$, $\mathrm{Re}\,(z) = x \le \sqrt{x^2 + y^2} = |z|$. Also, $|\bar{z}| = |z|$, and therefore

$$|z_1 + z_2|^2 \le |z_1|^2 + 2\,|z_1 \bar{z}_2| + |z_2|^2$$

$$= |z_1|^2 + 2\,|z_1||z_2| + |z_2|^2$$

$$= (|z_1| + |z_2|)^2.$$

(k)   We leave the proof of this part as an exercise for the student.

There is an obvious identity between complex numbers and points of a plane: the complex number $x + iy$ corresponds to the point with coordinates (x, y). This rather obvious geometric representation is very illuminating and important in the development of the theory of complex numbers. A plane with points representing complex numbers is called the *Argand diagram*. The x-axis and the y-axis are called the *real axis* and the *imaginary axis* respectively.

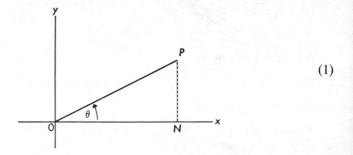

(1)

The distance $\sqrt{x^2 + y^2}$ from the origin to the point $P = (x, y)$ is the modulus of $x + iy$. The lengths of NP and ON are clearly the imaginary and the real parts of $x + iy$. Before we continue our study of complex numbers via the Argand diagram we shall remind the student of the definitions of the trigonometric functions and of two well-known theorems concerning these functions.

Let P be a point on a circle S of unit radius whose center is at the origin O. Let A be the point $(1, 0)$ and let the perpendicular from P to the x-axis cut the axis at the point N.

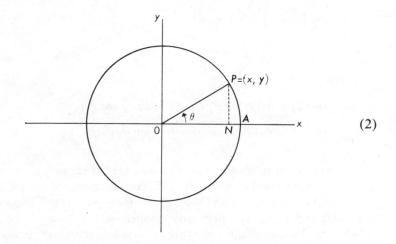

(2)

Let the angle AOP be θ measured in radians. Recall that an angle of one radian is the angle at the center of S subtended by an arc of length 1, that is, 1 radian $= 360/2\pi$ degrees. Also, the angle AOP is considered to be positive if the rotation from OA to OP is counterclockwise, and negative if it is clockwise. Let y be the length of the line segment NP counted positive or negative according as P is above or below the x-axis. The length x of the line segment ON is considered positive or negative according as P is to the right or to the left of the y-axis. Then we define the functions *sine, cosine, tangent* (abbreviated to sin, cos and tan) as follows:

$$\sin \theta = y,$$

$$\cos \theta = x,$$

$$\tan \theta = \frac{\sin \theta}{\cos \theta} = \frac{y}{x}, \qquad \text{if } x = \cos \theta \neq 0.$$

Note that if P and P' are on the unit circle, $AOP = \theta$ and $AOP' = \theta'$, and if $\sin \theta = \sin \theta'$, $\cos \theta = \cos \theta'$, then P and P' coincide and θ and θ' must either be equal or differ by a multiple of $360°$ ($=2\pi$ radians). Thus $\sin \theta = \sin \theta'$ and $\cos \theta = \cos \theta'$ together imply that $\theta' = \theta + 2k\pi$ for some integer k.

Theorem 3.4 *If θ, θ_1 and θ_2 are any angles measured in radians then*

(a) $\sin(-\theta) = -\sin\theta,$

$\cos(-\theta) = \cos\theta,$

$\sin\left(\dfrac{\pi}{2} - \theta\right) = \cos\theta,$

$\cos\left(\dfrac{\pi}{2} - \theta\right) = \sin\theta,$

$\sin^2\theta + \cos^2\theta = 1.$

Moreover,

(b) $\sin(\theta_1 + \theta_2) = \sin\theta_1\cos\theta_2 + \sin\theta_2\cos\theta_1,$

$\cos(\theta_1 + \theta_2) = \cos\theta_1\cos\theta_2 - \sin\theta_1\sin\theta_2.$

Proof.

(a)   These formulas are proved by direct reference to (2). For example, if $P = (x, y)$ is the point on the unit circle corresponding to the angle θ and Q is the point corresponding to the angle $-\theta$ then Q is the reflection of P in the x-axis (P and Q are symmetrically situated with respect to the x-axis). It follows that the coordinates of Q are $(x, -y)$ and therefore $\cos(-\theta) = \cos\theta$ and $\sin(-\theta) = -\sin\theta$. We leave the proof of the other three formulas as an exercise for the student.

(b)   We shall first prove a preliminary result. Let B and D be points on the unit circle and let α be the angle DOB.

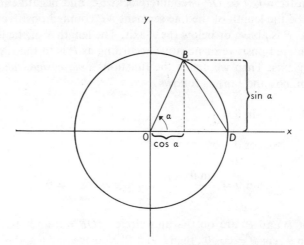

We want to evaluate the length BD in terms of α. Clearly only the relative positions of B and D matter and we can rotate the whole unit circle until D

is the point $(1, 0)$ on the x-axis and the coordinates of B are $(\cos \alpha, \sin \alpha)$. Then, using the distance formula for d, the length of BD, we obtain

$$d^2 = (1 - \cos \alpha)^2 + (0 - \sin \alpha)^2$$

$$= 1 - 2 \cos \alpha + \cos^2 \alpha + \sin^2 \alpha \tag{3}$$

$$= 2 - 2 \cos \alpha.$$

Now, let P and Q be points on the unit circle with coordinates $(\cos \theta, \sin \theta)$ and $(\cos \varphi, \sin \varphi)$, that is, θ and φ are the angles AOP and AOQ. Then the angle QOP is $\theta - \varphi$ and, by (3) with h denoting the length of PQ, we have

$$h^2 = 2 - 2 \cos (\theta - \varphi). \tag{4}$$

We can also compute h^2 directly from the distance formula

$$h^2 = (\cos \theta - \cos \varphi)^2 + (\sin \theta - \sin \varphi)^2 \tag{5}$$

$$= \cos^2 \theta + \sin^2 \theta + \cos^2 \varphi + \sin^2 \varphi - 2 \cos \theta \cos \varphi - 2 \sin \theta \sin \varphi$$

$$= 2 - 2(\cos \theta \cos \varphi + \sin \theta \sin \varphi).$$

Thus from (4) and (5)

$$\cos (\theta - \varphi) = \cos \theta \cos \varphi + \sin \theta \sin \varphi. \tag{6}$$

Now, set $\theta = \theta_1$ and $\varphi = -\theta_2$. Then, by part (a),

$$\cos (\theta_1 + \theta_2) = \cos \theta_1 \cos \theta_2 - \sin \theta_1 \sin \theta_2. \tag{7}$$

In (6) set $\theta = \dfrac{\pi}{2} - \theta_1$, $\varphi = \theta_2$ and compute that

$$\sin (\theta_1 + \theta_2) = \cos \left(\frac{\pi}{2} - \theta_1 - \theta_2 \right)$$

$$= \cos \left(\frac{\pi}{2} - \theta_1 \right) \cos \theta_2 + \sin \left(\frac{\pi}{2} - \theta_1 \right) \sin \theta_2$$

$$= \sin \theta_1 \cos \theta_2 + \cos \theta_1 \sin \theta_2.$$

We now return to the Argand diagram.

Definition 3.3   (Amplitude)   *Let $z = x + iy \neq 0$, where x and y are real, and let $P = (x, y)$ be the corresponding point on the Argand diagram. Then the angle NOP between the positive direction of the x-axis and OP is called the amplitude of z and is denoted by* amp (z).

Note that the point $P = \left(\dfrac{x}{|z|}, \dfrac{y}{|z|} \right)$ is on the unit circle since

$$\left(\frac{x}{|z|} \right)^2 + \left(\frac{y}{|z|} \right)^2 = \frac{x^2 + y^2}{|z|^2} = 1$$

and thus

$$\frac{x}{|z|} = \cos \theta, \qquad \frac{y}{|z|} = \sin \theta, \qquad \theta = \text{amp}\,(z). \tag{8}$$

Hence if $x \neq 0$,

$$\tan\,(\text{amp}\,(z)) = \frac{y}{x} = \frac{\text{Im}\,(z)}{\text{Re}\,(z)}. \tag{9}$$

Moreover, if $|z|$ is denoted by r then (8) can be written in the form

$$\text{Re}\,(z) = r \cos \theta, \qquad \text{Im}\,(z) = r \sin \theta \tag{10}$$

and therefore

$$z = r(\cos \theta + i \sin \theta). \tag{11}$$

The right-hand side of (11) is called the *polar form* of z.

EXAMPLE 3.2

Express $z = \dfrac{10 + i2}{3 - i2}$ in the form $r(\cos \theta + i \sin \theta)$. We first reduce z to

the form $x + iy$. We multiply the numerator and the denominator of z by the conjugate of the denominator:

$$z = \frac{(10 + i2)(3 + i2)}{(3 - i2)(3 + i2)}$$

$$= \frac{26 + i26}{9 + 4}$$

$$= 2 + i2.$$

Thus

$$r = |z| = \sqrt{2^2 + 2^2} = 2\sqrt{2}$$

and

$$z = 2\sqrt{2}\left(\frac{1}{\sqrt{2}} + i\frac{1}{\sqrt{2}}\right) = 2\sqrt{2}\left(\cos\frac{\pi}{4} + i\sin\frac{\pi}{4}\right).$$

Theorem 3.5 *Let* $z_j = r_j\,(\cos \theta_j + i \sin \theta_j) \neq 0$, *where* $r_j = |z_j|$ *and* $\theta_j = \text{amp}\,(z_j)$, $j = 1, \ldots, n$. *Then*

$$\prod_{j=1}^{n} z_j = r(\cos \theta + i \sin \theta), \tag{12}$$

where

$$r = \prod_{j=1}^{n} r_j$$

and

$$\theta = \sum_{j=1}^{n} \theta_j.$$

Proof. We use induction on n. If $n = 1$ then (12) becomes $z_1 = r_1 (\cos \theta_1 + i \sin \theta_1)$. Assume that (12) holds for products of $n - 1$ complex numbers, that is,

$$\prod_{j=1}^{n-1} z_j = \prod_{j=1}^{n-1} r_j [\cos (\sum_{j=1}^{n-1} \theta_j) + i \sin (\sum_{j=1}^{n-1} \theta_j)].$$

Then

$$\prod_{j=1}^{n} z_j = (\prod_{j=1}^{n-1} z_j) z_n$$

$$= (\prod_{j=1}^{n-1} r_j)[\cos (\sum_{j=1}^{n-1} \theta_j) + i \sin (\sum_{j=1}^{n-1} \theta_j)] r_n (\cos \theta_n + i \sin \theta_n)$$

$$= (\prod_{j=1}^{n} r_j)[(\cos (\sum_{j=1}^{n-1} \theta_j) \cos \theta_n - \sin (\sum_{j=1}^{n-1} \theta_j) \sin \theta_n)$$

$$+ i(\sin (\sum_{j=1}^{n-1} \theta_j) \cos \theta_n + \cos (\sum_{j=1}^{n-1} \theta_j) \sin \theta_n)]$$

$$= (\prod_{j=1}^{n} r_j)[\cos (\sum_{j=1}^{n-1} \theta_j + \theta_n) + i \sin (\sum_{j=1}^{n-1} \theta_j + \theta_n)]$$

$$= r(\cos \theta + i \sin \theta).$$

We are now in a position to state and prove the basic theorem in the algebra of complex numbers.

Theorem 3.6   (De Moivre's Theorem) *Let t be an integer and let $z = r(\cos \theta + i \sin \theta)$ where $r > 0$ and θ is real. Then*

$$z^t = r^t(\cos t\theta + i \sin t\theta). \tag{13}$$

Proof. If t is a positive integer then (13) follows from Theorem 3.5 by setting $z_1 = \cdots = z_t = z$. We prove next that (13) holds if $t = -1$.

$$z^{-1} = \frac{1}{r(\cos \theta + i \sin \theta)}$$

$$= r^{-1} \frac{\cos \theta - i \sin \theta}{(\cos \theta + i \sin \theta)(\cos \theta - i \sin \theta)}$$

$$= r^{-1} \frac{\cos \theta - i \sin \theta}{\cos^2 \theta + \sin^2 \theta}$$

$$= r^{-1}(\cos (-\theta) + i \sin (-\theta)).$$

Hence, if t is a negative integer we can set $t = -n$ where $n > 0$. Then

$$z^t = z^{-n} = (z^n)^{-1}$$

$$= (r^n(\cos n\theta + i \sin n\theta))^{-1}$$

$$= r^{-n}(\cos (-n\theta) + i \sin (-n\theta))$$

$$= r^t(\cos t\theta + i \sin t\theta).$$

If $t = 0$ then $z^t = z^0 = 1$ by convention and thus

$$r^t(\cos t\theta + i \sin t\theta) = r^0(\cos 0 + i \sin 0) = 1(1 + i0) = 1.$$

EXAMPLE 3.3

Express $\cos 3\theta$ as a polynomial in $\cos \theta$. Let

$$z = \cos \theta + i \sin \theta.$$

Then

$$z^3 = \cos 3\theta + i \sin 3\theta.$$

On the other hand,

$$z^3 = (\cos \theta + i \sin \theta)^3$$

$$= \cos^3 \theta + 3i \cos^2 \theta \sin \theta - 3 \cos \theta \sin^2 \theta - i \sin^3 \theta$$

$$= \cos \theta(\cos^2 \theta - 3 \sin^2 \theta) + i(3 \cos^2 \theta \sin \theta - \sin^3 \theta).$$

Hence, equating the real parts,

$$\cos 3\theta = \cos \theta(\cos^2 \theta - 3 \sin^2 \theta)$$

$$= \cos \theta(\cos^2 \theta - 3(1 - \cos^2 \theta))$$

$$= 4 \cos^3 \theta - 3 \cos \theta.$$

EXAMPLE 3.4

Let $w_1 = -1 + i\sqrt{3}$ and $w_2 = -1 - i\sqrt{3}$. Show that $w_1^3 = w_2^3 = 2^3$. Putting w_1 and w_2 in polar form (recall that $\cos 2\pi/3 = -\frac{1}{2}$, $\sin 2\pi/3 = \sqrt{3}/2$, $\cos 4\pi/3 = -\frac{1}{2}$, $\sin 4\pi/3 = \sqrt{3}/2$) we have

$$|w_1| = |w_2| = 2,$$

$$w_1 = 2\left(\cos \frac{2\pi}{3} + i \sin \frac{2\pi}{3}\right), \qquad w_2 = 2\left(\cos \frac{4\pi}{3} + i \sin \frac{4\pi}{3}\right).$$

Then, by Theorem 3.6 with $t = 3$, we have

$$w_1^3 = 2^3\left(\cos 3\left(\frac{2\pi}{3}\right) + i \sin 3\left(\frac{2\pi}{3}\right)\right)$$

$$= 8(\cos 2\pi + i \sin 2\pi)$$

$$= 8,$$

and similarly

$$w_2^3 = 2^3 \left(\cos 3\left(\frac{4\pi}{3}\right) + i \sin 3\left(\frac{4\pi}{3}\right) \right)$$

$$= 8(\cos 4\pi + i \sin 4\pi)$$

$$= 8.$$

We also know, of course, that if $w_3 = 2 = 2 (\cos 0 + i \sin 0)$ then $w_3^3 = 8$.

In looking at Example 3.4 we see that there are at least three distinct complex numbers whose cubes are equal to 8. This motivates the following definition.

Definition 3.4   (Roots of a complex number)   *Let q be a positive integer. If z is a given complex number and w is a complex number such that $w^q = z$ then w is called a qth root of z. We shall denote any qth root of z by $z^{1/q}$.*

Theorem 3.7   *If q is a positive integer and z is a given nonzero complex number, $z = r(\cos \theta + i \sin \theta)$, then there are precisely q complex numbers which are qth roots of z. These are given in polar form by*

$$w_k = r^{1/q} \left(\cos \frac{\theta + 2\pi k}{q} + i \sin \frac{\theta + 2\pi k}{q} \right), \qquad k = 0, \dots, q-1. \quad (14)$$

Proof.   First observe that by Theorem 3.6

$$w_k^q = (r^{1/q})^q \left(\cos q\left(\frac{\theta + 2\pi k}{q}\right) + i \sin q\left(\frac{\theta + 2\pi k}{q}\right) \right)$$

$$= r(\cos (\theta + 2\pi k) + i \sin (\theta + 2\pi k))$$

$$= r(\cos \theta + i \sin \theta)$$

$$= z.$$

Now suppose $w = \rho(\cos \varphi + i \sin \varphi)$ is a qth root of z. Then

$$w^q = \rho^q(\cos q\varphi + i \sin q\varphi)$$

$$= z$$

$$= r(\cos \theta + i \sin \theta).$$

Since $w^q = z$ we have $\rho^q = |w|^q = |z| = r$ and hence $\rho = r^{1/q}$. Also

$$\cos q\varphi = \cos \theta,$$

and   (15)

$$\sin q\varphi = \sin \theta.$$

As we saw immediately before Theorem 3.4, the equations (15) can hold if and only if $q\varphi$ and θ differ by an integral multiple of 2π, that is,

$$q\varphi = \theta + 2\pi k,$$

$$\varphi = \frac{\theta + 2\pi k}{q}. \tag{16}$$

The angles $\varphi_k = (\theta + 2\pi k)/q$, $k = 0, \ldots, q-1$, are distinct and if k is any integer not in the set $\{0, \ldots, q-1\}$ then the corresponding value of φ will clearly differ from one of the φ_k by a multiple of 2π. Also, if

$$0 \le u \le v \le q - 1$$

and

$$\cos \varphi_u = \cos \varphi_v,$$

$$\sin \varphi_u = \sin \varphi_v,$$

then again we know that φ_u and φ_v must differ by an integral multiple of 2π, say, $|\varphi_v - \varphi_u| = h2\pi$. But

$$
\begin{aligned}
h2\pi &= |\varphi_v - \varphi_u| \\
&= \left| \frac{\theta + 2\pi v}{q} - \frac{\theta + 2\pi u}{q} \right| \\
&= \frac{2\pi(v - u)}{q} \\
&< 2\pi.
\end{aligned}
$$

Hence $h = 0$ and $u = v$. We have proved that the q complex numbers on the right in equation (14) are all the q distinct qth roots of z.

EXAMPLE 3.5

Find all the nth roots of 1, that is, find all complex numbers z such that $z^n = 1$, n an integer. According to Theorem 3.7, the distinct nth roots of 1 are the n complex numbers

$$\cos\left(\frac{2k\pi}{n}\right) + i \sin\left(\frac{2k\pi}{n}\right), \qquad k = 0, 1, \ldots, n - 1.$$

Note that the nth roots of 1 lie in the Argand diagram on the unit circle and that their amplitudes are 0, $2\pi/n$, $4\pi/n$, $\ldots$, $2(n-1)\pi/n$. But these are the vertices of the n-sided regular polygon inscribed in the unit circle whose one vertex is at $(1, 0)$. For example, the 12th roots of 1 are situated in the Argand diagram as shown below.

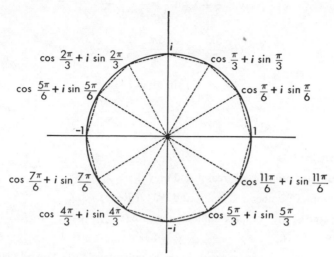

Definition 3.5   (Rational power of a complex number)   *If p and q are integers, q > 0, then $z^{p/q}$ is the pth power of any of the qth roots of z. Any one of these numbers $z^{p/q}$ is called a p/q power of z.*

We can now give a more complete version of Theorem 3.6.

Theorem 3.8   *If p and q are integers, q > 0, and $z = r(\cos\theta + i\sin\theta)$ is a nonzero complex number in polar form then all of the p/q powers of z are given by*

$$r^{p/q}\left(\cos p\left(\frac{\theta + 2\pi k}{q}\right) + i\sin p\left(\frac{\theta + 2\pi k}{q}\right)\right), \quad k = 0,\ldots,q-1. \quad (17)$$

Proof.   By Theorem 3.7, the numbers $z^{1/q}$ are given by

$$r^{1/q}\left(\cos\left(\frac{\theta + 2\pi k}{q}\right) + i\sin\left(\frac{\theta + 2\pi k}{q}\right)\right), \quad k = 0,\ldots,q-1. \quad (18)$$

We then apply Theorem 3.6 to (18) to obtain immediately the result (17).

EXAMPLE 3.6

Find the $\frac{2}{3}$ powers of i. First note that $i = \cos\dfrac{\pi}{2} + i\sin\dfrac{\pi}{2}$ and hence $i^{2/3}$ is any of the three numbers

$$\cos\frac{2}{3}\left(\frac{\pi}{2} + 2\pi k\right) + i\sin\frac{2}{3}\left(\frac{\pi}{2} + 2\pi k\right), \quad k = 0, 1, 2.$$

These are

$$\cos\frac{\pi}{3} + i\sin\frac{\pi}{3} = \frac{1}{2} + i\frac{\sqrt{3}}{2},$$

$$\cos\frac{5\pi}{3} + i\sin\frac{5\pi}{3} = \frac{1}{2} - i\frac{\sqrt{3}}{2},$$

$$\cos 3\pi + i\sin 3\pi = -1.$$

Quiz

Answer **true** or **false**:

1. A complex number z is real if and only if $z = \bar{z}$.
2. A complex number z is real if and only if $\text{Re}\,(z) = |z|$.
3. If z_1 and z_2 are complex numbers then $\text{Re}\,(z_1 z_2) = \text{Re}\,(z_1)\,\text{Re}\,(z_2)$.
4. $(-i)^2 + 1 = 0$.
5. If z_1 and z_2 are complex numbers on the unit circle in the Argand diagram then $z_1 z_2$ is on the unit circle.
6. If z_1 and z_2 are complex numbers then $z_1^2 + z_2^2 = 0$ if and only if $z_1 = z_2 = 0$.
7. $\cos\pi + i\sin\pi = -1$.
8. If a, b, and c are given real numbers, $a \neq 0$, then there exists a complex number z such that $az^2 + bz + c = 0$.
9. If z is any complex number then $(z + \bar{z})(z - \bar{z}) = 0$.
10. If $r_1(\cos\theta_1 + i\sin\theta_1) = r_2(\cos\theta_2 + i\sin\theta_2)$ where r_1 and r_2 are positive real numbers and θ_1, θ_2 are real, $-\pi < \theta_1 \leq \theta_2 \leq \pi$, then $r_1 = r_2$ and $\theta_1 = \theta_2$.

Exercises

1. Show that $1/z = \bar{z}/|z|^2$, if $z \neq 0$.
2. Evaluate $\sin\pi/3$, $\cos\pi/3$ and $\tan\pi/3$.
3. Find the real and imaginary parts of $(\sqrt{3} + i)^{93}$.
4. Express $z = i4\sqrt{3}/(1 + i\sqrt{3})$ in the form $z = r(\cos\theta + i\sin\theta)$.
5. Prove that $|z_1 z_2 \cdots z_k| = |z_1||z_2|\cdots|z_k|$.
6. Prove Theorem 3.3(k).
7. Show that $|z_1/z_2| = |z_1|/|z_2|$, $z_2 \neq 0$.
8. Find the $\frac{2}{3}$ powers of $-1 + i$.
9. Find all the nth roots of -1.
10. Show that if h and k are integers and $\cos 2h\pi/n + i\sin 2h\pi/n = \cos 2k\pi/n + i\sin 2k\pi/n$, then $h \equiv k \bmod n$.

11. An nth root of 1 is said to be *primitive* if it is not a kth root of 1 for $1 < k \le n$. Show that $\cos 2p\pi/n + i \sin 2p\pi/n$ is a primitive nth root of 1 if and only if g.c.d. $(p, n) = 1$.

12. Show that if u is a primitive nth root of 1 then $u, u^2, \ldots, u^{n-1}$ are all the distinct nth roots of 1.

13. Prove that $|z_1 + z_2| = |z_1| + |z_2|$ if and only if one of the numbers z_1 and z_2 is a nonnegative real multiple of the other.

14. Show that the set of complex numbers $\{m + in \mid m, n \text{ integers}\}$ with the usual addition and multiplication, forms a ring isomorphic to the ring of 2-square matrices of the form $\begin{bmatrix} m & -n \\ n & m \end{bmatrix}$, m and n integers, with matrix addition and matrix multiplication. (See Example 1.2, page 116.)

15. Show that the function $\varphi(z) = \bar{z}$ is an isomorphism function mapping the ring of complex numbers onto itself.

4.4 Polynomials

Our immediate goal in this section is to define a polynomial over a ring R. The reader has encountered polynomials in mathematics courses for at least the last five years: the phrase "let z be an unknown (or indeterminate)" is indeed a familiar one. Expressions like $z + 1$, $3z^5 - 4z^3 + 2z - 7$ and the algebraic rules governing them are part of every student's mathematical equipment. Thus the magic symbols z or x or y, etc., pulled from nowhere, come endowed with many properties. For example, if a is in the ring R then $az = za$; the laws governing addition and multiplication in R also work for z and yet z is not any particular number in R; although $z \ne 0$, nor for that matter is z a divisor of zero, it is not permissible in computing with polynomials to write z^{-1}. The problem we face is to make sense of something that the student has used for many years without sacrificing any of its utility.

Definition 4.1 (Indeterminate. Polynomial) *Let R_1 and R_2 be rings with a multiplicative identity 1 and assume that $R_1 \subset R_2$ and the operations in R_1 and R_2 are the same (we shall denote the addition by " $+$ " and the multiplication by juxtaposition to reduce the notation). Let z be an element of R_2 having the following two properties:*

(a) *z commutes with every element of R_1;*
(b) *if $a_n z^n + a_{n-1} z^{n-1} + \cdots + a_1 z + a_0 = 0$, $a_k \in R_1$, $k = 0, 1, \ldots, n$, then $a_0 = a_1 = \cdots = a_n = 0$.*
Then z is called an indeterminate (or unknown) over R_1. Any element of the form

$$a_n z^n + a_{n-1} z^{n-1} + \cdots + a_0 = \sum_{k=0}^{n} a_k z^k, \qquad (1)$$

where $a_k \in R_1$, $k = 0, \ldots, n$, is called a polynomial in z over R_1. (We interpret z^0 to be 1.) If every element of R_2 is of the form (1) then we write $R_1[z] = R_2$ and R_2 is called the ring of polynomials in z over R_1.

In Section 4.5 we shall show that given any ring R_1 with a multiplicative identity there exists a ring R_2 containing R_1 and satisfying the following properties:

(a)   the operations in R_2, restricted to elements in R_1, are the same as the operations in R_1;

(b) R_2 contains an element z which is an indeterminate over R_1;

(c) $R_2 = R_1[z]$, that is, every element of R_2 has the form (1).

We will now standardize and extend our agreements about notation for polynomials.

Definiton 4.2   **(Notation for polynomials)**   *Let R be a ring with a multiplicative identity and let z be an indeterminate over R.*

(a)   *An arbitrary polynomial in z will be denoted by an expression such as*

$$f(z) = \sum_{k=0}^{n} a_k z^k, \qquad a_k \in R. \tag{2}$$

The elements a_k in (2) are called the coefficients of the polynomial $f(z)$.

(b)   *The largest integer d for which $a_d \neq 0$ in (2) is called the degree of $f(z)$. We write*

$$\deg f(z) = d. \tag{3}$$

If $f(z) = a_0 \neq 0$ then $\deg f(z) = 0$, by definition. The degree is not defined for the polynomial $f(z) = 0$.

(c)   *The addition and multiplication formulas for polynomials can be expressed as follows:*

$$\sum_{k=0}^{n} a_k z^k + \sum_{k=0}^{n} b_k z^k = \sum_{k=0}^{n} (a_k + b_k) z^k; \tag{4}$$

$$\left(\sum_{k=0}^{n} a_k z^k \right)\left(\sum_{k=0}^{n} b_k z^k \right) = \sum_{m=0}^{2n} \left(\sum_{k=0}^{m} a_k b_{m-k} \right) z^m$$

$$= \sum_{m=0}^{2n} \left(\sum_{i+j=m} a_i b_j \right) z^m. \tag{5}$$

(d)   *If $f(z) \in R[z]$, $c \in R$ and R is a commutative ring then the specialization of f to c, written $f(c)$, is defined to be*

$$f(c) = \sum_{k=0}^{n} a_k c^k.$$

The   element $f(c) \in R$ is also called the value of f at c. For many purposes, however, R cannot be assumed to be commutative; for example, R might very *well be a ring of matrices. There are two possibilities for the value of $f(z)$ at c that we wish to distinguish*:

$$f_r(c) = \sum_{k=0}^{n} a_k c^k \tag{6}$$

and

$$f_l(c) = \sum_{k=0}^{n} c^k a_k. \tag{7}$$

The value $f_r(c)$ is called the right hand value of $f(z)$ at c and $f_l(c)$ is called the left hand value of $f(z)$ at c.

(e) *If R is commutative, $c \in R$, and $f(c) = 0$, then c is called a root or a zero of $f(z)$.*

(f) *If $d = \deg f(z)$ then the coefficient a_d of z^d is called the leading coefficient of $f(z)$. The coefficient a_0 is called the constant term. If $a_d = 1$ then the polynomial is said to be monic.*

The central problem in algebra during the 16th, 17th, 18th and 19th centuries was the determination of the structure of the roots of a polynomial. The difficulties posed by this problem have occupied the attentions of some of the most creative mathematicians: Tartaglia, Cardan, Newton, Lagrange, Abel, Galois, and Gauss, to mention a few. The fields of group theory, algebraic number theory, ring theory, and algebraic geometry have come into existence as a result of the study of the equation

$$\sum_{k=0}^{n} a_k z^k = 0.$$

We shall return to this problem in some detail in Section 4.6.

Our next project in this section will be to show that many of the important results about integers have almost direct analogues for polynomials. We begin by observing some elementary properties of the degree of a polynomial (see Definition 4.2).

Theorem 4.1 *Let R be a ring with a multiplicative identity and let z be an indeterminate over R. If $f(z)$ and $g(z)$ are polynomials in $R[z]$ then*

$$\deg f(z)g(z) \le \deg f(z) + \deg g(z). \tag{8}$$

If R has no zero divisors (see Definition 1.2(x)) then (8) is equality. Also, if the leading coefficient of either polynomial is a unit in R then (8) is equality.

Proof. Suppose that

$$f(z) = a_p z^p + a_{p-1} z^{p-1} + \cdots + a_0, \qquad a_p \ne 0,$$

and

$$g(z) = b_q z^q + b_{q-1} z^{q-1} + \cdots + b_0, \qquad b_q \ne 0.$$

Then the leading coefficient of $f(z)g(z)$ is just $a_p b_q$. If $a_p b_q \ne 0$ then the largest integer k for which the kth coefficient of $f(z)g(z)$ is not zero is obviously $k = p + q$; that is, the leading coefficient of $f(z)g(z)$ is $a_p b_q$. Thus

$$\deg f(z)g(z) = p + q = \deg f(z) + \deg g(z).$$

If a_p is a unit then $a_p b_q \neq 0$ otherwise (since a_p^{-1} exists) we would have $0 = a_p^{-1}(a_p b_q) = b_q$ contrary to assumption. Similarly if b_q is a unit then $a_p b_q \neq 0$. In general, however, the ring may have zero divisors and we cannot assume that $a_p b_q \neq 0$. Thus the degree of $f(z)g(z)$ will be at most $p + q$.

EXAMPLES 4.1

(a) If R has no zero divisors and $a(z)b(z) = 1$ then from (8) we conclude that $\deg a(z) = \deg b(z) = 0$. Thus, if $a(z)$ has an inverse in $R[z]$, then $a(z) = a_0 \in R$.

(b) Let R be the ring of all 2×2 matrices with integer entries. Let

$$f(z) = \begin{bmatrix} 0 & 1 \\ 0 & 0 \end{bmatrix} z^2 + \begin{bmatrix} 1 & -1 \\ 1 & 1 \end{bmatrix} z + \begin{bmatrix} 1 & 0 \\ 0 & 1 \end{bmatrix},$$

and

$$g(z) = \begin{bmatrix} 0 & 1 \\ 0 & 0 \end{bmatrix} z + \begin{bmatrix} -1 & 0 \\ 0 & 1 \end{bmatrix}.$$

Then

$$f(z)g(z) = \begin{bmatrix} 0 & 1 \\ 0 & 0 \end{bmatrix}\begin{bmatrix} 0 & 1 \\ 0 & 0 \end{bmatrix} z^3 + h(z)$$

where $\deg h(z) \leq 2$. However,

$$\begin{bmatrix} 0 & 1 \\ 0 & 0 \end{bmatrix}^2 = \begin{bmatrix} 0 & 0 \\ 0 & 0 \end{bmatrix}$$

and hence

$$\deg f(z)g(z) < 3 = \deg f(z) + \deg g(z).$$

As was the case with the ring of integers our most important result about polynomials concerns the division process. In Theorem 2.2 in this chapter the absolute value played an important role in measuring how close the division was to being "exact". A precisely analogous part is played by the degree for polynomial division. Once again we remind the reader of Definition 1.4 in which a unit in a ring is defined as an element possessing a multiplicative inverse. In the following theorem we shall have two "divisions" exhibited because we are not initially assuming that R is a commutative ring. It is important in the applications of this material to subsequent courses in linear algebra and general algebra to be familiar with the peculiarities of this two-sided division.

Theorem 4.2 (Division algorithm) *Let R be a ring with a multiplicative identity, denoted by* 1. *Let z be an indeterminate over R. Set*

$$a(z) = \sum_{t=0}^{n} a_t z^t \in R[z]$$

and

$$b(z) = \sum_{t=0}^{m} b_t z^t \in R[z]$$

where $a_n \neq 0$ and b_m is a unit in R. Then there exist unique polynomials $q(z)$, $r(z)$, $s(z)$ and $u(z)$ in $R[z]$ satisfying

$$a(z) = q(z)b(z) + r(z), \tag{9}$$

and

$$a(z) = b(z)s(z) + u(z), \tag{10}$$

where

$$\deg r(z) < \deg b(z) \qquad or \qquad r(z) = 0, \tag{11}$$

and

$$\deg u(z) < \deg b(z) \qquad or \qquad u(z) = 0. \tag{12}$$

Proof. The proof of (9) is by induction on n, the degree of $a(z)$. We shall deal initially with the case in which $n = 0$. Suppose first that $n = 0$ and $m > 0$ so that $a(z) = a_0$. For $m > 0$ we can set $q(z) = 0$ and $r(z) = a_0$. Then

$$q(z)b(z) + r(z) = 0 + a_0 = a(z).$$

If $n = 0$ and $m = 0$ then $b(z) = b_0$ and $b_0 \,(=b_m)$ is assumed to be a unit. Then set $q(z) = a_0 b_0^{-1}$ and $r(z) = 0$ so that

$$a(z) - q(z)b(z) = a_0 - a_0 b_0^{-1} b_0$$

$$= a_0 - a_0$$

$$= 0$$

$$= r(z).$$

We have disposed of $n = 0$. Now suppose the theorem (i.e., formula (9)) holds for all polynomials $a(z)$ of degree at most $n - 1$ and assume that $\deg a(z) = n > 0$. If $m > n$ set $q(z) = 0$ and $r(z) = a(z)$. If $m \leq n$, let $\alpha(z) \in R[z]$ be defined by

$$\alpha(z) = a(z) - a_n b_m^{-1} z^{n-m} b(z). \tag{13}$$

Then from (13) we compute that

$$\alpha(z) = a(z) - a_n b_m^{-1} z^{n-m} \sum_{t=0}^{m} b_t z^t$$

$$= a(z) - a_n b_m^{-1} z^{n-m}(b_m z^m + b_{m-1} z^{m-1} + \cdots + b_0)$$

$$= a(z) - (a_n b_m^{-1} b_m z^n + \cdots) \tag{14}$$

$$= a(z) - (a_n z^n + \cdots)$$

$$= (a_n z^n + \cdots) - (a_n z^n + \cdots).$$

In both of the latter brackets the " dots " stand for terms of degree less than n. In the calculation (14) we have repeatedly used the fact that the indeterminate z commutes with everything in $R[z]$ (see Definition 4.1). Thus (14) shows that deg $\alpha(z) < n$ (or $\alpha(z) = 0$) and the induction step may be applied to it in order to secure polynomials $q_1(z)$ and $r_1(z)$ in $R[z]$ for which

$$\alpha(z) = q_1(z)b(z) + r_1(z), \tag{15}$$

where $r_1(z) = 0$ or deg $r_1(z) < $ deg $b(z)$. But then from (13) and (15) we have

$$a(z) = \alpha(z) + a_n b_m^{-1} z^{n-m} b(z)$$

$$= q_1(z)b(z) + r_1(z) + a_n b_m^{-1} z^{n-m} b(z) \tag{16}$$

$$= (q_1(z) + a_n b_m^{-1} z^{n-m})b(z) + r_1(z)$$

and deg $r_1(z) < $ deg $b(z)$ or $r_1(z) = 0$. We set $q(z) = q_1(z) + a_n b_m^{-1} z^{n-m}$ and $r(z) = r_1(z)$ and (16) becomes (9) with condition (11) satisfied. The proof of (10) is virtually identical and is relegated to the exercises. We now proceed to prove that formula (9) and condition (11) determine $q(z)$ and $r(z)$ uniquely. For, suppose that

$$a(z) = q(z)b(z) + r(z)$$

$$= Q(z)b(z) + \rho(z)$$

where

$$\text{deg } \rho(z) < \text{deg } b(z) \qquad \text{or} \qquad \rho(z) = 0.$$

Then

$$(q(z) - Q(z))b(z) = \rho(z) - r(z). \tag{17}$$

If $q(z) - Q(z) = 0$ then $\rho(z) - r(z) = 0$ and uniqueness is proved. If $q(z) - Q(z)$ were not zero then since the leading coefficient in $b(z)$ is a unit it would follow immediately that $(q(z) - Q(z))b(z) \neq 0$. Thus we could compute the degrees of both sides of (17) to obtain from Theorem 4.1

$$\text{deg } (q(z) - Q(z))b(z) = \text{deg } (q(z) - Q(z)) + \text{deg } b(z)$$

$$\geq \text{deg } b(z). \tag{18}$$

But $\deg(\rho(z) - r(z)) < \deg b(z)$, which is incompatible with (18). Thus $q(z) = Q(z)$ and the uniqueness of $q(z)$ and $r(z)$ is established. A similar argument proves the uniqueness of $s(z)$ and $u(z)$.

EXAMPLES 4.2

(a)   Let R be the ring of 2×2 matrices with integer entries. Then R possesses the multiplicative identity $\begin{bmatrix} 1 & 0 \\ 0 & 1 \end{bmatrix}$. Moreover $\begin{bmatrix} 0 & 1 \\ -1 & 0 \end{bmatrix}$ is a unit in R since $\begin{bmatrix} 0 & 1 \\ -1 & 0 \end{bmatrix}^{-1} = \begin{bmatrix} 0 & -1 \\ 1 & 0 \end{bmatrix}$. Let

$$a(z) = \begin{bmatrix} 2 & 1 \\ 0 & 0 \end{bmatrix} z^2 + \begin{bmatrix} 0 & 0 \\ 1 & 0 \end{bmatrix} z + \begin{bmatrix} 1 & 0 \\ 0 & 1 \end{bmatrix},$$

$$b(z) = \begin{bmatrix} 0 & 1 \\ -1 & 0 \end{bmatrix} z + \begin{bmatrix} 1 & 1 \\ 1 & 1 \end{bmatrix}.$$

Following (13) we compute

$$\alpha(z) = a(z) - \begin{bmatrix} 2 & 1 \\ 0 & 0 \end{bmatrix} \begin{bmatrix} 0 & -1 \\ 1 & 0 \end{bmatrix} z\, b(z)$$

$$= \begin{bmatrix} 2 & 1 \\ 0 & 0 \end{bmatrix} z^2 + \begin{bmatrix} 0 & 0 \\ 1 & 0 \end{bmatrix} z + \begin{bmatrix} 1 & 0 \\ 0 & 1 \end{bmatrix}$$

$$\qquad - \begin{bmatrix} 2 & 1 \\ 0 & 0 \end{bmatrix} \begin{bmatrix} 0 & -1 \\ 1 & 0 \end{bmatrix} z \left(\begin{bmatrix} 0 & 1 \\ -1 & 0 \end{bmatrix} z + \begin{bmatrix} 1 & 1 \\ 1 & 1 \end{bmatrix} \right)$$

$$= \begin{bmatrix} 2 & 1 \\ 0 & 0 \end{bmatrix} z^2 + \begin{bmatrix} 0 & 0 \\ 1 & 0 \end{bmatrix} z + \begin{bmatrix} 1 & 0 \\ 0 & 1 \end{bmatrix} - \begin{bmatrix} 2 & 1 \\ 0 & 0 \end{bmatrix} z^2 - \begin{bmatrix} 2 & 1 \\ 0 & 0 \end{bmatrix} \begin{bmatrix} -1 & -1 \\ 1 & 1 \end{bmatrix} z$$

$$= \left(\begin{bmatrix} 0 & 0 \\ 1 & 0 \end{bmatrix} - \begin{bmatrix} 2 & 1 \\ 0 & 0 \end{bmatrix} \begin{bmatrix} -1 & -1 \\ 1 & 1 \end{bmatrix} \right) z + \begin{bmatrix} 1 & 0 \\ 0 & 1 \end{bmatrix}$$

$$= \left(\begin{bmatrix} 0 & 0 \\ 1 & 0 \end{bmatrix} - \begin{bmatrix} -1 & -1 \\ 0 & 0 \end{bmatrix} \right) z + \begin{bmatrix} 1 & 0 \\ 0 & 1 \end{bmatrix}$$

$$= \begin{bmatrix} 1 & 1 \\ 1 & 0 \end{bmatrix} z + \begin{bmatrix} 1 & 0 \\ 0 & 1 \end{bmatrix}.$$

Thus $\alpha(z) = \begin{bmatrix} 1 & 1 \\ 1 & 0 \end{bmatrix} z + \begin{bmatrix} 1 & 0 \\ 0 & 1 \end{bmatrix}$. Now deg $\alpha(z) = 1$ and since deg $b(z) = 1$ we must repeat the process with $\alpha(z)$. We compute

$$\alpha(z) - \begin{bmatrix} 1 & 1 \\ 1 & 0 \end{bmatrix}\begin{bmatrix} 0 & -1 \\ 1 & 0 \end{bmatrix} b(z)$$

$$= \begin{bmatrix} 1 & 1 \\ 1 & 0 \end{bmatrix} z + \begin{bmatrix} 1 & 0 \\ 0 & 1 \end{bmatrix} - \begin{bmatrix} 1 & 1 \\ 1 & 0 \end{bmatrix}\begin{bmatrix} 0 & -1 \\ 1 & 0 \end{bmatrix}\left(\begin{bmatrix} 0 & 1 \\ -1 & 0 \end{bmatrix} z + \begin{bmatrix} 1 & 1 \\ 1 & 1 \end{bmatrix} \right)$$

$$= \begin{bmatrix} 1 & 1 \\ 1 & 0 \end{bmatrix} z + \begin{bmatrix} 1 & 0 \\ 0 & 1 \end{bmatrix} - \begin{bmatrix} 1 & 1 \\ 1 & 0 \end{bmatrix} z - \begin{bmatrix} 1 & 1 \\ 1 & 0 \end{bmatrix}\begin{bmatrix} -1 & -1 \\ 1 & 1 \end{bmatrix}$$

$$= \begin{bmatrix} 1 & 0 \\ 0 & 1 \end{bmatrix} - \begin{bmatrix} 0 & 0 \\ -1 & -1 \end{bmatrix}$$

$$= \begin{bmatrix} 1 & 0 \\ 1 & 2 \end{bmatrix}.$$

Thus

$$a(z) - \begin{bmatrix} 2 & 1 \\ 0 & 0 \end{bmatrix}\begin{bmatrix} 0 & -1 \\ 1 & 0 \end{bmatrix} z b(z) = \alpha(z)$$

$$= \begin{bmatrix} 1 & 1 \\ 1 & 0 \end{bmatrix}\begin{bmatrix} 0 & -1 \\ 1 & 0 \end{bmatrix} b(z) + \begin{bmatrix} 1 & 0 \\ 1 & 2 \end{bmatrix},$$

$$a(z) = \left(\begin{bmatrix} 2 & 1 \\ 0 & 0 \end{bmatrix}\begin{bmatrix} 0 & -1 \\ 1 & 0 \end{bmatrix} z + \begin{bmatrix} 1 & 1 \\ 1 & 0 \end{bmatrix}\begin{bmatrix} 0 & -1 \\ 1 & 0 \end{bmatrix} \right) b(z) + \begin{bmatrix} 1 & 0 \\ 1 & 2 \end{bmatrix}$$

$$= \left(\begin{bmatrix} 1 & -2 \\ 0 & 0 \end{bmatrix} z + \begin{bmatrix} 1 & -1 \\ 0 & -1 \end{bmatrix} \right) b(z) + \begin{bmatrix} 1 & 0 \\ 1 & 2 \end{bmatrix}.$$

In this example

$$q(z) = \begin{bmatrix} 1 & -2 \\ 0 & 0 \end{bmatrix} z + \begin{bmatrix} 1 & -1 \\ 0 & -1 \end{bmatrix}$$

and

$$r(z) = \begin{bmatrix} 1 & 0 \\ 1 & 2 \end{bmatrix}.$$

We may check that

$$b(z)q(z) + r(z) = \left(\begin{bmatrix} 0 & 1 \\ -1 & 0 \end{bmatrix} z + \begin{bmatrix} 1 & 1 \\ 1 & 1 \end{bmatrix} \right)\left(\begin{bmatrix} 1 & -2 \\ 0 & 0 \end{bmatrix} z \right.$$

$$\left. + \begin{bmatrix} 1 & -1 \\ 0 & -1 \end{bmatrix} \right) + \begin{bmatrix} 1 & 0 \\ 1 & 2 \end{bmatrix}$$

$$= \begin{bmatrix} 0 & 0 \\ -1 & 2 \end{bmatrix} z^2 + \begin{bmatrix} 1 & -3 \\ 0 & -1 \end{bmatrix} z + \begin{bmatrix} 2 & -2 \\ 2 & 0 \end{bmatrix}$$

$$\neq a(z).$$

We see then that it makes a difference on what side we perform the division.

(b)   Let R be the ring of integers, assume that p is an odd positive integer and let

$$a(z) = z^p + z^{p-1} + z^{p-2} + \cdots + z + 1$$

and

$$b(z) = z + 1.$$

Then $b(z)$ has a unit as leading coefficient, i.e., 1, and the hypotheses of Theorem 4.2 apply. Once again let

$$\alpha(z) = a(z) - z^{p-1}(z + 1)$$

$$= \sum_{k=0}^{p} z^k - (z^p + z^{p-1})$$

$$= \sum_{k=0}^{p-2} z^k + (z^p + z^{p-1}) - (z^p + z^{p-1})$$

$$= \sum_{k=0}^{p-2} z^k.$$

Furthermore,

$$\sum_{k=0}^{p-2} z^k - z^{p-3}(z + 1) = \sum_{k=0}^{p-2} z^k - (z^{p-2} + z^{p-3})$$

$$= \sum_{k=0}^{p-4} z^k + (z^{p-2} + z^{p-3}) - (z^{p-2} + z^{p-3})$$

$$= \sum_{k=0}^{p-4} z^k.$$

It is clear that we may continue in this way, decreasing the number of terms in the polynomial at hand by two at each stage. Since p is odd we finally obtain 0. That is,

$$a(z) - z^{p-1}(z + 1) = z^{p-3}(z + 1) + \sum_{k=0}^{p-4} z^k$$

$$= z^{p-3}(z + 1) + z^{p-5}(z + 1) + \sum_{k=0}^{p-6} z^k$$

$$= \cdots$$

$$= z^{p-3}(z + 1) + z^{p-5}(z + 1) + \cdots + z^{p-p}(z + 1),$$

and hence

$$a(z) = (z^{p-1} + z^{p-3} + \cdots + z^2 + 1)(z + 1).$$

Thus $q(z) = z^{p-1} + z^{p-3} + \cdots + z^2 + 1$ and $r(z) = 0$. Notice here that the value of $a(z)$ at -1, that is, $a(-1)$, is

$$(-1)^p + (-1)^{p-1} + \cdots + (-1) + 1 = -1 + 1 - 1 + 1 - 1 + 1 \cdots -1 + 1$$

in which there are the same number of 1's as -1's. Hence $a(-1) = 0$. As we shall see in a moment, the facts that $a(-1) = 0$ and $r(z) = 0$ are intimately related.

Theorem 4.3   (Remainder theorem)   *Let R be a ring with a multiplicative identity denoted by* 1. *Let z be an indeterminate over R and let $a(z) \in R[z]$. Let $c \in R$. Then there exist unique polynomials $q(z)$ and $s(z)$ in $R[z]$ satisfying*

$$a(z) = q(z)(z - c) + a_r(c) \tag{19}$$

and

$$a(z) = (z - c)s(z) + a_l(c). \tag{20}$$

(Recall Definition 4.2(d) in which the right- and left-hand values of $a(z)$ at c are defined.)

Proof.   According to Theorem 4.2 we can find unique polynomials $q(z)$ and $r(z) \in R[z]$ such that

$$a(z) = q(z)(z - c) + r(z). \tag{21}$$

Moreover, $r(z) = 0$ or $\deg r(z) = 0$. Thus, $r(z) \in R$ under any circumstances, say, $r(z) = d$. Next let

$$q(z) = \sum_{t=0}^{m} c_t z^t$$

so that

$$q(z)(z - c) = \sum_{t=0}^{m} c_t z^t (z - c)$$

$$= \sum_{t=0}^{m} c_t (z^{t+1} - cz^t).$$

Hence the right-hand value of $q(z)(z - c)$ at c is just

$$\sum_{t=0}^{m} c_t (c^{m+1} - cc^m) = \sum_{t=0}^{m} c_t (c^{m+1} - c^{m+1})$$

$$= 0.$$

It now follows from (21) that

$$a_r(c) = r_r(c).$$

But, of course, $r(z) = d$ so $r_r(c) = d$. In other words,

$$a_r(c) = r(z)$$

and (21) becomes (19). The verification of (20) is done in essentially the same way and is left as an exercise.

In case R is a commutative ring we need not distinguish between right- and left-hand values of a polynomial. These will of course be the same. In fact, in what we do in the remainder of this chapter we shall need to consider only those polynomials whose coefficients are real or complex numbers. Thus we have

Theorem 4.4   *Let the ring R be either the real or the complex numbers and let z be an indeterminate over R. If $a(z)$ and $b(z)$ are in $R[z]$, $b(z) \neq 0$, then there exist unique polynomials $q(z)$ and $r(z)$ satisfying*

$$a(z) = q(z)b(z) + r(z) \tag{22}$$

and

$$\deg r(z) < \deg b(z) \qquad or \qquad r(z) = 0. \tag{23}$$

Also if $c \in R$ then there exists a unique polynomial $s(z)$ such that

$$a(z) = s(z)(z - c) + a(c). \tag{24}$$

Proof.   In Theorem 4.2 the distinction between "right" and "left" division disappears. Also, if $b(z) \neq 0$ then the leading coefficient of $b(z)$ is a unit. This is so because every nonzero real or complex number has an inverse. Thus (22) follows immediately from Theorem 4.2. Similarly, the distinction between $a_r(c)$ and $a_l(c)$ disappears and both become $a(c)$ (see Definition 4.2(d)). Hence (24) follows from Theorem 4.3.

Definition 4.3   (Divisibility)   *Let R be either the real numbers or the complex numbers, and let z be an indeterminate over R.*

   (i)   *If $a(z)$ and $b(z)$ are in $R[z]$ and $b(z) \neq 0$ then $b(z)$ is a divisor of $a(z)$ if there exists $c(z) \in R[z]$ such that $a(z) = b(z)c(z)$. We write $b(z)\,|\,a(z)$.*

   (ii)   *A unit in $R[z]$ is a polynomial in $R[z]$ which has an inverse, also in $R[z]$; that is, a unit is just a nonzero number in R (see Example 4.1(a)).*

   (iii)   *If $a(z)$ and $b(z)$ are in $R[z]$ and u is a unit for which $a(z) = ub(z)$ then $a(z)$ and $b(z)$ are called associates.*

   (iv)   *If $b(z)\,|\,a(z)$ and $b(z)$ is neither a unit nor an associate of $a(z)$ then $b(z)$ is called a proper divisor of $a(z)$.*

   (v)   *A polynomial is called prime or irreducible if it is not a unit and has no proper divisors.*

   (vi)   *A nonzero polynomial is called composite if it has proper divisors.*

If the reader will look back at Definition 2.1 in this chapter, he will find that the above terms are word for word the same ones we used for integers. In fact we shall prove a sequence of theorems that is almost identical to the development of divisibility for integers. The role of the absolute value of an integer will here be played by the degree of a polynomial.

EXAMPLES   4.3

   (a)   Find the remainder obtained by dividing $b(z) = z - 3$ into $a(z) = z^4 - 5z^2 + z - 2$. To solve this example we can apply Theorem 4.4 directly. Thus by (24) we have

$$a(z) = b(z)q(z) + a(3).$$

So the remainder is

$$a(3) = 3^4 - 5 \cdot 3^2 + 3 - 2 = 37.$$

(b)   Show that if p is an odd positive integer then

$$(z + 1) | (z^p + z^{p-1} + \cdots + z + 1).$$

Again, by (24),

$$z^p + \cdots + 1 = (z + 1)q(z) + ((-1)^p + (-1)^{p-1} + \cdots + (-1) + 1).$$

Since p is odd there are $(p + 1)/2$ ones and $(p + 1)/2$ minus ones in the remainder. Hence it must be 0 and the divisibility is proved.

(c)   Find all the roots of $f(z) = z^4 + 2z^3 + z + 2$.
By inspection try the value -1:

$$f(-1) = (-1)^4 + 2(-1)^3 + (-1) + 2$$

$$= 0.$$

Hence $f(-1) = 0$, that is, -1 is a root of $f(z)$ (see Definition 4.2(e)). Thus, by Theorem 4.4, $(z + 1) | f(z)$. In fact the process described in the division algorithm yields

$$z^4 + 2z^3 + z + 2 = (z + 1)(z^3 + z^2 - z + 2).$$

One can see immediately by inspection that

$$(-2)^3 + (-2)^2 - (-2) + 2 = 0$$

and hence

$$(z + 2) | (z^3 + z^2 - z + 2).$$

In fact

$$z^3 + z^2 - z + 2 = (z + 2)(z^2 - z + 1).$$

Now $z^2 - z + 1$ has complex roots $1 + 3i$ and $1 - 3i$ (use the quadratic formula) and we have

$$f(z) = (z + 1)(z + 2)(z - (1 + 3i))(z - (1 - 3i)).$$

Theorem 4.5   *Let z be an indeterminate over R.*

(a)   *If $a(z)$ and $b(z)$ are in $R[z]$ and $a(z)b(z) = 0$ then either $a(z) = 0$ or $b(z) = 0$.*

(b)   *If $a(z) \neq 0$ and $a(z)b(z) = a(z)c(z)$ then $b(z) = c(z)$.*

(c)   *If $a(z) | b(z)$ and $b(z) | c(z)$ then $a(z) | c(z)$.*

(d)   *If $a(z) | b(z)$ and $a(z) | c(z)$ then $a(z) | (m(z)b(z) + n(z)c(z))$ for any $m(z)$ and $n(z)$ in $R[z]$.*

(e)   *If $a(z) | b(z)$ and $b(z) | a(z)$ then $a(z) = ub(z)$ where $u \in R$.*

(f)   *If $c \in R$ and $a(z) \in R[z]$ then $a(c) = 0$ if and only if $(z - c) | a(z)$.*

Proof.

(a)   Let a_p and b_q be the leading coefficients of $a(z)$ and $b(z)$ respectively. Then $a(z)b(z)$ has $a_p b_q$ as leading coefficient and this must be 0. Hence $a_p = 0$ or $b_q = 0$, that is, $a(z) = 0$ or $b(z) = 0$.

(b)   We see immediately that $a(z)\,(b(z) - c(z)) = 0$ and hence $b(z) - c(z) = 0$ from (a).

(c)   Write $b(z) = q_1(z)a(z)$, $c(z) = q_2(z)b(z)$ so that $c(z) = q_2(z)q_1(z)a(z)$, that is, $a(z)\,|\,c(z)$.

(d)   The proof is left as an exercise.

(e)   Write $b(z) = q_1(z)a(z)$, $a(z) = q_2(z)b(z)$. Then

$$a(z) = q_1(z)q_2(z)a(z), \qquad a(z)(1 - q_1(z)q_2(z)) = 0.$$

Hence, by (b), $q_1(z)q_2(z) = 1$ and from Theorem 4.1 it follows that $\deg q_1(z) + \deg q_2(z) = 0$, that is, $q_1(z) \in R$ and $q_2(z) \in R$.

(f)   By (24) we can write $a(z) = s(z)(z - c) + a(c)$. Hence $(z - c)\,|\,a(z)$ if and only if $a(c) = 0$.

EXAMPLES 4.4

(a)   If R denotes the real numbers then show that $p(z) = z^2 + z + 1$ is a prime polynomial. To see this suppose $p(z) = a(z)b(z)$ so that $\deg p(z) = \deg a(z) + \deg b(z)$. If $a(z)$ (and $b(z)$) were a proper divisor of $p(z)$ then $\deg a(z) = 1$; that is, $a(z) = a_1 z + a_0$. Then $a(-a_1^{-1}a_0) = 0$ so that $p(-a_1^{-1}a_0) = 0$. In other words, there is a real number $r_0 = -a_1^{-1}a_0$ that satisfies

$$r_0^2 + r_0 + 1 = 0.$$

But according to Theorem 3.2, Chapter 3, applied to $|r_0|$,

$$-r_0 = r_0^2 + 1 \geq 2\,|r_0|.$$

Hence $-r_0 \geq 2\,|r_0|$. This can only happen if $r_0 = 0$. But $p(0) = 1$, a contradiction.

(b)   If R is the field of real numbers and n is a positive integer show that $p(z) = z^n - (n - 1)z + (n - 1)$ has no nonnegative real roots. Suppose that $p(r) = 0$ and $r \geq 0$. Then

$$r^n + (n - 1) = (n - 1)r. \tag{25}$$

According to Theorem 3.2, Chapter 3, again we have

$$r^n + n - 1 \geq nr,$$

which contradicts (25).

Definition 4.4   (Greatest common divisor)   *Let* $\{a_1(z), \ldots, a_n(z)\}$ *be a set of n polynomials in $R[z]$, not all zero. If $d(z) \in R[z]$ and $d(z) \mid a_i(z)$, $i = 1, \ldots, n$, then $d(z)$ is called a common divisor of $a_1(z), \ldots, a_n(z)$. If for any $h(z)$ such that $h(z) \mid a_i(z)$, $i = 1, \ldots, n$, it is the case that $h(z) \mid d(z)$ then $d(z)$ is called a greatest common divisor (abbreviated g.c.d.) of $a_1(z), \ldots, a_n(z)$. This is written*

$$d(z) = \text{g.c.d.}\,(a_1(z), \ldots, a_n(z)).$$

If $\deg d(z) = 0$ *then* $a_1(z), \ldots, a_n(z)$ *are said to be relatively prime.*

Theorem 4.6

(a)   *There is only one monic g.c.d. of a set of polynomials and any two g.c.d.'s are associated polynomials. Hereafter the unique monic g.c.d. will be called the g.c.d. and will be denoted by*

$$d(z) = (a_1(z), \ldots, a_n(z)).$$

(b)   *If* $a_1(z), \ldots, a_n(z)$ *are in $R[z]$ then the g.c.d. of these polynomials always exists and moreover there exist polynomials $m_1(z), \ldots, m_n(z)$ for which*

$$d(z) = \sum_{i=1}^{n} m_i(z)a_i(z). \tag{26}$$

Proof.

(a)   If $d_1(z)$ and $d_2(z)$ are g.c.d.'s of $a_1(z), \ldots, a_n(z)$ then $d_1(z) \mid d_2(z)$ and $d_2(z) \mid d_1(z)$ because each is a common divisor and, by Definition 4.4, each must divide any other g.c.d. But then Theorem 4.5(e) tells us that $d_1(z)$ and $d_2(z)$ are associates:

$$d_1(z) = u d_2(z), \qquad u \in R. \tag{27}$$

If the leading coefficients of $d_1(z)$ and $d_2(z)$ are both 1 then clearly $u = 1$ since the coefficients of equal polynomials must be the same (see Exercise 1) and, from (27), $d_1(z) = d_2(z)$.

(b)   Let M be the totality of polynomials of the form

$$\sum_{i=1}^{n} m_i(z)a_i(z). \tag{28}$$

It is obvious that if $\alpha(z)$ and $\beta(z)$ are in M so are $\alpha(z) + \beta(z)$ and $c(z)\alpha(z)$, where $c(z)$ is any polynomial in $R[z]$. Among all the polynomials in M let $d(z)$ be a monic polynomial whose degree is minimal, i.e., $\deg d(z) \leq \deg \alpha(z)$ for any $\alpha(z) \in M$. Such a polynomial exists because the degrees of polynomials are nonnegative integers and any nonempty set of nonnegative integers certainly contains a least integer. Now suppose $d(z)$ is not a divisor of $a_k(z)$ for some $k = 1, \ldots, n$. Then according to Theorem 4.4 there exist polynomials $q(z)$ and $r(z) \neq 0$, $\deg r(z) < \deg d(z)$, for which

$$r(z) = a_k(z) + q(z)d(z).$$

Now $d(z) \in M$, $a_k(z) \in M$ and hence, by the preceding remarks, $r(z) \in M$. But $d(z)$ is supposed to be a polynomial of least degree in M. This contradiction means that our assumption that $d(z)$ is not a divisor of $a_k(z)$ is wrong. Thus $d(z)$ is a common divisor of $a_1(z), \ldots, a_n(z)$. But more is true. For, let $h(z)$ be a common divisor of $a_1(z), \ldots, a_n(z)$. Then we can write

$$a_i(z) = q_i(z)h(z), \qquad i = 1, \ldots, n.$$

Now $d(z) \in M$ so that $d(z)$ can be written in the form (28):

$$
\begin{aligned}
d(z) &= \sum_{i=1}^{n} m_i(z)a_i(z) \\
&= \sum_{i=1}^{n} m_i(z)q_i(z)h(z) \qquad\qquad (29) \\
&= \left(\sum_{i=1}^{n} m_i(z)q_i(z) \right)h(z).
\end{aligned}
$$

If we set $q(z) = \sum_{i=1}^{n} m_i(z)q_i(z)$ we see from (29) that $d(z) = q(z)h(z)$, that is, $h(z)\,|\,d(z)$. Thus any common divisor of $a_1(z), \ldots, a_n(z)$ is a divisor of $d(z)$. Hence $d(z)$ is the g.c.d. of $a_1(z), \ldots, a_n(z)$. This completes the proof of (b).

The preceding result is defective in the sense that it does not tell us how to produce the g.c.d. of two polynomials. In other words, it is not constructive. In our next theorem we will devise a procedure for obtaining the g.c.d. of two polynomials which is almost identical in form to Theorem 2.4, the Euclidean Algorithm.

Theorem 4.7 (Euclidean Algorithm) *Let $a(z)$ and $b(z)$ be nonzero polynomials in $R[z]$. Using the division process described in Theorem 4.4 consider the following sequence:*

$$
\begin{aligned}
a(z) &= b(z)q_1(z) + r_1(z), & \deg r_1(z) &< \deg b(z), \\
b(z) &= r_1(z)q_2(z) + r_2(z), & \deg r_2(z) &< \deg r_1(z), \\
r_1(z) &= r_2(z)q_3(z) + r_3(z), & \deg r_3(z) &< \deg r_2(z), \qquad (30)
\end{aligned}
$$

$$\cdot \quad \cdot \quad \cdot \quad \cdot \quad \cdot \quad \cdot \quad \cdot \quad \cdot \quad \cdot \quad \cdot \quad \cdot \quad \cdot \quad \cdot \quad \cdot \quad \cdot \quad \cdot$$

$$r_{k-1}(z) = r_k(z)q_{k+1}(z) + r_{k+1}(z), \qquad \deg r_{k+1}(z) < \deg r_k(z),$$

$$r_k(z) = r_{k+1}(z)q_{k+2}(z).$$

Then

$$r_{k+1}(z) = (a(z), b(z)). \qquad\qquad (31)$$

Proof.   In other words, perform the indicated sequence of divisions and since

$$0 \le \deg r_{k+1}(z) < \cdots < \deg r_1(z) < \deg b(z)$$

the procedure must terminate after at most deg $b(z)$ steps. We first prove that $r_{k+1}(z)$ is a divisor of both $a(z)$ and $b(z)$. From the last equation in (30)

$$r_{k+1}(z) \mid r_k(z),$$

and by repeated applications of Theorem 4.5(d),

$r_{k+1}(z) \mid r_{k-1}(z)$ because $r_k(z)q_{k+1}(z) + r_{k+1}(z) = r_{k-1}(z);$

$r_{k+1}(z) \mid r_{k-2}(z)$ because $r_{k-1}(z)q_k(z) + r_k(z) = r_{k-2}(z);$

.   .   .   .

$r_{k+1}(z) \mid r_1(z)$ because $r_2(z)q_3(z) + r_3(z) = r_1(z);$

$r_{k+1}(z) \mid b(z)$ because $r_1(z)q_2(z) + r_2(z) = b(z);$

and finally

$r_{k+1}(z) \mid a(z)$ because $b(z)q_1(z) + r_1(z) = a(z).$

Hence $r_{k+1}(z) \mid a(z)$ and $r_{k+1}(z) \mid b(z)$. We next use an induction argument to show that the process in (30) actually produces polynomials $m(z)$ and $n(z)$ for which

$$r_{k+1}(z) = m(z)a(z) + n(z)b(z).$$

Thus, we want to prove by induction that there exist polynomials $m(z)$ and $n(z)$ in $R[z]$ such that

$$r_s(z) = m_s(z)a(z) + n_s(z)b(z), \qquad s = 1, \ldots, k+1. \tag{32}$$

For $s = 1$,

$$r_1(z) = a(z) - q_1(z)b(z),$$

and for $s = 2$,

$$\begin{aligned}
r_2(z) &= b(z) - r_1(z)q_2(z) \\
&= b(z) - (a(z) - b(z)q_1(z))q_2(z) \\
&= -q_2(z)a(z) + (1 + q_1(z)q_2(z))b(z).
\end{aligned}$$

Assume then that $r_t(z) = m_t(z)a(z) + n_t(z)b(z)$ for $t < s$. Then

$$\begin{aligned}
r_s(z) &= r_{s-2}(z) - r_{s-1}(z)q_{s-2}(z) \\
&= m_{s-2}(z)a(z) + n_{s-2}(z)b(z) - (m_{s-1}(z)a(z) + n_{s-1}(z)b(z))q_{s-2}(z) \\
&= (m_{s-2}(z) - m_{s-1}(z)q_{s-2}(z))a(z) + (n_{s-2}(z) - n_{s-1}(z)q_{s-2}(z))b(z) \\
&= m_s(z)a(z) + n_s(z)b(z).
\end{aligned}$$

In particular, for $s = k+1$

$$r_{k+1}(z) = m_{k+1}(z)a(z) + n_{k+1}(z)b(z). \tag{33}$$

We have proved that $r_{k+1}(z)$ must divide $a(z)$ and $b(z)$ and hence by definition must divide $(a(z), b(z))$. On the other hand, from (33) and Theorem 4.5(d) we can conclude that $(a(z), b(z)) \mid r_{k+1}(z)$ and Theorem 4.5(e) completes the proof.

EXAMPLES 4.5

(a) Find the g.c.d. of $a(z) = z^4 + 2z^3 - 9z^2 - 2z + 8$ and $b(z) = z^3 - 7z + 6$. We write

$$z^4 + 2z^3 - 9z^2 - 2z + 8 = (z + 2)(z^3 - 7z + 6) + (-2z^2 + 6z - 4),$$

$$z^3 - 7z + 6 = \left(-\frac{z}{2} - \frac{3}{2}\right)(-2z^2 + 6z - 4).$$

Thus a g.c.d. is $-2z^2 + 6z - 4$ which we render monic, i.e., the g.c.d. is $z^2 - 3z + 2$.

(b) Let $a(z) = 2z^5 + 2z^4 + 4z^3 - z^2 - z - 2$ and $b(z) = 2z^4 + 2z^3 + 5z^2 + z + 2$. Let $d(z) = $ g.c.d. $(a(z), b(z))$. Find polynomials $m(z)$ and $n(z)$ such that

$$d(z) = m(z)a(z) + n(z)b(z).$$

We first use the Euclidean Algorithm to calculate $d(z)$:

$$2z^5 + 2z^4 + 4z^3 - z^2 - z - 2 = (2z^4 + 2z^3 + 5z^2 + z + 2)(z)$$
$$+ (-z^3 - 2z^2 - 3z - 2), \qquad (34)$$

$$2z^4 + 2z^3 + 5z^2 + z + 2 = (-z^3 - 2z^2 - 3z - 2)(-2z + 2)$$
$$+ (3z^2 + 3z + 6), \qquad (35)$$

$$-z^3 - 2z^2 - 3z - 2 = (3z^2 + 3z + 6)(-\tfrac{1}{3}z - \tfrac{1}{3}).$$

Hence $3z^2 + 3z + 6$ is a g.c.d. of $a(z)$ and $b(z)$. Thus $d(z) = z^2 + z + 2$. Now, from (35), $3z^2 + 3z + 6 = b(z) - (-z^3 - 2z^2 - 3z - 2)(-2z + 2)$ and, using (34),

$$3z^2 + 3z + 6 = b(z) - (a(z) - zb(z))(-2z + 2)$$

$$= (2z - 2)a(z) + (-2z^2 + 2z + 1)b(z).$$

Therefore,

$$d(z) = z^2 + z + 2$$

$$= (\tfrac{2}{3}z - \tfrac{2}{3})a(z) + (-\tfrac{2}{3}z^2 + \tfrac{2}{3}z + \tfrac{1}{3})b(z).$$

(c) Let $a(z) = z^4 + z^3 - z^2 - 4z - 12$, $b(z) = z^4 - 5z - 6$ and $c(z) = z^5 + z^4 + 3z^3 - z^2 - z - 3$. Evaluate the g.c.d of the three polynomials.

Find polynomials $m(z)$, $n(z)$ and $p(z)$ such that g.c.d.$(a(z),b(z),c(z)) = m(z)a(z) + n(z)b(z) + p(z)c(z)$. First we compute a g.c.d. of $a(z)$ and $b(z)$:

$$z^4 + z^3 - z^2 - 4z - 12 = (z^4 - 5z - 6)(1) + (z^3 - z^2 + z - 6), \quad (36)$$

$$z^4 - 5z - 6 = (z^3 - z^2 + z - 6)(z + 1).$$

Thus $d(z) = $ g.c.d.$(a(z), b(z)) = z^3 - z^2 + z - 6$. Now, g.c.d.$(a(z), b(z), c(z))$ = g.c.d.$($g.c.d.$(a(z), b(z)), c(z))$ (see Exercise 2). Again, we use the Euclidean Algorithm:

$$z^5 + z^4 + 3z^3 - z^2 - z - 3 = (z^3 - z^2 + z - 6)(z^2 + 2z + 4)$$
$$+ (7z^2 + 7z + 21), \quad (37)$$

$$z^3 - z^2 + z - 6 = (7z^2 + 7z + 21)(\tfrac{1}{7}z - \tfrac{2}{7}),$$

and obtain

$$\text{g.c.d.}(a(z), b(z), c(z)) = z^2 + z + 3.$$

From (37) we have

$$7z^2 + 7z + 21 = c(z) - (z^2 + 2z + 4)\,d(z)$$

and from (36)

$$d(z) = a(z) - b(z).$$

Thus

$$\text{g.c.d.}(a(z), b(z), c(z)) = z^2 + z + 3$$
$$= (-\tfrac{1}{7}z^2 - \tfrac{2}{7}z - \tfrac{4}{7})a(z) + (\tfrac{1}{7}z^2 + \tfrac{2}{7}z + \tfrac{4}{7})b(z) + \tfrac{1}{7}c(z).$$

Hence

$$m(z) = -\tfrac{1}{7}z^2 - \tfrac{2}{7}z - \tfrac{4}{7}, \qquad n(z) = \tfrac{1}{7}z^2 + \tfrac{2}{7}z + \tfrac{4}{7} \qquad \text{and} \qquad p(z) = \tfrac{1}{7}.$$

Theorem 4.8 *Let $a(z)$, $b(z)$ and $c(z)$ be polynomials in $R[z]$, z an indeterminate over R. If $a(z) \mid b(z)c(z)$ and $(a(z), b(z)) = 1$ then $a(z) \mid c(z)$. In words, if $a(z)$ divides the product of two polynomials $b(z)$, $c(z)$, and $a(z)$ and $b(z)$ are relatively prime then $a(z)$ must divide $c(z)$.*

Proof. Since $(a(z), b(z)) = 1$, it follows by Theorem 4.6(b) that

$$1 = m(z)a(z) + n(z)b(z)$$

for appropriate polynomials $m(z)$ and $n(z)$ in $R[z]$. Thus

$$c(z) = m(z)a(z)c(z) + n(z)b(z)c(z).$$

Now $a(z) \mid m(z)a(z)c(z)$ and $a(z) \mid n(z)b(z)c(z)$. Hence, by Theorem 4.5(d), $a(z) \mid c(z)$.

Theorem 4.9   *Assume that all polynomials are in $R[z]$, z an indeterminate over R. Then*

(a) *if $p(z)$ is prime and $p(z) \mid \prod_{i=1}^{n} a_i(z)$ then $p(z) \mid a_k(z)$ for some k;*

(b) *if $(a(z), b(z)) = d(z)$ and $a(z) = a'(z)d(z)$, $b(z) = b'(z)d(z)$ then $(a'(z), b'(z)) = 1$;*

(c) *if $c(z) \mid a(z)$, $c(z) \mid b(z)$ and $c(z)$ is monic and $c(z) \neq (a(z), b(z))$, then $\deg c(z) < \deg (a(z), b(z))$.*

Proof.

(a)   We use an induction on n. If $n = 2$ the result follows from Theorem 4.8. For, $p(z)$ is a prime polynomial dividing $a_1(z)a_2(z)$ and thus $p(z) \mid a_1(z)$, or $(p(z), a_1(z)) = 1$ and then $p(z) \mid a_2(z)$. Now assume the result holds for products of fewer than n factors. Then, by Theorem 4.8, if

$$p(z) \mid a_1(z)(\prod_{i=2}^{n} a_i(z))$$

then either $p(z) \mid a_1(z)$ or $p(z) \mid \prod_{i=2}^{n} a_i(z)$. But in the latter case $p(z) \mid a_k(z)$ for some k, $2 \leq k \leq n$, by the induction hypothesis.

(b)   By Theorem 4.6(b) there exist polynomials $m(z)$ and $n(z)$ such that

$$d(z) = m(z)a(z) + n(z)b(z).$$

Thus

$$d(z) = m(z)a'(z)d(z) + n(z)b'(z)d(z)$$

and by Theorem 4.5(b) we have

$$1 = m(z)a'(z) + n(z)b'(z).$$

Hence $(a'(z), b'(z)) \mid 1$ so that $(a'(z), b'(z)) = 1$.

(c)   We defer the proof until Exercise 3.

Our major result here is the following theorem that shows that any polynomial can be factored into prime polynomials uniquely to within order and associates.

Theorem 4.10   *Every nonzero nonunit polynomial $a(z)$ is a prime or a product of prime polynomials. Moreover, this factorization is unique up to associates and order in the following sense: if*

$$a(z) = \prod_{i=1}^{r} p_i(z) = \prod_{j=1}^{s} q_j(z),$$

where $p_1(z), \ldots, p_r(z)$, $q_1(z), \ldots, q_s(z)$ are prime polynomials, then $r = s$ and $p_i(z) = v_i q_{\sigma(i)}(z)$ for some permutation $\sigma \in S_r$ and nonzero elements $v_i \in R$, $i = 1, \ldots, r$.

Proof.   The proof is by induction on the degree of $a(z)$. Assume then that $\deg a(z) = 1$. If $a(z)$ were composite then $a(z) = b(z)c(z)$ and $1 = \deg a(z)$

$= \deg b(z) + \deg c(z)$. It follows that either $\deg b(z) = 0$ or $\deg c(z) = 0$, i.e., either $b(z)$ or $c(z)$ is in R. Thus any polynomial of degree 1 has no proper divisors. Assume now that a factorization into primes is possible for any polynomial of degree at most $n - 1$. If $\deg a(z) = n$ then either $a(z)$ is a prime, in which case we are done, or $a(z)$ is composite, $a(z) = b(z)c(z)$ where $b(z)$ and $c(z)$ are proper divisors of $a(z)$. Then $\deg a(z) = \deg b(z) + \deg c(z)$ and since neither $b(z)$ nor $c(z)$ is in R we conclude that $\deg b(z) \le n - 1$ and $\deg c(z) \le n - 1$. We apply the induction hypothesis to $b(z)$ and $c(z)$ so that we may write each of them as a product of primes. Thus $a(z) = b(z)c(z)$ can be written as a product of primes. We now proceed to the uniqueness. Let

$$\prod_{i=1}^{r} p_i(z) = \prod_{j=1}^{s} q_j(z) \tag{38}$$

where $p_1(z), \ldots, p_r(z)$, $q_1(z), \ldots, q_s(z)$ are prime polynomials. It is just a matter of notational convenience to assume that $r \le s$. The uniqueness argument will be by induction on r. If $r = 1$ then the left side of (38) is a prime and hence the right side cannot be composite, that is, $s = 1$ and $p_1(z) = q_1(z)$. Suppose that $r > 1$ and that the uniqueness part of the theorem holds for products of fewer than r primes. Then, from (38), $p_1(z) | \prod_{j=1}^{s} q_j(z)$ and hence, by Theorem 4.9(a), $p_1(z) | q_k(z)$ for some k. But $q_k(z)$ is a prime and hence by definition its only divisors are units or associates, that is, $p_1(z) = v q_k(z)$, $v \in R$. Thus, by Theorem 4.5(b),

$$v \prod_{i=2}^{r} p_i(z) = \prod_{\substack{j=1 \\ j \ne k}}^{s} q_j(z). \tag{39}$$

Now we may absorb the unit v into any of the remaining $p_i(z)$ so that (39) is a statement of equality of the products of two sets of primes. But by the induction hypothesis, $r - 1 = s - 1$, that is, $r = s$, and $p_i(z) = v_i q_{\tau(i)}(z)$, $i = 2, \ldots, r$, where τ is a 1-1 function on $\{2, \ldots, r\}$ onto $\{1, \ldots, k-1, k+1, \ldots, r\}$, and $v_i \in R$, $i = 2, \ldots, r$. Define $\sigma \in S_r$ by $\sigma(1) = k$, $\sigma(i) = \tau(i)$, $i = 2, \ldots, r$. Thus, to within order and unit multiples, the p_i's and the q_i's are the same.

Quiz

Answer **true** or **false**:

1. $(z + 1) | (z^7 + z^6 + z^5 + z^3 + 2)$.

2. Let $a(z) = \begin{bmatrix} 1 & -1 \\ 1 & 0 \end{bmatrix} z^2 + \begin{bmatrix} 1 & 1 \\ 1 & -1 \end{bmatrix} z + \begin{bmatrix} -3 & -4 \\ -3 & -5 \end{bmatrix}$ where z is an indeterminate

    over the ring of all 2×2 matrices with real number entries. If $c = \begin{bmatrix} 1 & 2 \\ 1 & 1 \end{bmatrix}$ then

    $a_r(c) = \begin{bmatrix} 0 & 0 \\ 0 & 0 \end{bmatrix}$ but $a_l(c) \ne \begin{bmatrix} 0 & 0 \\ 0 & 0 \end{bmatrix}$.

3. If $p_1(z), \ldots, p_r(z)$ are distinct prime polynomials in $R[z]$, where R is the real numbers, and $m_1, \ldots, m_r, n_1, \ldots, n_r$ are nonnegative integers such that

$$\prod_{i=1}^{r} (p_i(z))^{m_i} = \prod_{i=1}^{r} (p_i(z))^{n_i}$$

then $m_i = n_i$, $i = 1, \ldots, r$.

4. The number $\sqrt{2}$ is an indeterminate over the ring of rational numbers.

5. The number i is an indeterminate over the ring of real numbers.

In the following five questions let R be the ring of 2×2 matrices with real entries and assume that z is an indeterminate over R. All polynomials are in $R[z]$. The "0" refers to the zero matrix in R.

6. If $a(z) \neq 0$ and $a(z)b(z) = a(z)c(z)$ then $b(z) = c(z)$.

7. If $a(z)$ and $b(z)$ are both different from 0 then $\deg a(z)b(z) = \deg a(z) + \deg b(z)$.

8. If $a(z)b(z) \in R$ then both $a(z)$ and $b(z)$ are in R.

9. For any $c \in R$, $(za(z))_r(c) = (a(z)z)_r(c)$.

10. If $\deg a(z) = \deg b(z) = 1$ and $a_r(c) = b_r(c)$ for all $c \in R$, $c \neq 0$, then $a(z) = b(z)$.

In the following questions R is either the real or the complex numbers and z is an indeterminate over R.

11. Any polynomial in $R[z]$ of degree 1 has no proper divisors.

12. If R is the ring of real numbers then $z^2 + 1$ is a prime.

13. If R is the ring of real numbers then $z^3 + 1$ is a prime.

14. $(2z^2 + 4, 2z^2 + 2) = 2$.

15. $(a(z), b(z))^2 = ((a(z))^2, (b(z))^2)$.

Exercises

1. Let z be an indeterminate over R and let $a_0, \ldots, a_n, b_0, \ldots, b_m$ be elements in R, $a_n \neq 0$, $b_m \neq 0$. Show that

$$\sum_{i=0}^{n} a_i z^i = \sum_{i=0}^{m} b_i z^i$$

implies $n = m$ and

$$a_i = b_i, \qquad i = 0, \ldots, n.$$

2. Prove that

$$(a(z), b(z), c(z)) = ((a(z), b(z)), c(z))$$

for any polynomials $a(z)$, $b(z)$ and $c(z)$ in $R[z]$.

3. Prove Theorem 4.9(c).

4. Assume that z is an indeterminate over I_3, the ring of residue classes modulo 3. Let $a(z) = [1]z^3 + [1]z + [2]$ and $b(z) = [2]z + [2]$. Show that $a([c]) = b([c])$ for every $[c]$ in I_3. Are $a(z)$ and $b(z)$ equal polynomials?

5. Find a polynomial $a(z)$ of degree 3 with coefficients in the ring of 2×2 real matrices such that $a_r(A) = a_l(B) = \begin{bmatrix} 0 & 0 \\ 0 & 0 \end{bmatrix}$ for given matrices A and B.

6. Let $R[z]$ be the ring of polynomials with coefficients in the ring of 2×2 matrices with integer entries. Let

$$a(z) = \begin{bmatrix} 2 & 4 \\ -2 & 2 \end{bmatrix} z + \begin{bmatrix} 1 & 6 \\ 2 & 4 \end{bmatrix}.$$

Show that for any matrix $A = \begin{bmatrix} a & b \\ c & d \end{bmatrix}$ with integer entries both $a_r(A)$ and

$a_l(A)$ are different from zero.

In the remaining exercises all polynomials are assumed to be in $R[z]$ where R is the ring of real numbers.

7. Compute the g.c.d. of $z^4 + 5z^3 + 5z^2 - 2z$ and $z^6 - 10z^4 + 3z^3 + z^2 + 3z - 1$.

8. Show that the g.c.d. of $a(z) = z^4 - z^2 + 1$ and $b(z) = z^5 - z^3 + 2z^2 - 2$ is equal to 1. Find polynomials $m(z)$ and $n(z)$ such that $m(z)a(z) + n(z)b(z) = 1$.

9. Let $a(z) = z^3 + 2z^2 - z - 2$, $b(z) = z^4 + z^3 + 2z - 4$ and $c(z) = z^5 + z^3 - 2z$. Compute $(a(z), b(z))$, $(a(z), c(z))$, $(b(z), c(z))$ and $(a(z), b(z), c(z))$. Verify that

$$\begin{aligned}
(a(z), b(z), c(z)) &= ((a(z), b(z)), c(z)) \\
&= ((a(z), c(z)), b(z)) \\
&= ((b(z), c(z)), a(z)).
\end{aligned}$$

10. If $a(z)$, $b(z)$ and $c(z)$ are the polynomials in Exercise 9 find polynomials $m(z)$, $n(z)$, and $p(z)$ such that

$$m(z)a(z) + n(z)b(z) + p(z)c(z) = z - 1.$$

4.5   Construction of an Indeterminate

In Definition 4.1 of the preceding section we defined what is meant by an indeterminate z over a ring R_1. Immediately thereafter we stated that the existence of an indeterminate could be established. The construction that we are about to embark upon in this section is used in many parts of mathematics. However, if the reader is prepared to accept the existence of an indeterminate over any ring, then the contents of this section are peripheral to the remainder of the book.

Definition 5.1   (The set R^X)   *Let X be an arbitrary set and let R be a ring. The set R^X is the totality of functions $f : X \to R$ which have a nonzero value* *in R for at most a finite number of elements in X. An operation of addition, $\oplus$, is defined between elements of R^X by*

$$(f \oplus g)(x) = f(x) + g(x) \tag{1}$$

for every $x \in R$. If an operation " $+$ " between pairs of elements of X is available then an operation of multiplication, $\otimes$, can be defined between functions in R^X by

$$(f \otimes g)(x) = \sum_{u+v=x} f(u)g(v). \tag{2}$$

The notation in (2) is explained as follows: the sum on the right in (2) is over all pairs u and v in X satisfying $u + v = x$; the product $f(u)g(v)$ is the product of the two elements $f(u)$ and $g(v)$ in R. To avoid introducing another notation we have indicated the multiplication in R by juxtaposition. It should be pointed out that although X may be an infinite set there are only a finite number of nonzero summands appearing on the right in (2). The summation symbol means only that the nonzero terms are to be added and we do not concern ourselves here with any notions of infinite summation.

EXAMPLES 5.1

(a)   Let X be the set of nonnegative integers and let R be the ring of real numbers. Then for $x = 3$, (2) becomes

$$(f \otimes g)(3) = f(0)g(3) + f(1)g(2) + f(2)g(1) + f(3)g(0).$$

Consider the function $e \in R^X$ for which $e(0) = 1$ and $e(x) = 0$, $x \neq 0$. Then, for any $f \in R^X$, (2) yields

$$(f \otimes e)(x) = \sum_{u+v=x} f(u)e(v). \tag{3}$$

Now $e(v) = 0$ for $v \neq 0$ and hence $f(u)e(v) = f(u)0 = 0$. But when $v = 0$, $u = x$ in (3) and hence $f(u)e(0) = f(x)$. Thus (3) becomes

$$(f \otimes e)(x) = f(x), \qquad x \in X.$$

In other words, $f \otimes e = f$, and a similar argument shows that $e \otimes f = f$. Thus the function e acts as a multiplicative identity in R^X.

(b)   Let X be the set of integers 0, 1 with an operation " $+$ " given by the table

+	0	1
0	0	1
1	1	0

In other words, X is isomorphic to the residue class ring of integers modulo 2.

Let R be the ring of real numbers. Then, if f and g are in R^X, we compute that

$$(f \otimes g)(0) = \sum_{u+v=0} f(u)g(v) = f(0)g(0) + f(1)g(1),$$

$$(f \otimes g)(1) = \sum_{u+v=1} f(u)g(v) = f(0)g(1) + f(1)g(0)$$

and

$$(f \oplus g)(0) = f(0) + g(0),$$

$$(f \oplus g)(1) = f(1) + g(1).$$

Henceforth, the set X will be assumed to be the nonnegative integers together with the operation of addition. Thus the elements of R^X can be thought of as sequences of elements of R having only a finite number of nonzero terms. We have the following fundamental result concerning R^X.

Theorem 5.1 *Let X be the set of nonnegative integers together with the operation of addition. Let R be a ring. Then*

(a) *the set R^X with the operations given in Definition 5.1 is a ring;*
(b) *if R has a multiplicative identity then so does R^X;*
(c) *if R is commutative so is R^X;*
(d) *the ring R^X contains a ring R_1 which is isomorphic to R. Moreover if R contains a multiplicative identity then there exists an element $z \in R^X$ which commutes with every element of R_1. If*

$$(a_n \otimes z^n) \oplus (a_{n-1} \otimes z^{n-1}) \oplus \cdots \oplus (a_1 \otimes z) \oplus a_0, \quad a_k \in R_1, \quad k = 0, \ldots, n, \tag{4}$$

is the zero function then $a_k = 0$, $k = 0, \ldots, n$. Here n is a positive integer and z^k means $z \otimes \cdots \otimes z$ in which z appears k times. Furthermore, every element in R^X is of the form (4). Thus z is an indeterminate over R_1 and $R^X = R_1[z]$.

Proof.

(a)   We must first show that R^X is closed under addition, $\oplus$, and multiplication, $\otimes$. Let f and g be in R^X. Then clearly $f \oplus g$ is a function on X with values in R and since $(f \oplus g)(x) = f(x) + g(x)$ it follows that $f \oplus g$ can be different from 0 only if at least one of $f(x)$ or $g(x)$ is not 0. Hence $(f \oplus g)(x)$ is nonzero for at most a finite number of values of $x \in X$. By definition

$$(f \otimes g)(x) = \sum_{u+v=x} f(u)g(v). \tag{5}$$

Now $f(u)$ and $g(v)$ are nonzero for at most a finite number of pairs of integers u and v in X. Suppose $u_1, \ldots, u_m$ are all the elements of X where f has a non-zero value and $v_1, \ldots, v_n$ are all the elements of X where g has a nonzero value. Suppose $x \in X$ is not of the form $u_i + v_j$ for some i and j. Then if u and v are in X and satisfy $u + v = x$ it must be the case that either $f(u) = 0$ or $g(v) = 0$. In other words, there are no nonzero summands in (5) for such an x.

We have proved that $f \otimes g$ is nonzero for at most mn values of x in X; that is, $f \otimes g \in R^X$.

Our next chore will be to verify the associative law for multiplication. Let f, g, and h be elements of R^X. Note that

$$(f \otimes g)(x) = \sum_{u+v=x} f(u)g(v)$$

$$= f(0)g(x) + f(1)g(x-1) + \cdots + f(x-1)g(1) + f(x)g(0)$$

$$= \sum_{s \in X} f(s)g(x-s)$$

$$= \sum_{u \in X} f(x-u)g(u).$$

Then

$$((f \otimes g) \otimes h)(x) = \sum_{u+v=x} (f \otimes g)(u)h(v)$$

$$= \sum_{u+v=x} \left(\sum_{s+t=u} f(s)g(t) \right) h(v)$$

$$= \sum_{u \in X} \left(\sum_{s \in X} f(s)g(u-s) \right) h(x-u)$$

$$= \sum_{s \in X} f(s) \left(\sum_{u \in X} g(u-s)h(x-u) \right).$$

Now

$$\sum_{u \in X} g(u-s)h(x-u) = (g \otimes h)(x-s)$$

and hence

$$((f \otimes g) \otimes h)(x) = \sum_{s \in X} f(s)(g \otimes h)(x-s)$$

$$= (f \otimes (g \otimes h))(x).$$

In other words,

$$(f \otimes g) \otimes h = f \otimes (g \otimes h).$$

We have verified rules (i) and (ii) for $\otimes$ in Definition 1.1. It is easy to check that the remaining rules are valid once we define the 0 in R^X. But this is trivial: simply define the 0 to be the function which is 0 for every element in X. Then, of course, $-f$ is the function whose value is $-f(x)$ for each $x \in X$. We leave the verification of (iii), (iv), (v) and (vi) of Definition 1.1 to the student.

(b)   Let i denote the multiplicative identity in R. Then define $e \in R^X$ by

$$e(0) = i,$$

$$e(u) = 0, \qquad u \neq 0.$$

Then

$$(e \otimes f)(x) = \sum_{u \in X} e(u) f(x - u)$$

$$= e(0) f(x)$$

$$= i(f(x))$$

$$= f(x).$$

Hence $e \otimes f = f$ and similarly $f \otimes e = f$.

(c) If R is commutative, i.e., $r_1 r_2 = r_2 r_1$ for all r_1, r_2 in R, then for any f and g in R^X,

$$(f \otimes g)(x) = \sum_{u \in X} f(u) g(x - u)$$

$$= \sum_{u \in X} g(x - u) f(u)$$

$$= \sum_{v \in X} g(v) f(x - v)$$

$$= (g \otimes f)(x).$$

Hence $f \otimes g = g \otimes f$.

(d) Define a function $\varphi : R \to R^X$ by

$$\varphi(r) = f_r,$$

where $f_r \in R^X$ is defined by

$$f_r(0) = r,$$

$$f_r(u) = 0, \qquad u \neq 0.$$

If $\varphi(r) = \varphi(s)$ then $f_r = f_s$ and hence $f_r(0) = r = f_s(0) = s$. Thus φ is 1-1. Also

$$\varphi(r + s) = f_{r+s}$$

and hence

$$f_{r+s}(u) = 0, \qquad u \neq 0,$$

$$f_{r+s}(0) = r + s$$

$$= f_r(0) + f_s(0)$$

$$= (f_r \oplus f_s)(0).$$

In other words,

$$\varphi(r + s) = \varphi(r) \oplus \varphi(s).$$

We also compute that

$$\varphi(rs) = f_{rs}$$

and

$$(f_r \otimes f_s)(x) = \sum_{u \in X} f_r(u) f_s(x - u)$$

$$= f_r(0) f_s(x)$$

$$= r f_s(x).$$

Now unless $x = 0$ it follows that $f_s(x) = 0$. If $x = 0$ then $f_s(0) = s$. Hence whether x is 0 or not

$$(f_r \otimes f_s)(x) = f_{rs}(x),$$

that is,

$$\varphi(rs) = \varphi(r) \otimes \varphi(s).$$

Now let R_1 be the set of all the functions f_r in R^X and combine these according to the operations in R^X. We have already proved that

$$f_r \oplus f_s = f_{r+s},$$

and

$$f_r \otimes f_s = f_{rs}.$$

Moreover, f_0 is the zero function and $f_{-r} = -f_r$. We have proved that R is isomorphic to the ring R_1 and φ is an isomorphism. To prove the last part of (d) assume now that R has a multiplicative identity i and define z to be the element in R^X defined by

$$z(1) = i,$$

$$z(x) = 0, \qquad x \neq 1.$$

To begin with we must show that

$$f_r \otimes z = z \otimes f_r$$

for any $r \in R$; in other words, z commutes with any element of R_1. But if f is any element of R^X then for $x \geq 1$

$$(f \otimes z)(x) = \sum_{u \in X} f(u)z(x - u)$$
$$= f(x - 1)i$$
$$= f(x - 1).$$

If $x = 0$ then the only term that can appear in the preceding sum is the one corresponding to $u = 0$ because X is the set of nonnegative integers. Thus

$$(f \otimes z)(0) = f(0)z(0) = 0.$$

Similarly,

$$(z \otimes f)(0) = \sum_{u \in X} z(u)f(0 - u)$$
$$= z(0)f(0)$$
$$= 0.$$

If $x \geq 1$ then

$$(z \otimes f)(x) = \sum_{u \in X} z(u)f(x - u)$$
$$= z(1)f(x - 1)$$
$$= i(f(x - 1))$$
$$= f(x - 1). \tag{6}$$

Thus z commutes with anything in R^X and hence with anything in R_1. It also follows from (6) that if $x \geq k$ then

$$
\begin{aligned}
(z^k \otimes f)(x) &= (z \otimes (z^{k-1} \otimes f))(x) \\
&= (z^{k-1} \otimes f)(x-1) \\
&= (z \otimes (z^{k-2} \otimes f))(x-1) \\
&= (z^{k-2} \otimes f)(x-2) \\
&\quad \cdot \quad \cdot \quad \cdot \quad \cdot \quad \cdot \quad \cdot \quad \cdot \quad \cdot \\
&= f(x-k).
\end{aligned} \tag{7}
$$

If $x < k$ it is clear from (7) and the fact that $(z \otimes f)(0) = 0$, that $(z^k \otimes f)(x) = 0$. We now proceed to verify the defining condition for an indeterminate over R_1 given in Definition 4.1(b). Let $a_k = f_{r_k}$, $k = 0, \ldots, n$, and suppose that

$$
\begin{aligned}
g &= (a_n \otimes z^n) \oplus (a_{n-1} \otimes z^{n-1}) \oplus \cdots \oplus (a_1 \otimes z) \oplus a_0 \\
&= 0,
\end{aligned}
$$

i.e., g is the zero function in R^X. Then if $x = 0$,

$$
\begin{aligned}
0 = g(0) &= (f_{r_n} \otimes z^n)(0) + \cdots + (f_{r_1} \otimes z)(0) + f_{r_0}(0) \\
&= f_{r_0}(0) \\
&= r_0.
\end{aligned}
$$

Hence $r_0 = 0$ and thus $a_0 = f_{r_0}$ is the zero in R_1. Next we see that

$$
\begin{aligned}
0 = g(1) \\
&= (f_{r_n} \otimes z^n)(1) + \cdots + (f_{r_1} \otimes z)(1) \\
&= f_{r_1}(1-1) \\
&= f_{r_1}(0) \\
&= r_1.
\end{aligned}
$$

Hence $r_1 = 0$ and thus $a_1 = f_{r_1}$ is the zero in R_1. We proceed to evaluate $g(2)$ and prove that $r_2 = 0$, and so on, until we have proved that $r_0, \ldots, r_n$ are all 0 in R and hence that $a_0, \ldots, a_n$ are all zero in R_1.

To complete the proof of the theorem we must show that any element of R^X is of the form (4). Thus let $f \in R^X$ and suppose that

$$
0 \leq u_1 < \cdots < u_p
$$

are the integers for which the values of f are not zero, that is,

$$
f(u_t) = r_t \neq 0, \qquad t = 1, \ldots, p.
$$

We assert that in fact

$$f = (f_{r_p} \otimes z^{u_p}) \oplus (f_{r_{p-1}} \otimes z^{u_{p-1}}) \oplus \cdots \oplus (f_{r_1} \otimes z^{u_1}) \tag{8}$$

(z^0 means the identity function e in R^X). According to (7) if $x > u_t$ (and hence $x - u_t > 0$) then

$$(f_{r_t} \otimes z^{u_t})(x) = f_{r_t}(x - u_t) \tag{9}$$

$$= 0,$$

because $f_{r_t}(x)$ is only nonzero for $x = 0$.
If $x < u_t$ then, as we have seen,

$$(f_{r_t} \otimes z^{u_t})(x) = 0. \tag{10}$$

That is to say, if $x \neq u_t$ then

$$(f_{r_t} \otimes z^{u_t})(x) = 0. \tag{11}$$

If $x = u_t$ then by (7)

$$(f_{r_t} \otimes z^{u_t})(u_t) = f_{r_t}(u_t - u_t)$$

$$= f_{r_t}(0) \tag{12}$$

$$= r_t.$$

It follows from (11) and (12) that the value of the right side of (8) at x is r_t if $x = u_t$ for some $t = 1, \ldots, p$, and zero otherwise. In other words, this value is precisely $f(x)$ and the proof is complete.

Before we go on, we verify that the representation of an $f \in R^X$ as in (4) yields the standard rules of polynomial computation given in Definition 4.2(c). Suppose then that

$$f = \sum_{k=0}^{n} a_k \otimes z^k \tag{13}$$

and

$$g = \sum_{k=0}^{n} b_k \otimes z^k \tag{14}$$

where a_k and b_k are in R_1, and we have introduced zero a_k's or b_k's, if necessary, to make the same number of summands appear in both (13) and (14). If we add f and g we obtain

$$f \oplus g = \left(\sum_{k=0}^{n} a_k \otimes z^k \right) \oplus \left(\sum_{k=0}^{n} b_k \otimes z^k \right)$$

$$= \sum_{k=0}^{n} (a_k \oplus b_k) \otimes z^k. \tag{15}$$

If we multiply f and g we can compute, using the distributive law in the ring R^X,

$$f \otimes g = (\sum_{k=0}^{n} a_k \otimes z^k) \otimes (\sum_{p=0}^{n} b_p \otimes z^p)$$

$$= \sum_{k=0}^{n} [(a_k \otimes z^k) \otimes (\sum_{p=0}^{n} b_p \otimes z^p)]$$

$$= \sum_{k=0}^{n} (\sum_{p=0}^{n} a_k \otimes z^k \otimes b_p \otimes z^p).$$

Now z commutes with everything in R^X and hence

$$a_k \otimes z^k \otimes b_p \otimes z^p = a_k \otimes b_p \otimes z^k \otimes z^p$$

$$= a_k \otimes b_p \otimes z^{k+p}.$$

Thus,

$$f \otimes g = \sum_{k=0}^{n} \sum_{p=0}^{n} a_k \otimes b_p \otimes z^{k+p}$$

$$= \sum_{m=0}^{2n} (\sum_{k=0}^{m} a_k \otimes b_{m-k}) \otimes z^m.$$

In other words,

$$f \otimes g = \sum_{m=0}^{2n} c_m \otimes z^m, \qquad c_m = \sum_{k=0}^{m} a_k \otimes b_{m-k}, \qquad m = 0, \ldots, 2n. \quad (16)$$

Before we go on let us pause to reflect on precisely what Theorem 5.1 tells us. It says: suppose we have a ring R (assumed to have a multiplicative identity to make life a little simpler); then R^X contains an indeterminate z and a subset R_1 which is a ring such that
  (a) R_1 is isomorphic to R,
  (b) $R^X = R_1[z]$.
Our original goal was to find a ring S and an element $z \in S$ such that
  (c) S contains R and the operations in R are the same as the operations in S,
  (d) $S = R[z]$ and z is an indeterminate over R.
In other words, we want to construct an indeterminate over R itself and not its carbon copy R_1, in R^X, as shown in the diagram.

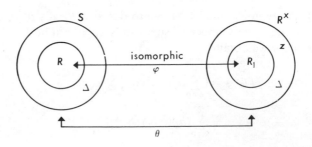

But the resolution of our little dilemma is really quite easy. Just take the "annulus" Δ, consisting of those elements in R^X that are not in R_1, paste it around R, and call the resulting object S:

$$S = R \cup \Delta. \tag{17}$$

The indeterminate z is in Δ and hence it is transferred into S. Now we must define appropriate operations for S. (We shall denote the multiplication in S by juxtaposition and the addition in S by $+$.) Before we do this let θ be the function defined on S to R^X by

$$\theta(f) = f, \qquad f \in \Delta,$$

$$\theta(r) = \varphi(r) = f_r, \qquad r \in R. \tag{18}$$

Obviously θ is 1-1 by definition. Now, if s_1 and s_2 are two elements in S we define

$$s_1 + s_2 = \theta^{-1}[\theta(s_1) \oplus \theta(s_2)],$$

$$s_1 s_2 = \theta^{-1}[\theta(s_1) \otimes \theta(s_2)]. \tag{19}$$

In other words, to compute $s_1 + s_2$ in S just go over to R^X via θ, add the two images in R^X, and then come back to S via θ^{-1}. Similarly for the product $s_1 s_2$. We can now state, using the preceding notation, the following fundamental result.

Theorem 5.2   (Existence of an indeterminate)   *Let R be a ring with a multiplicative identity. Then there exists a ring S containing R such that*
  (a)   *the operations in S, restricted to R, are the same as the operations in R;*
  (b)   *S contains an element z which is an indeterminate over R;*
  (c)   *$S = R[z]$.*

Proof.
  (a)   Suppose r_1 and r_2 are in R. Then according to (19) and the definition of θ in (18) we have

$$r_1 + r_2 = \theta^{-1}[\theta(r_1) \oplus \theta(r_2)]$$

$$= \theta^{-1}(f_{r_1} \oplus f_{r_2})$$

$$= \theta^{-1}(f_{r_1 + r_2})$$

$$= r_1 + r_2.$$

In other words, the addition "$+$" in S, when applied to elements in R, coincides with the addition "$+$" in R. An entirely analogous statement holds for the multiplication in S. The ring axioms in Definition 1.1 for the operations in S are easily verified using only (19) and the corresponding properties in R^X. For example, we verify associativity of multiplication:

$$(s_1s_2)s_3 = \theta^{-1}\{\theta(s_1s_2) \otimes \theta(s_3)\}$$

$$= \theta^{-1}\{\theta[\theta^{-1}(\theta(s_1) \otimes \theta(s_2))] \otimes \theta(s_3)\}$$

$$= \theta^{-1}\{(\theta(s_1) \otimes \theta(s_2)) \otimes \theta(s_3)\}$$

$$= \theta^{-1}\{\theta(s_1) \otimes (\theta(s_2) \otimes \theta(s_3))\}$$

$$= \theta^{-1}\{\theta(s_1) \otimes \theta[\theta^{-1}(\theta(s_2) \otimes \theta(s_3))]\}$$

$$= \theta^{-1}\{\theta(s_1) \otimes \theta(s_2s_3)\}$$

$$= s_1(s_2s_3).$$

It follows by similar direct verifications that S is a ring using the operations given in (19).

(b) The element z is in S. We must prove that it is an indeterminate over R. First observe that z commutes with everything in R. For, if $r \in R$, then from (19),

$$zr = \theta^{-1}(\theta(z) \otimes \theta(r))$$

$$= \theta^{-1}(z \otimes f_r)$$

$$= \theta^{-1}(f_r \otimes z)$$

$$= \theta^{-1}(\theta(r) \otimes \theta(z))$$

$$= rz.$$

Suppose that some polynomial in z over R is 0:

$$a_nz^n + a_{n-1}z^{n-1} + \cdots + a_1z + a_0 = 0, \qquad a_k \in R, \qquad k = 0, \ldots, n. \quad (20)$$

By (19) applied to (20), we have

$$\theta^{-1}(\sum_{k=0}^{n} \theta(a_kz^k)) = 0,$$

and since $\theta(0)$ is the 0 in R_1 (we shall not distinguish between them notationally) we have

$$\sum_{k=0}^{n} \theta(\theta^{-1}[\theta(a_k) \otimes \theta(z^k)]) = 0,$$

or simplifying,

$$\sum_{k=0}^{n} \theta(a_k) \otimes z^k = 0, \qquad \theta(a_k) \in R_1.$$

But z is an indeterminate over R_1 and hence $\theta(a_k) = 0$, $k = 0, \ldots, n$. Again, since θ is 1-1 and $\theta(0) = 0$ it follows that $a_k = 0$, $k = 0, \ldots, n$. Thus (20) implies that $a_k = 0$, $k = 0, \ldots, n$, and hence z is an indeterminate over R.

(c)   To prove that $S = R[z]$ we again use the corresponding property in R^X. Any element of R^X is of the form

$$f = \sum_{k=0}^{n} \alpha_k \otimes z^k, \qquad \alpha_k \in R_1.$$

Applying θ^{-1} to f we obtain from (19)

$$\theta^{-1}(f) = \sum_{k=0}^{n} \theta^{-1}(\alpha_k \otimes z^k)$$

$$= \sum_{k=0}^{n} \theta^{-1}[\theta(\theta^{-1}(\alpha_k)) \otimes \theta(z^k)]$$

$$= \sum_{k=0}^{n} b_k z^k$$

where $b_k = \theta^{-1}(\alpha_k) \in R$, $k = 0, \ldots, n$. In other words, any element in S is a polynomial in z over R. Hence $S = R[z]$.

We may now proceed to use the notational conventions described in Definition 4.2. That is, it is no longer necessary to distinguish (notationally) the operations in R and $R[z]$.

Quiz

Answer **true** or **false**:

1. If R is a ring and X is the set of nonnegative integers then $R^X \cap R = \varnothing$.

2. If R is the ring of real numbers and X is the set of nonnegative integers and $f \in R^X$ then $f \otimes f = 0$ implies that $f = 0$.

3. In the preceding question, if R is changed to be I_4, the residue class ring of integers modulo 4, then the same statement still holds.

(In the following questions the notation will be that of Theorem 5.1.)

4. If r and s are in R then $f_{rs} = f_r \otimes f_s$.

5. If $r \in R$ then $(f_r \otimes z)(0) = r$.

6. If $r \in R$ then $(f_r \otimes z^2 \otimes f_r)(0) = r^2$.

7. The multiplicative identity in R^X is f_1.

8. If $f \in R^X$ then $(z^2 \otimes f)(3) = f(2)$.

9. If $r_1, \ldots, r_k$ are in R and

$$f_{r_1} \oplus (f_{r_2} \otimes z) \oplus (f_{r_3} \otimes z^2) \oplus \cdots \oplus (f_{r_k} \otimes z^{k-1}) = 0$$

then $r_1 = \cdots = r_k = 0$.

10. z^2 commutes with everything in R_1.

Exercises

1. Prove that the rules of Definition 1.1(iii), (iv), (v), and (vi) hold for the ring R^X in Theorem 5.1.

2. If X is the set in Example 5.1(b), how many elements are there in the set X^X? Write down addition and multiplication tables for X^X.

4.6   Theory of Equations

In this section we shall study the structure of the roots of a polynomial in terms of the coefficients in the polynomial. We shall begin by introducing the idea of symmetry.

Let R be either the real or the complex numbers and let x_1 be an indeterminate over R. Then, as we saw in the preceding two sections, the set of polynomials $R[x_1]$ forms a ring with 1 as multiplicative identity. Thus we can construct an indeterminate x_2 over the ring $R[x_1]$ and again we have the ring of polynomials in x_2 over $R[x_1]$, i.e., $R[x_1][x_2]$. By definition, the elements of this latter ring are polynomials in x_2 with coefficients in $R[x_1]$:

$$a_n(x_1)x_2^n + a_{n-1}(x_1)x_2^{n-1} + \cdots + a_1(x_1)x_2 + a_0(x_1). \tag{1}$$

Each $a_k(x_1)$ is itself a polynomial in x_1 and, since x_2 commutes with everything in $R[x_1]$, we can write (1) as

$$a_{mn}x_1^m x_2^n + \cdots + a_{11}x_1 x_2 + a_{10}x_1 + a_{01}x_2 + a_{00} \tag{2}$$

where each $a_{ij} \in R$, $i = 0, \ldots, m$, $j = 0, \ldots, n$. In other words, the polynomials (2) are of the form

$$\sum_{(i,j)=(0,0)}^{(m,n)} a_{ij}x_1^i x_2^j \tag{3}$$

where the summation extends over all pairs of integers (i, j), $i = 0, \ldots, m$, $= 0, \ldots, n$, and as before x_1^0, x_2^0 are interpreted as 1. It follows that $R[x_1][x_2] = R[x_2][x_1]$. For, if x_2 is an indeterminate over $R[x_1]$ then x_1 is an indeterminate over $R[x_2]$ (see Exercise 1) and each of $R[x_1][x_2]$ and $R[x_2][x_1]$ is simply the set of all polynomials of the form (3). We shall write $R[x_1][x_2]$ in a somewhat more sensible way as $R[x_1, x_2]$. We can repeat the process and obtain an indeterminate x_3 over $R[x_1, x_2]$ and construct the ring of polynomials in the three indeterminates, $R[x_1, x_2, x_3]$. In general, we will denote the ring of polynomials in p indeterminates constructed in this way by

$$R[x_1, \ldots, x_p]. \tag{4}$$

A typical element of $R[x_1, \ldots, x_p]$ is denoted by

$$f(x_1, \ldots, x_p) = \sum_\omega a_\omega x_1^{\omega_1} x_2^{\omega_2} \cdots x_p^{\omega_p}, \tag{5}$$

where $a_\omega \in R$, $\omega = (\omega_1, \ldots, \omega_p)$, $0 \leq \omega_1 \leq n_1$, $0 \leq \omega_2 \leq n_2, \ldots, 0 \leq \omega_p \leq n_p$, in which $n_1, \ldots, n_p$ are fixed positive integers depending on the polynomial $f(x_1, \ldots, x_p)$. The *degree* of $f(x_1, \ldots, x_p)$ in (5) is just the largest integer $\omega_1 + \cdots + \omega_p$ for which $a_\omega \neq 0$. We denote this integer by $\deg f(x_1, \ldots, x_p)$.

EXAMPLE 6.1

If $f(x_1, x_2, x_3) = x_1^2 x_2 + 3x_2^3 + 5x_1 x_2 x_3^2$, then $\deg f(x_1, x_2, x_3) = 4$.

Definition 6.1   (Symmetric polynomials) *Let* $f(x_1, \ldots, x_p) \in R[x_1, \ldots, x_p]$. *Then* $f(x_1, \ldots, x_p)$ *is said to be symmetric if for each permutation* $\sigma \in S_p$

$$f(x_{\sigma(1)}, \ldots, x_{\sigma(p)}) = f(x_1, \ldots, x_p). \tag{6}$$

EXAMPLES 6.2

(a)   The polynomial $x_1 x_2 + x_1 x_3 + x_2 x_3$ is symmetric. For, all possible products $x_i x_j$, $i \neq j$, appear exactly once and, since $\sigma \in S_3$ is a 1-1 onto function, precisely these products will appear exactly once among $x_{\sigma(i)} x_{\sigma(j)}$, $i \neq j$.

(b)   The polynomial $x_1^n + \cdots + x_p^n$ is symmetric. For, if $\sigma \in S_p$, then $x_{\sigma(1)}^n + \cdots + x_{\sigma(p)}^n$ is clearly the same as $x_1^n + \cdots + x_p^n$ since each term x_j^n appears precisely once in both expressions.

(c)   The polynomial $f(x_1, x_2) = x_1^3 + x_1 x_2$ is not symmetric. Let $\sigma = (1\ 2)$. Then

$$f(x_{\sigma(1)}, x_{\sigma(2)}) = f(x_2, x_1) = x_2^3 + x_1 x_2 \neq x_1^3 + x_1 x_2 = f(x_1, x_2).$$

In studying the relations between the roots and the coefficients of a polynomial the most important class of symmetric functions for our purposes is described in the following definition.

Definition 6.2 (Elementary symmetric functions) *Let* $1 \leq r \leq p$ *and let* $Q_{r,p}$ *denote the set of all strictly increasing sequences* $\omega = (\omega_1, \ldots, \omega_r)$ *where* $1 \leq \omega_1 < \omega_2 < \cdots < \omega_r \leq p$. *Then the* r*th elementary symmetric function of* $x_1, \ldots, x_p$ *is defined by*

$$E_r(x_1, \ldots, x_p) = \sum_{\omega \in Q_{r,p}} x_{\omega_1} x_{\omega_2} \cdots x_{\omega_r}.$$

For completeness we set $E_0(x_1, \ldots, x_p) = 1$.

EXAMPLES 6.3

(a) $E_1(x_1, \ldots, x_p) = x_1 + \cdots + x_p$.

(b) $E_2(x_1, x_2, x_3, x_4) = x_1 x_2 + x_1 x_3 + x_1 x_4 + x_2 x_3 + x_2 x_4 + x_3 x_4$.

(c) $E_p(x_1, \ldots, x_p) = x_1 x_2 \cdots x_p = \prod_{j=1}^{p} x_j$.

(d) The number of sequences in $Q_{r,p}$ is $\binom{p}{r}$.

We prove the assertion in (d) by induction on p. For $p = 1$ there is nothing to prove. Assume that $p > 1$ and that for any integer m, $1 \leq m \leq p - 1$, the number of sequences in $Q_{m,p-1}$ is $\binom{p-1}{m}$. If $r = 1$ then clearly the number of sequences in $Q_{r,p}$ is $p = \binom{p}{1}$. If $r > 1$ then the strictly increasing sequences of length r chosen from $1, \ldots, p$ can be separated into two classes: those that involve p and those that do not. Any sequence that involves p can be constructed by attaching p to an increasing sequence of length $r - 1$ chosen from $1, \ldots, p - 1$. Any sequence that does not involve p is an increasing sequence of length r chosen from $1, \ldots, p - 1$. By the induction hypothesis there are $\binom{p-1}{r-1}$ increasing sequences that end in p and $\binom{p-1}{r}$ increasing sequences that do not end in p. Thus there are

$$\binom{p-1}{r-1} + \binom{p-1}{r} = \binom{p}{r}$$

(see Chapter 1, Section 1.1, formula (8)) strictly increasing sequences of length r involving the integers $1, \ldots, p$.

Definition 6.3   (Lexicographic order)

(a) *Let* $\alpha = (\alpha_1, \ldots, \alpha_p)$ *and* $\beta = (\beta_1, \ldots, \beta_p)$ *be two sequences of non-negative integers. We say that the sequence* α *is higher than the sequence* β *(or that* β *is lower than* α*) in the lexicographic order, and write* $\alpha \succ \beta$*, if the first nonzero difference* $\alpha_j - \beta_j$*,* $j = 1, \ldots, p$*, is positive.*

(b) *Let*

$$f(x_1, \ldots, x_p) = \sum_{\omega} a_\omega x_1^{\omega_1} x_2^{\omega_2} \cdots x_p^{\omega_p} \tag{7}$$

be a nonzero polynomial in $R[x_1, \ldots, x_p]$*, where* $a_\omega \in R$ *and the* $\omega = (\omega_1, \ldots, \omega_p)$ *are distinct sequences of nonnegative integers. We say that a term* $a_\alpha x_1^{\alpha_1} x_2^{\alpha_2} \cdots x_p^{\alpha_p}$*,* $a_\alpha \neq 0$*, is higher in lexicographic order than a term* $a_\beta x_1^{\beta_1} x_2^{\beta_2} \cdots x_p^{\beta_p}$ *if the sequence* $\alpha = (\alpha_1, \ldots, \alpha_p)$ *is higher in lexicographic order than the sequence* $\beta = (\beta_1, \ldots, \beta_p)$*. A term* $a_\alpha x_1^{\alpha_1} x_2^{\alpha_2} \cdots x_p^{\alpha_p}$*,* $a_\alpha \neq 0$*, of* $f(x_1, \ldots, x_p)$*, is called the leading term of* $f(x_1, \ldots, x_p)$ *if it is higher in lexicographic order than any other term (with a nonzero coefficient) of* $f(x_1, \ldots, x_p)$*.*

EXAMPLES 6.4

(a) The sequence $(3, 5, 0, 0, 0)$ is higher in lexicographic order than the sequence $(3, 4, 5, 6, 6)$. Indeed, the first difference, $3 - 3$, is zero while the second, $5 - 4$, is positive.

(b)   The term $-2x_1^3x_2^5$ is higher in lexicographic order than the term $9x_1^3x_2^4x_3^5x_4^6x_5^6$. In fact, by Definition 6.3 and the preceding example, $-2x_1^3x_2^5$ is the leading term of the polynomial $-2x_1^3x_2^5 + 9x_1^3x_2^4x_3^5x_4^6x_5^6$.

(c)   Arrange the terms of the polynomial $f(x_1, x_2, x_3) = 2x_2^4 - x_2^3x_3 + 3x_1^2x_3 - 2x_1x_2^2 + x_2x_3 - x_1 + 5$ in lexicographic order with the leading term in the first position. We note that the sequences corresponding to terms with nonzero coefficients are $(0, 4, 0)$, $(0, 3, 1)$, $(2, 0, 1)$, $(1, 2, 0)$, $(0, 1, 1)$, $(1, 0, 0)$, $(0, 0, 0)$. It is easily seen that $(2, 0, 1) \succ (1, 2, 0) \succ (1, 0, 0) \succ (0, 4, 0) \succ (0, 3, 1) \succ (0, 1, 1) \succ (0, 0, 0)$. Thus the leading term of $f(x_1, x_2, x_3)$ is $3x_1^2x_3$ and the required ordering is

$$3x_1^2x_3 - 2x_1x_2^2 - x_1 + 2x_2^4 - x_2^3x_3 + x_2x_3 + 5.$$

The most important theorem concerning the elementary symmetric functions is the following.

Theorem 6.1   (Basis theorem for symmetric polynomials)   *Let $f(x_1,\ldots, x_p) \in R[x_1,\ldots, x_p]$ be a symmetric polynomial. Then there exists a polynomial $\psi(x_1,\ldots, x_p) \in R[x_1,\ldots, x_p]$ such that*

$$f(x_1,\ldots, x_p) = \psi(E_1(x_1,\ldots, x_p), E_2(x_1,\ldots, x_p),\ldots, E_p(x_1,\ldots, x_p)). \quad (8)$$

(The notation in (8) means that each x_i is replaced by $E_i(x_1,\ldots, x_p)$ in $\psi(x_1,\ldots, x_p)$, $i = 1,\ldots, p$.) Moreover, the coefficients appearing in $\psi(x_1,\ldots, x_p)$ are obtained from the coefficients in $f(x_1,\ldots, x_p)$ by addition and subtraction only.

Proof.   The method of attack in this proof is analogous to the methods used in the division algorithm for polynomials (see Theorem 4.2). Namely, we devise an ordering for the terms, subtract the leading term, and then proceed by induction. For notational economy we first agree to write expressions like (8) without all the x_j's appearing, that is,

$$f = \psi(E_1,\ldots, E_p). \quad (9)$$

Let $\deg f(x_1,\ldots, x_p) = n$. It is clear that we can write the polynomial $f(x_1,\ldots, x_p)$ in the form

$$f(x_1,\ldots, x_p) = \sum_\omega a_\omega \prod_{t=1}^{p} x_t^{\omega_t} \quad (10)$$

where the summation extends over all sequences $\omega = (\omega_1,\ldots, \omega_p)$, for which $0 \le \omega_i \le n$, $i = 1,\ldots, p$, and where a_ω is zero in case the term $\prod_{t=1}^{p} x_t^{\omega_t}$ does not really appear in $f(x_1,\ldots, x_p)$. Now let $a_\gamma x_1^{\gamma_1} x_2^{\gamma_2} \cdots x_p^{\gamma_p}$ be the leading term of the polynomial $f(x_1,\ldots, x_p)$. We try to choose nonnegative integers $s_1,\ldots, s_p$ such that the leading term of the polynomial

$$E_1^{s_1} E_2^{s_2} \cdots E_p^{s_p} \quad (11)$$

is $x_1^{\gamma_1} x_2^{\gamma_2} \cdots x_p^{\gamma_p}$. It is clear that the leading term of $E_1^{s_1}$ is just $x_1^{s_1}$, the leading term of $E_2^{s_2}$ is $x_1^{s_2} x_2^{s_2}$, the leading term of $E_3^{s_3}$ is $x_1^{s_3} x_2^{s_3} x_3^{s_3}$,..., the leading (and only) term of $E_p^{s_p}$ is $x_1^{s_p} x_2^{s_p} \cdots x_p^{s_p}$. Thus the leading term of (11) is just the product of all these leading terms, namely

$$x_1^{s_1}(x_1^{s_2}x_2^{s_2})(x_1^{s_3}x_2^{s_3}x_3^{s_3}) \cdots (x_1^{s_p}x_2^{s_p} \cdots x_p^{s_p}),$$

which is equal to

$$x_1^{\sigma_p}x_2^{\sigma_{p-1}} \cdots x_p^{\sigma_1} \tag{12}$$

in which we have introduced the notation

$$\sigma_{p-k} = s_{k+1} + \cdots + s_p, \qquad k = 0, \ldots, p-1.$$

In order to make (12) equal to $x_1^{\gamma_1} x_2^{\gamma_2} \cdots x_p^{\gamma_p}$ we want to choose the nonnegative integers $s_1, \ldots, s_p$ so that

$$s_1 + \cdots + s_p = \gamma_1,$$

$$s_2 + \cdots + s_p = \gamma_2,$$

$$\cdot \quad \cdot \quad \cdot \quad \cdot \quad \cdot \quad \cdot \tag{13}$$

$$s_{p-1} + s_p = \gamma_{p-1},$$

$$s_p = \gamma_p.$$

Thus from (13) we see that the integers $s_1, \ldots, s_p$ have to be chosen so that

$$s_p = \gamma_p,$$

$$s_{p-1} = \gamma_{p-1} - \gamma_p,$$

$$\cdot \quad \cdot \quad \cdot \quad \cdot \quad \cdot \quad \cdot \tag{14}$$

$$s_2 = \gamma_2 - \gamma_3,$$

$$s_1 = \gamma_1 - \gamma_2.$$

So far we have yet to use the hypothesis that $f(x_1, \ldots, x_p)$ is symmetric. We do this to prove that $\gamma_1 \geq \gamma_2 \geq \cdots \geq \gamma_p$ so that the equations (14) produce nonnegative integers for the values of the s_j, $j = 1, \ldots, p$. Suppose on the contrary that $\gamma_k < \gamma_{k+1}$ for some k. Recall that

$$a_\gamma x_1^{\gamma_1} \cdots x_k^{\gamma_k} x_{k+1}^{\gamma_{k+1}} \cdots x_p^{\gamma_p} \tag{15}$$

is the leading term of the symmetric polynomial $f(x_1, \ldots, x_p)$. Let σ be the transposition $(k \ \ k+1)$. Then one of the terms in $f(x_{\sigma(1)}, \ldots, x_{\sigma(p)}) = f(x_1, \ldots, x_p)$ is

$$a_\gamma x_{\sigma(1)}^{\gamma_1} \cdots x_{\sigma(k)}^{\gamma_k} x_{\sigma(k+1)}^{\gamma_{k+1}} \cdots x_{\sigma(p)}^{\gamma_p}$$

which is just

$$a_\gamma x_1^{\gamma_1} \cdots x_k^{\gamma_{k+1}} x_{k+1}^{\gamma_k} \cdots x_p^{\gamma_p}. \tag{16}$$

But if $\gamma_k < \gamma_{k+1}$ then $(\gamma_1, \ldots, \gamma_{k+1}, \gamma_k, \ldots, \gamma_p) > (\gamma_1, \ldots, \gamma_k, \gamma_{k+1}, \ldots, \gamma_p)$ and thus the term (16) is higher in lexicographic order than the term (15).

This, however, contradicts our assumption that (15) is the leading term of $(x_1, \ldots, x_p)$. Thus we conclude that $\gamma_1 \geq \gamma_2 \geq \cdots \geq \gamma_p$ and the nonnegative integers $s_1, \ldots, s_p$ in (14) are determined. Now form the difference

$$f_1 = f - a_\gamma E_1^{s_1} E_2^{s_2} \cdots E_p^{s_p}. \tag{17}$$

Then the leading term of f_1 must be strictly lower in lexicographic order than the leading term of f since the term (15) cancels in (17). We repeat the whole process with f_1 which is also obviously symmetric, and continue in this fashion, at each stage producing a symmetric polynomial whose leading term is strictly lower than the leading term at the immediately preceding stage. The process must terminate since there are only a finite number of sequences $\omega = (\omega_1, \ldots, \omega_p)$ lower than $\gamma = (\gamma_1, \ldots, \gamma_p)$. Formally, we can write the proof by induction on the position of the leading term in the lexicographic order.

EXAMPLES 6.5

(a) Write $f(x_1, x_2, x_3) = x_1 x_2 + x_1 x_3 + x_2 x_3 + x_1^2 + x_2^2 + x_3^2$ in the form (10) and list the sequences ω for which the corresponding coefficient $a_\omega \neq 0$. To do this we observe that $\deg f(x_1, x_2, x_3) = 2 = n$ and $p = 3$. We thus are interested in sequences of the form $(\omega_1, \omega_2, \omega_3)$ in which $0 \leq \omega_i \leq 2$, $i = 1, 2, 3$. These are $(2, 2, 2)$, $(2, 2, 1)$, $(2, 2, 0)$, $(2, 1, 2)$, $(2, 1, 1)$, $(2, 1, 0)$, $(2, 0, 2)$, $(2, 0, 1)$, $(2, 0, 0)$, $(1, 2, 2)$, and so on. We can write

$$f(x_1, x_2, x_3) = \sum_\omega a_\omega x_1^{\omega_1} x_2^{\omega_2} x_3^{\omega_3}$$

in which $a_\omega = 1$ for $\omega = (1, 1, 0), (1, 0, 1), (0, 1, 1), (2, 0, 0), (0, 2, 0), (0, 0, 2)$ and $a_\omega = 0$ for all other choices of ω.

(b) Express $f(x_1, \ldots, x_p) = \sum_{i=1}^p x_i^2$ as a polynomial in the elementary symmetric functions by the method in Theorem 6.1. Here clearly the leading term is x_1^2 and the corresponding sequence is $\gamma = (\gamma_1, \ldots, \gamma_p) = (2, 0, \ldots, 0)$. Thus from (14) we see that $s_2 = \cdots = s_p = 0$, $s_1 = \gamma_1 - \gamma_2 = 2$. Hence we form

$$f - E_1^2 = \sum_{i=1}^p x_i^2 - \left(\sum_{i=1}^p x_i \right)^2$$

$$= \sum_{i=1}^p x_i^2 - \left(\sum_{i=1}^p x_i^2 + \sum_{i \neq j} x_i x_j \right)$$

$$= - \sum_{i \neq j} x_i x_j$$

$$= -2 \sum_{1 \leq i < j \leq p} x_i x_j$$

$$= -2 E_2.$$

Thus $f = E_1^2 - 2E_2$.

Theorem 6.2 Let $f(x_1, \ldots, x_p, z) = a \prod_{j=1}^{p}(z - x_j) \in R[x_1, \ldots, x_p, z]$ where $x_1, \ldots, x_p, z$ are $p + 1$ indeterminates over R and $a \in R$. Then

$$f(x_1, \ldots, x_p, z) = a \sum_{k=0}^{p} (-1)^k E_k(x_1, \ldots, x_p) z^{p-k}. \tag{18}$$

Proof. The proof is by induction on p with nothing to prove for $p = 1$. Thus suppose that $p > 1$ and that (18) holds for $p - 1$; that is,

$$a \prod_{j=1}^{p-1}(z - x_j) = a \sum_{k=0}^{p-1} (-1)^k E_k(x_1, \ldots, x_{p-1}) z^{p-1-k}. \tag{19}$$

Multiplying both sides of (19) by $(z - x_p)$ we have

$$a \prod_{j=1}^{p}(z - x_j) = a \sum_{k=0}^{p-1} (-1)^k E_k(x_1, \ldots, x_{p-1}) z^{p-k} \tag{20}$$
$$+ a \sum_{k=0}^{p-1} (-1)^{k+1} E_k(x_1, \ldots, x_{p-1}) x_p z^{p-1-k}.$$

In the second summation in (20) replace the dummy index k by $k - 1$ so that this summation becomes

$$a \sum_{k=1}^{p} (-1)^k E_{k-1}(x_1, \ldots, x_{p-1}) x_p z^{p-k}. \tag{21}$$

Separating the first $(k = 0)$ term from the first summation in (20) and the last $(k = p)$ term from (21) we have

$$a \prod_{j=1}^{p}(z - x_j) = a[z^p + (-1)^p E_{p-1}(x_1, \ldots, x_{p-1}) x_p \tag{22}$$
$$+ \sum_{k=1}^{p-1} (-1)^k (E_k(x_1, \ldots, x_{p-1}) + E_{k-1}(x_1, \ldots, x_{p-1}) x_p) z^{p-k}].$$

But (see Exercise 3) it is very easy to check that

$$E_k(x_1, \ldots, x_{p-1}) + E_{k-1}(x_1, \ldots, x_{p-1}) x_p = E_k(x_1, \ldots, x_p),$$

$$E_{p-1}(x_1, \ldots, x_{p-1}) x_p = \left(\prod_{j=1}^{p-1} x_j \right) x_p$$

$$= \prod_{j=1}^{p} x_j$$

$$= E_p(x_1, \ldots, x_p).$$

Hence (22) becomes

$$a \prod_{j=1}^{p}(z - x_j) = a[z^p + (-1)^p E_p(x_1, \ldots, x_p) + \sum_{k=1}^{p-1} (-1)^k E_k(x_1, \ldots, x_p) z^{p-k}]$$

$$= a \sum_{k=0}^{p} (-1)^k E_k(x_1, \ldots, x_p) z^{p-k}$$

and the induction is complete.

We remind the reader before going on that the equality between two polynomials

$$f(x_1, \ldots, x_p) = \sum_{\omega} a_\omega \prod_{t=1}^{p} x_t^{\omega_t}, \qquad a_\omega \in R,$$

and

$$g(x_1, \ldots, x_p) = \sum_{\omega} b_\omega \prod_{t=1}^{p} x_t^{\omega_t}, \qquad b_\omega \in R,$$

means that the coefficients are all the same, that is, $a_\omega = b_\omega$ for all ω under consideration. It follows immediately that if $f(x_1, \ldots, x_p) = g(x_1, \ldots, x_p)$ and we replace some of the x_i by numbers c_i in R then the results will be equal also; for example,

$$f(x_1, c_2, x_3, \ldots, x_p) = \sum_{\omega} a_\omega x_1^{\omega_1} c_2^{\omega_2} x_3^{\omega_3} \cdots x_p^{\omega_p}$$

$$= \sum_{\omega} b_\omega x_1^{\omega_1} c_2^{\omega_2} x_3^{\omega_3} \cdots x_p^{\omega_p}$$

$$= g(x_1, c_2, x_3, \ldots, x_p).$$

From this observation we prove an important result.

Theorem 6.3   *If z is any indeterminate over R and*

$$g(z) = a \prod_{j=1}^{p} (z - c_j) \in R[z], \quad c_j \in R, \ j = 1, \ldots, p,$$

then

$$g(z) = a \sum_{k=0}^{p} (-1)^k E_k(c_1, \ldots, c_p) z^{p-k}. \tag{23}$$

Proof.   In (18) replace x_i by c_i, $i = 1, \ldots, p$, to obtain (23).

As we indicated in Section 4.4, one of the central problems in algebra for several centuries concerned the existence of roots of polynomials. In the second half of the eighteenth century the French mathematician d'Alembert finally succeeded in proving a theorem that has come to be known as the "Fundamental Theorem of Algebra". Unfortunately, no purely algebraic proof of this theorem can be made and thus we will not attempt to prove the result here. It is claimed that d'Alembert's original proof was defective in that it assumed a certain proposition concerning minima of continuous functions without "proof". In the opinion of the present authors, the subsequent proof that was given just shifted the responsibility for d'Alembert's "defect" to an item known as "the axiom of continuity". Whether d'Alembert's assumption is harder to believe than the axiom of continuity is a matter of opinion. In any event, the Fundamental Theorem of Algebra is a remarkable result that shows the importance of the complex numbers.

Theorem 6.4 **(Fundamental Theorem of Algebra)** *Let R be the ring of complex numbers and let z be an indeterminate over R. Let $f(z) = \sum_{k=0}^{n} a_k z^k \in R[z]$, $a_n \neq 0$. Then $f(z)$ has a complex root. In other words, any polynomial with complex coefficients has a complex root.*

Thus, although we had to invent irrationals in order that polynomials with rational coefficients have roots (e.g., $z^2 - 2$), and complex numbers in order that polynomials with real coefficients have roots (e.g., $z^2 + 1$), it is not necessary to invent any "new" numbers in order that an arbitrary polynomial with complex coefficients shall have a root.

As an immediate corollary to Theorems 6.3 and 6.4 we have

Theorem 6.5 *Let R be the ring of complex numbers and z an indeterminate over R. Let $f(z) = \sum_{k=0}^{n} a_k z^k \in R[z]$, $a_n \neq 0$. Then $f(z)$ has n complex roots, $c_1, \ldots, c_n$. That is,*

$$f(z) = a_n \prod_{i=1}^{n} (z - c_i). \tag{24}$$

Moreover,

$$\frac{a_{n-k}}{a_n} = (-1)^k E_k(c_1, \ldots, c_n), \qquad k = 0, \ldots, n. \tag{25}$$

Proof. Clearly $a_n^{-1} f(z)$ has the same roots as $f(z)$. By Theorem 6.4, let c_n be a root of $f(z)$ and then, by Theorem 4.5(f), $(z - c_n) \mid a_n^{-1} f(z)$. Let $a_n^{-1} f(z) = q(z)(z - c_n)$. It is obvious that $\deg q(z) = n - 1$ and hence we may proceed by induction on the degree of the polynomial (see Exercise 5.). Thus we may write $q(z) = \prod_{j=1}^{n-1} (z - c_j)$ so that

$$a_n^{-1} f(z) = q(z)(z - c_n)$$

$$= \prod_{j=1}^{n-1} (z - c_j)(z - c_n)$$

$$= \prod_{j=1}^{n} (z - c_j)$$

and (24) is proved. To obtain (25) we just apply (23); for,

$$\sum_{k=0}^{n} a_k z^k = a_n \prod_{i=1}^{n} (z - c_i) = a_n \sum_{k=0}^{n} (-1)^k E_k(c_1, \ldots, c_n) z^{n-k}$$

and hence matching the coefficients of these equal polynomials we have

$$a_{n-k} = a_n (-1)^k E_k(c_1, \ldots, c_n).$$

EXAMPLE 6.6

Find the sum of the squares of the roots of the polynomial $f(z) = z^9 + z^7 + z^3 + z^2 + z - 1$. Let $c_1, \ldots, c_9$ be the roots of $f(z)$. From Example 6.5(b) we know that

$$\sum_{i=1}^{9} x_i^2 = (E_1(x_1, \ldots, x_9))^2 - 2E_2(x_1, \ldots, x_9),$$

so that according to (25) (since $a_9 = 1$)

$$E_1(c_1, \ldots, c_9) = -\frac{a_8}{a_9} = 0,$$

$$E_2(c_1, \ldots, c_9) = \frac{a_7}{a_9} = 1.$$

Hence

$$\sum_{i=1}^{9} c_i^2 = -2.$$

Except in the case of an equation of a very special type or of low degree, we cannot, in general, evaluate the roots of a given polynomial equation. Occasionally we can determine some of the roots, e.g., the rational roots, and roots of largest modulus; or we sometimes can localize the real roots in certain intervals of the real line, or the complex roots in certain regions of the complex plane. In some problems it may be of importance to determine if a given polynomial has multiple roots, i.e., if it can be factorized in the form $(z - a)^k q(z)$ where $q(z)$ is a polynomial and k is an integer greater than 1.

Definition 6.4   (Derivative)   *Let* $f(z) = \sum_{t=0}^{n} a_t z^t$ *be a polynomial of degree* *n. If* $n > 0$*, the first derivative of* $f(z)$ *is defined by*

$$f'(z) = \sum_{t=1}^{n} t a_t z^{t-1}$$

$$= \sum_{s=0}^{n-1} (s + 1) a_{s+1} z^s.$$

The first derivative of 0 *and of any polynomial of degree* 0 *is defined to be* 0*. For* $m > 1$ *we define recursively* $f^{(m)}(z)$*, the* m*th derivative of* $f(z)$*, as the first derivative of the* $(m - 1)$*th derivative of* $f(z)$*.*

It should be noted that Definition 6.4 agrees with the well-known differential calculus formula for the derivative of a polynomial function. For our present purpose, however, Definition 6.4 is quite adequate and the subtle concept of a limit is not required here.

Theorem 6.6   *If* $f(z)$ *and* $g(z)$ *are polynomials,* a, b *and* c *complex numbers, and* k *is a positive integer, then*

$$(af(z) + bg(z))' = af'(z) + bg'(z), \tag{26}$$

$$(f(z)g(z))' = f'(z)g(z) + f(z)g'(z), \tag{27}$$

$$((z - c)^k)' = k(z - c)^{k-1}. \tag{28}$$

Proof.   Let $f(z) = \sum_{t=0}^{m} c_t z^t$, $g(z) = \sum_{t=0}^{n} d_t z^t$ and suppose that $m \geq n$. Then

$$af(z) + bg(z) = \sum_{t=0}^{m} (ac_t + bd_t)z^t,$$

where $d_{n+1} = \cdots = d_m = 0$, and, by Definition 6.4,

$$(af(z) + bg(z))' = \sum_{t=1}^{m} t(ac_t + bd_t)z^{t-1}$$

$$= a\sum_{t=1}^{m} tc_t z^{t-1} + b\sum_{t=1}^{n} td_t z^{t-1}$$

$$= af'(z) + bg'(z).$$

Next,

$$f(z)g(z) = \sum_{t=0}^{m+n} \left(\sum_{i+j=t} c_i d_j \right)z^t$$

where $\sum_{i+j=t}$ indicates that the summation extends over all nonnegative i and j for which $i + j = t$. If either $f(z)$ or $g(z)$ is 0 or of degree 0 then the formula (27) clearly holds. Otherwise

$$(f(z)g(z))' = \sum_{t=1}^{m+n} t\left(\sum_{i+j=t} c_i d_j \right)z^{t-1}$$

$$= \sum_{t=1}^{m+n} \left(\sum_{i+j=t} (i+j)c_i d_j \right)z^{t-1}$$

$$= \sum_{t=1}^{m+n} \left(\sum_{i+j=t} ic_i d_j \right)z^{t-1} + \sum_{t=1}^{m+n} \left(\sum_{i+j=t} jc_i d_j \right)z^{t-1}$$

$$= \sum_{s=0}^{m+n-1} \left(\sum_{i+j=s} (i+1)c_{i+1} d_j \right)z^s + \sum_{s-0}^{m+n-1} \left(\sum_{i+j-s} (j+1)c_i d_{j+1} \right)z^s.$$

Now note that, by formula (5), Section 4.4, with $a_i = (i+1)c_{i+1}$ and $b_j = d_j$,

$$\left(\sum_{i=0}^{m-1} (i+1)c_{i+1} z^i \right)\left(\sum_{j=0}^{n} d_j z^j \right) = \sum_{s=0}^{m+n-1} \left(\sum_{i+j=s} (i+1)c_{i+1} d_j \right)z^s$$

and similarly

$$\left(\sum_{i=0}^{m} c_i z^i \right)\left(\sum_{j=0}^{n-1} (j+1)d_{j+1} z^j \right) = \sum_{s=0}^{m+n-1} \left(\sum_{i+j=s} c_i(j+1)d_{j+1} \right)z^s.$$

Therefore,

$$(f(z)g(z))' = \left(\sum_{i=0}^{m-1} (i+1)c_{i+1} z^i \right)\left(\sum_{j=0}^{n} d_j z^j \right) + \left(\sum_{i=0}^{m} c_i z^i \right)\left(\sum_{j=0}^{n-1} (j+1)d_{j+1} z^j \right)$$

$$= f'(z)g(z) + f(z)g'(z).$$

The formula (28) is readily proved by induction on k. It holds for $k = 1$ where $(z - c)^0$ is interpreted as 1. Now, assume that $k > 1$ and that

$$((z - c)^{k-1})' = (k-1)(z - c)^{k-2}.$$

Then, using (27),

$$((z - c)^k)' = ((z - c)(z - c)^{k-1})'$$
$$= (z - c)^{k-1} + (z - c)(k - 1)(z - c)^{k-2}$$
$$= k(z - c)^{k-1}.$$

EXAMPLE 6.7

Let $f(z) = z^4 - z^2 + 1$ and $g(z) = z^4 + z^2 + 1$. Then $f'(z) = 4z^3 - 2z$, $g'(z) = 4z^3 + 2z$ and, by (27),

$$(f(z)g(z))' = (4z^3 - 2z)(z^4 + z^2 + 1) + (z^4 - z^2 + 1)(4z^3 + 2z)$$
$$= 8z^7 + 4z^3.$$

On the other hand, we can compute

$$f(z)g(z) = (z^4 + 1)^2 - z^4 = z^8 + z^4 + 1$$

and obtain directly from Definition 6.4:

$$(f(z)g(z))' = (z^8 + z^4 + 1)'$$
$$= 8z^7 + 4z^3.$$

Definition 6.5   (Multiple zero)   *If $f(z)$ is a polynomial and $f(z) = (z - c)^k g(z)$ where k is a positive integer and $g(z)$ is a polynomial not divisible by $z - c$, then c is said to be a zero (or a root) of $f(z)$ of multiplicity k. A zero of multiplicity 1 is called a simple zero (or a simple root).*

Theorem 6.7   *A number c is a zero of multiplicity k of a polynomial $f(z)$ if and only if c is a zero of $f(z)$ and a zero of $f'(z)$ of multiplicity $k - 1$. In particular, c is a simple zero of $f(z)$ if and only if $f(c) = 0$ and $f'(c) \neq 0$.*

Proof.   Suppose that $f(z) = (z - c)^k g(z)$, where k is a positive integer and $g(z)$ is a polynomial not divisible by $z - c$. Then, by Theorem 6.6,

$$f'(z) = k(z - c)^{k-1}g(z) + (z - c)^k g'(z)$$
$$= (z - c)^{k-1}r(z), \tag{29}$$

where $r(z) = kg(z) + (z - c)g'(z)$. Thus c is a zero of $f(z)$ of multiplicity k provided $r(z)$ is not divisible by $z - c$. Suppose that $r(z) = (z - c)^t s(z)$ where $t \geq 1$ and $s(z)$ is a polynomial. Then

$$g(z) = \frac{1}{k}(z - c)((z - c)^{t-1}s(z) - g'(z))$$

and thus, $z - c$ divides $g(z)$, contradicting our hypothesis. To prove the converse we show that if $f(z) = (z - c)^t g(z)$ and $f'(z) = (z - c)^{k-1} s(z)$, where t and k are positive integers and $g(z)$, $s(z)$ are polynomials not divisible by $z - c$, then $t = k$. For, by (29), $f'(z) = (z - c)^{t-1} r(z)$ where $r(z)$ is a polynomial not divisible by $z - c$. Thus

$$(z - c)^{t-1} r(z) = (z - c)^{k-1} s(z)$$

and, since $z - c$ does not divide either $r(z)$ or $s(z)$, it follows by Theorem 4.8 that $t - 1 = k - 1$ and hence $t = k$.

Note that c may be a zero of $f'(z)$ without being a zero of $f(z)$. For example, if $f(z) = z^3 - 3z^2 + 3z + 2$, then $f(1) = 3 \neq 0$ while $f'(z) = 3z^2 - 6z + 3 = 3(z - 1)^2$.

Further information about the zeros of a polynomial can be obtained by studying the localization of the zeros of its derivative (a polynomial of a smaller degree) but such results involve concepts which are beyond the scope of this book. We now state two important results on polynomials with real coefficients. In conformity with common usage we shall occasionally refer to the zeros (roots) of the polynomial $f(z)$ as the roots of the "polynomial equation $f(z) = 0$".

Theorem 6.8 *If a is a root of a polynomial equation with real coefficients then its complex conjugate, $\bar{a}$, is also a root of the equation.*

Proof. Let a be a root of equation $\sum_{t=0}^{n} b_t z^t = 0$. Then, since $\bar{b}_t = b_t$,

$$\sum_{t=0}^{n} b_t \bar{a}^t = \sum_{t=0}^{n} \bar{b}_t \bar{a}^t$$

$$= \overline{\sum_{t=0}^{n} b_t a^t}$$

$$= 0.$$

We remark that the preceding result is, in general, false for polynomials with complex coefficients.

The next result, due to Gauss, provides an easy method of finding all rational roots of an equation with integer coefficients. Note that any polynomial equation with rational coefficients can be transformed into one with integer coefficients by multiplying both sides of the equation by a common denominator of all the coefficients.

Theorem 6.9 *If a polynomial with integer coefficients, $\sum_{t=0}^{n} a_t z^t$, has a rational zero p/q, where p and q are relatively prime, then $p \mid a_0$ and $q \mid a_n$.*

Proof.   If p and q are relatively prime and p/q is a zero of the polynomial $\sum_{t=0}^{n} a_t z^t$, then

$$\sum_{t=0}^{n} a_t \frac{p^t}{q^t} = 0$$

and thus

$$\sum_{t=0}^{n} a_t p^t q^{n-t} = 0. \tag{30}$$

We therefore have

$$a_n p^n = -q \sum_{t=0}^{n-1} a_t p^t q^{n-t-1}$$

and $q \mid a_n p^n$. Since $q \nmid p$, and thus $q \nmid p^n$, it follows from Theorem 2.6 that $q \mid a_n$. Similarly, (30) yields

$$a_0 q^n = -p \sum_{t=1}^{n} a_t p^{t-1} q^{n-t}$$

and thus $p \mid a_0$.

EXAMPLE 6.8

Find all the rational zeros of the polynomial $f(z) = z^4 + 2z^3 - 2z^2 - 3z + 2$. By Theorem 6.9, a rational root of $f(z)$ must be an integer and must divide 2. Hence the candidates for rational roots are -1, 1, -2 and 2. We compute $f(-1) = 2$, $f(1) = 0$, $f(-2) = 0$, $f(2) = 20$. Thus the only rational zeros of $f(z)$ are 1 and -2. The other two zeros may be either irrational or complex (in which case they would be conjugate (see Theorem 6.8)). In fact, it is easy to compute that the remaining zeros are $-\frac{1}{2} \pm \frac{1}{2}\sqrt{5}$.

We shall now obtain a remarkable result, due to Sturm (1829), on the localization of real roots of a polynomial with real coefficients. We first require two results normally found in calculus books.

Theorem 6.10   *Let $f(z) = \sum_{t=0}^{n} a_t z^t$, where a_t are real, and suppose that b is a real number such that $f(b) > 0$. Then there exists a positive number ε such that $f(s) > 0$ for any s satisfying $b - \varepsilon \le s \le b + \varepsilon$. Similarly, if c is a real number such that $f(c) < 0$ then there exists a positive number η such that $f(s) < 0$ for any s satisfying $c - \eta \le s \le c + \eta$.*

Proof.   Let δ be a real number of absolute value less than 1. Then

$$|f(b + \delta) - f(b)| = |\sum_{t=1}^{n} a_t((b + \delta)^t - b^t)|$$

$$\le \sum_{t=1}^{n} |a_t| |(b + \delta)^t - b^t|$$

$$\le M \sum_{t=1}^{n} |(b + \delta)^t - b^t|$$

where $M = \max_t |a_t|$. Now, by the binomial theorem (Theorem 1.1, Chapter 1),

$$|(b + \delta)^t - b^t| = |\sum_{i=0}^{t} \binom{t}{i} b^i \delta^{t-i} - b^t|$$

$$= |\sum_{i=0}^{t-1} \binom{t}{i} b^i \delta^{t-i}|$$

$$\leq \sum_{i=0}^{t-1} \binom{t}{i} |b|^i |\delta|^{t-i}$$

$$= |\delta| \sum_{i=0}^{t-1} \binom{t}{i} |b|^i |\delta|^{t-i-1}$$

$$\leq |\delta| \sum_{i=0}^{t-1} \binom{t}{i} |b|^i$$

$$\leq |\delta| N_t,$$

where $N_t = \sum_{i=0}^{t-1} \binom{t}{i} |b|^i$. Let $N = M \sum_{t=1}^{n} N_t$. Then

$$|f(b + \delta) - f(b)| \leq M \sum_{t=1}^{n} |\delta| N_t$$

$$= |\delta| N.$$

Let ε be any positive number smaller than both $f(b)/2N$ and 1. Then for any s satisfying $b - \varepsilon \leq s \leq b + \varepsilon$ we have from the preceding inequality with $b + \delta = s$

$$|f(s) - f(b)| \leq |s - b| N$$

$$\leq \varepsilon N$$

$$\leq \tfrac{1}{2} f(b).$$

Hence, by Example 2.8(a) in Chapter 3,

$$-\tfrac{1}{2} f(b) \leq f(s) - f(b) \leq \tfrac{1}{2} f(b),$$

and therefore

$$f(s) \geq \tfrac{1}{2} f(b) > 0.$$

To prove the second part of the theorem set $g(z) = -f(z)$. Then $g(z)$ is a polynomial with real coefficients and $g(c) > 0$. Thus, by the first part of the theorem, there exists a positive number η such that $g(s) > 0$, that is, $f(s) < 0$, for any s satisfying $c - \eta \leq s \leq c + \eta$.

Before we can prove our next result we have to remind the reader of the following property of real numbers.

If S is a nonempty set of real numbers bounded above (i.e., S is such a set that there exists a real number N such that $s \leq N$ for all $s \in S$), then there exists *exactly one real number d, called the least upper bound of S and denoted by* l.u.b.(*S*), *with the following properties:*

    (i) $s \leq d$ *for all* $s \in S$

and

    (ii)   *if c is a real number such that* $s \leq c$ *for all* $s \in S$ *then* $c \geq d$

(i.e., *for any* $\varepsilon > 0$ *there exists* s_1 *in S such that* $s_1 > d - \varepsilon$). This property is usually called "the least upper bound axiom" and is considered as a defining property of real numbers.

    Theorem 6.11   *If* $f(z)$ *is a polynomial with real coefficients and* $f(b) \neq 0$ *for any b satisfying* $a_1 \leq b \leq a_2$, *then* $f(a_1)$ *and* $f(a_2)$ *are either both positive or both negative.*

    Proof. Suppose that $f(a_1) > 0$ and $f(a_2) < 0$. Let S be the set of all numbers c such that $f(b) > 0$ for all b satisfying $a_1 \leq b \leq c$. Now, $a_1 \in S$ and thus S is nonempty. Also, $c < a_2$ for all $c \in S$ and thus S is bounded above. Hence, by the least upper bound axiom, there exists a number d with the properties: $c \leq d$ for all c in S and, for any $\varepsilon > 0$, there exists c_1 in S such that $c_1 > d - \varepsilon$. First, note that $d > a_1$, since, by Theorem 6.10, there exists $\varepsilon_1 > 0$ such that $f(b) > 0$ for all b satisfying $a_1 \leq b \leq a_1 + \varepsilon_1$. Clearly $d \leq a_2$. Consider $f(d)$. It cannot be negative, since by Theorem 6.10 there would exist $\varepsilon_2 > 0$ such that $f(b) < 0$ for all b satisfying $d - \varepsilon_2 \leq b \leq d$, contradicting the definition of d. Nor can $f(d)$ be positive. For then, by Theorem 6.10, there would exist $\varepsilon_3 > 0$ such that $f(b) > 0$ for all b satisfying $d \leq b \leq d + \varepsilon_3$, again contradicting the definition of d. Hence $f(d)$ must be 0. But this contradicts our hypothesis. Thus we cannot have $f(a_1) > 0$ and $f(a_2) < 0$. Now, suppose that $f(a_1) < 0$ and $f(a_2) > 0$. Set $g(x) = -f(x)$. Then $g(x)$ satisfies the condition of the theorem and $g(a_1) > 0$ while $g(a_2) < 0$ which is impossible by the preceding part of the proof.

    It is easy to see that Theorem 6.11 is equivalent to the statement that if $f(a_1)$ and $f(a_2)$ are of opposite sign then there exists a real number c, $a_1 \leq c \leq a_2$, such that $f(c) = 0$.

    Definition 6.6 **(Sturm sequence, Sturm function)** *Let* $f(z)$ *be a real polynomial of positive degree. Define polynomials* $f_t(z)$, $t = 0, \ldots, m$, *by*
$$f_0(z) = f(z),$$

$$f_1(z) = f'(z),$$

$$f_0(z) = f_1(z)q_1(z) - f_2(z), \qquad \deg f_2(z) < \deg f_1(z),$$

. . . .

$$f_{t-2}(z) = f_{t-1}(z)q_{t-1}(z) - f_t(z), \quad \deg f_t(z) < \deg f_{t-1}(z), \quad t = 2, \ldots, m - 1,$$

$$f_{m-1}(z) = f_m(z)q_m(z).$$

Note that the above process is essentially the Euclidean algorithm applied to polynomials $f(z)$ and $f'(z)$, where each remainder has been multiplied by -1. It follows (see the proof of Theorem 4.7) that

$$f_m(z)\,|\,f_t(z), \qquad t = 0, \ldots, m,$$

that is,

$$f_t(z) = f_m(z)g_t(z), \qquad t = 0, \ldots, m.$$

The sequence $g_0(z), g_1(z), \ldots, g_m(z)$ is called the Sturm sequence of $f(z)$. Let $S(a)$ denote the number of variations of sign in the sequence

$$g_0(a), g_1(a), \ldots, g_m(a). \tag{31}$$

That is to say, $S(a)$ is the number of occurrences in the sequence (31) of pairs of consecutive terms having opposite signs, any vanishing terms being ignored. The function S is called the Sturm function of $f(z)$.

EXAMPLE 6.9

Find $S(-4)$, $S(0)$ and $S(4)$ for

$$f(z) = z^4 - 2z^3 - 7z^2 + 20z - 12.$$

We have

$$f_0(z) = f(z), \qquad f_1(z) = f'(z) = 4z^3 - 6z^2 - 14z + 20,$$

and applying Definition 6.6 we obtain

$$f_0(z) = (\tfrac{1}{4}z - \tfrac{1}{8})f_1(z) - (\tfrac{17}{4}z^2 - \tfrac{53}{4}z + \tfrac{19}{2}).$$

Therefore

$$f_2(z) = \tfrac{17}{4}z^2 - \tfrac{53}{4}z + \tfrac{19}{2}.$$

Again,

$$f_1(z) = (\tfrac{16}{17}z + \tfrac{440}{289})f_2(z) - (\tfrac{800}{289}z - \tfrac{1600}{289})$$

and thus

$$f_3(z) = \tfrac{800}{289}(z - 2).$$

Finally,

$$f_2(z) = \tfrac{289}{3200}(17z - 19)f_3(z).$$

Hence,

$$g_0(z) = \tfrac{289}{800}(z^3 - 7z + 6),$$

$$g_1(z) = \tfrac{289}{400}(2z^2 + z - 5),$$

$$g_2(z) = \tfrac{289}{3200}(17z - 19),$$

$$g_3(z) = 1,$$

and we compute

$$g_0(-4) < 0, \qquad g_1(-4) > 0, \qquad g_2(-4) < 0, \qquad g_3(-4) > 0;$$

$$g_0(0) > 0, \qquad g_1(0) < 0, \qquad g_2(0) < 0, \qquad g_3(0) > 0;$$

$$g_0(4) > 0, \qquad g_1(4) > 0, \qquad g_2(4) > 0, \qquad g_3(4) > 0.$$

Thus $S(-4) = 3$, $S(0) = 2$, $S(4) = 0$.

Theorem 6.12 (**Sturm's theorem**) *If $f(z)$ is a polynomial with real coefficients and a and b are two real numbers, $a < b$, neither a zero of $f(z)$, then the number of distinct real zeros of $f(z)$ between a and b is equal to $S(a) - S(b)$.*

Proof. First suppose that $f(z)$ has no multiple zeros, i.e., that $f_0(z)$ and $f_1(z)$ have no factor of positive degree in common (see Theorem 6.7). This is equivalent to the assumption that $\deg f_m(z) = 0$, that is, $f_m(z)$ is a nonzero real number, since $f_m(z)$ divides all $f_j(z)$, $j = 1, \ldots, m$. Thus, in this case, $S(c)$ is equal to the number of variations of sign in the sequence $f_0(c), f_1(c), \ldots, f_m(c)$. Let $c_1 < \cdots < c_n$ be all the distinct real zeros of the polynomials $f_0(z), f_1(z), \ldots, f_{m-1}(z)$. By Theorem 6.11, if d_1 and d_2 are any real numbers such that $c_i < d_1 < d_2 \le c_{i+1}$ for some i, then none of the polynomials $f_j(z)$, $j = 1, \ldots, m$, has a zero between d_1 and d_2 and therefore, by Theorem 6.11, $S(d_1) = S(d_2)$. Let us examine what happens to the Sturm function $S(\xi)$ as ξ approaches and passes one of the numbers c_t. Suppose then that $f_i(c_t) = 0$ for some i and t. We shall assume first that $i > 0$, that is, $f_i(z) \ne f(z)$. Note that neither $f_{i-1}(c_t)$ nor $f_{i+1}(c_t)$ can be zero. Otherwise, by Theorem 4.4, $z - c_t$ would be a common factor of two consecutive $f_j(z)$ and thus of all the preceding $f_j(z)$ (in particular, $f_0(z)$ and $f_1(z)$) and therefore, by Theorem 6.7, c_t would be a multiple zero of $f(z)$. Let ξ be any real number satisfying $c_{t-1} < \xi < c_{t+1}$ (if $t = 1$ or $t = n$ then ξ satisfies $\xi < c_2$ or $c_{n-1} < \xi$, respectively). By Definition 6.6,

$$f_{i+1}(z) = f_i(z) q_i(z) - f_{i-1}(z)$$

and thus

$$f_{i+1}(c_t) = -f_{i-1}(c_t). \tag{32}$$

Now, $f_{i-1}(\xi) \ne 0$ and $f_{i+1}(\xi) \ne 0$ for any ξ, $c_{t-1} < \xi < c_{t+1}$. Thus, by Theorem 6.11, $f_{i-1}(\xi)$ has the same sign as $f_{i-1}(c_t)$ and $f_{i+1}(\xi)$ has the same sign as $f_{i+1}(c_t)$. Hence (32) implies that $f_{i+1}(\xi)$ and $f_{i-1}(\xi)$ have opposite signs for any ξ satisfying $c_{t-1} < \xi < c_{t+1}$. It follows that

$$f_{i-1}(\xi), \qquad f_i(\xi), \qquad f_{i+1}(\xi)$$

gives rise to exactly one variation of sign, whatever the value of $f_i(\xi)$. Hence $S(\xi)$ is constant in the interval considered. Next, let c_s be a zero of $f_0(z)$ and let M_1 be the set of real numbers ξ satisfying $c_{s-1} < \xi < c_s$ and M_2 the set of all real numbers ξ satisfying $c_s < \xi < c_{s+1}$. We show that $S(\xi_2) = S(\xi_1) - 1$ for any $\xi_1 \in M_1$ and $\xi_2 \in M_2$. Since $f_0(z)$ has no zeros in M_1, the numbers $f_0(\xi_1)$ have the same sign for all ξ_1 in M_1. Similarly the numbers $f_0(\xi_2)$ have the same sign for all ξ_2 in M_2. We first prove that if $\xi_1 \in M_1$ and $\xi_2 \in M_2$ then $f_0(\xi_1)$ and $f_0(\xi_2)$ differ in sign. By Theorem 4.4 there exists a polynomial $q(z)$ such that

$$f_0(z) = (z - c_s)q(z). \tag{33}$$

Now c_s is assumed to be a simple zero and therefore $q(c_s) \neq 0$. Also, $q(\xi) \neq 0$ for any ξ in M_1 or in M_2. Let ε be any positive number such that $c_s - \varepsilon$ is in M_1 and $c_s + \varepsilon$ is in M_2 and let L be the set of all real numbers ξ satisfying $c_s - \varepsilon \leq \xi \leq c_s + \varepsilon$. Then $q(\xi)$ has the same sign for all ξ in L. Also, we have from (33)

$$f_0(c_s - \varepsilon) = -\varepsilon q(c_s - \varepsilon) \tag{34}$$

and

$$f_0(c_s + \varepsilon) = \varepsilon q(c_s + \varepsilon). \tag{35}$$

Therefore $f_0(c_s - \varepsilon)$ and $f_0(c_s + \varepsilon)$ have opposite signs and it follows, by another application of Theorem 6.11, that $f_0(\xi_1)$ and $f_0(\xi_2)$ differ in sign for any ξ_1 in M_1 and ξ_2 in M_2. Next, we obtain from (33)

$$f_1(z) = f_0'(z) = q(z) + (z - c_s)q'(z),$$

and therefore for any real number η

$$f_1(c_s + \eta) = q(c_s + \eta) + \eta q'(c_s + \eta). \tag{36}$$

Now, choose a positive number $\varepsilon_1 \leq \varepsilon$ such that

$$|q(\xi)| > \varepsilon_1 |q'(\xi)| \tag{37}$$

for all ξ in L. [This can be accomplished in the following way. Let $\alpha = \text{l.u.b.}_{\xi \in L}(|q'(\xi)|)$ and $\beta = \text{l.u.b.}_{\xi \in L}(-|q(\xi)|)$. Recall that ε was chosen so that $q(\xi) \neq 0$, that is, $-|q(\xi)| < 0$, for all ξ in the closed interval L. It is a well-known property of l.u.b. (which we shall not prove here), that under these conditions $\beta < 0$. If $\alpha > 0$, choose ε_1 to be any positive number smaller than either ε or $-\beta/\alpha$. For, $-\beta \leq |q(\xi)|$ and $\alpha \geq |q'(\xi)|$ for any $\xi \in L$ and therefore $|q(\xi)| \geq -\beta/\alpha |q'(\xi)|$. If $\alpha = 0$ then $q'(\xi) = 0$ for all ξ in L and we can choose $\varepsilon_1 = \varepsilon$.] It follows from (36) and (37) that $f_1(c_s + \varepsilon_1)$ has the same sign as $q(c_s + \varepsilon_1)$ and, by another application of Theorem 6.11, that $f_1(\xi)$ and $q(\xi)$ have the same sign for all $\xi \in L$. On the other hand, we see from (34) and (35) that $f_0(c_s - \varepsilon)$ and $q(c_s - \varepsilon)$ have opposite signs while $f_0(c_s + \varepsilon)$ and $q(c_s + \varepsilon)$ agree in sign. Moreover, by Theorem 6.11, the sign of $f_1(\xi)$ is the same for all ξ in $M_1 \cup M_2$ and the sign of $f_0(\xi_i)$ is constant in M_i, $i = 1, 2$. Hence $f_0(\xi_1)$ and $f_1(\xi_1)$ differ in sign for any ξ_1 in M_1 while $f_0(\xi_2)$ and $f_1(\xi_2)$ agree in sign for any ξ_2 in M_2. It follows that $S(\xi_2) = S(\xi_1) - 1$. To sum up: if $f(z)$ has no multiple zeros, then the value of the Sturm function $S(\xi)$ does not change as ξ increases unless ξ passes through a real zero of

$f(z)$ in which case the value of $S(\xi)$ diminishes each time by 1. Hence if $f(z)$ has no multiple zeros, then the total number of real roots between a and b is equal to $S(a) - S(b)$. To conclude the proof suppose that $f(z)$ has multiple zeros. We see from Definition 6.6 and Theorem 4.7 that $f_m(z)$ is a g.c.d. of $f(z)$ and $f'(z)$. Now, $f(z) = f_m(z)g_0(z)$ and therefore Theorem 6.7 implies that the zeros of $g_0(z)$ are precisely the distinct zeros of $f(z)$ (see Exercise 9). Thus the zeros of $g_0(z)$ are all simple, and $g_0(z)$, $g_1(z)$, ..., $g_m(z)$ is the Sturm sequence both for $g_0(z)$ and for $f(z)$. The result follows.

EXAMPLE 6.10

Find the number of distinct real roots of

$$f(z) = z^4 - 2z^3 - 7z^2 + 20z - 12.$$

We found in Example 6.9 that

$$g_0(z) = \tfrac{289}{800}(z^3 - 7z + 6), \qquad g_1(z) = \tfrac{289}{400}(2z^2 + z - 5),$$

$$g_2(z) = \tfrac{289}{3200}(17z - 19), \qquad g_3(z) = 1$$

and that $S(-4) = 3$, $S(0) = 2$ and $S(4) = 0$. We check by direct computation that $f(-4) \neq 0$, $f(0) \neq 0$, and $f(4) \neq 0$. Thus there is one real root between -4 and 0 and two real roots between 0 and 4. Furthermore, $S(4) = 0$ and therefore there are no real roots greater than 4. In addition, since there are four polynomials in the Sturm sequence, there cannot be more than three variations of sign. Hence $f(z)$ cannot have real roots smaller than -4.

We shall conclude this section, the present chapter, and our book by obtaining explicit formulas for roots of certain algebraic (polynomial) equations. Let

$$a_n z^n + a_{n-1} z^{n-1} + \cdots + a_1 z + a_0 = 0, \tag{38}$$

be an equation of degree n, where $a_n, \ldots, a_0$ are complex numbers and $n \geq 2$. Clearly,

$$z^n + \alpha_{n-1} z^{n-1} + \cdots + \alpha_1 z + \alpha_0 = 0 \tag{39}$$

where $\alpha_j = a_j/a_n$, $j = 1, \ldots, n-1$, has the same roots as (38). Now, let $z = x - \alpha_{n-1}/n$. Then, for $k \geq 2$, $z^k = x^k - \alpha_{n-1}(k/n)x^{k-1} + p_{k-2}(x)$ where $p_{k-2}(x)$ is a polynomial in x of degree not exceeding $k - 2$ (see Theorem 1.1, Chapter 1). If we substitute $z = x - \alpha_{n-1}/n$ on the left hand side of equation (39), we obtain an equation of the form

$$x^n + b_{n-2} x^{n-2} + \cdots + b_1 x + b_0 = 0 \tag{40}$$

where $b_{n-2}, \ldots, b_0$ are complex numbers. Hence, if $r_1, \ldots, r_n$ are the roots of (40) then $r_1 - \alpha_{n-1}/n, \ldots, r_n - \alpha_{n-1}/n$ are the roots of (39) and thus of (38). Equation (40) is said to be in *reduced form*.

EXAMPLE 6.11

Put the quadratic equation

$$az^2 + bz + c = 0, \qquad a \neq 0, \tag{41}$$

in reduced form. Hence find its roots. We set $p = b/a$ and $q = c/a$. Equation (41) is equivalent to

$$z^2 + pz + q = 0. \tag{42}$$

Now in (42) substitute

$$z = x - \frac{p}{2} \tag{43}$$

and obtain

$$\left(x - \frac{p}{2}\right)^2 + p\left(x - \frac{p}{2}\right) + q = 0$$

or

$$x^2 = \frac{p^2}{4} - q.$$

Thus

$$x = \pm \tfrac{1}{2}\sqrt{p^2 - 4q}$$

and from (43)

$$z = \pm \tfrac{1}{2}\sqrt{p^2 - 4q} - \tfrac{1}{2}p$$

$$= \frac{1}{2a}(-b \pm \sqrt{b^2 - 4ac}).$$

In the following theorem we shall give Tartaglia's solution of the cubic equation (usually called "Cardan's formula") and Descartes' solution of the quartic equation. We shall assume that the equations are already in reduced form.

Theorem 6.13
(a)   *Let*

$$z^3 + pz + q = 0 \tag{44}$$

be a cubic equation with complex coefficients. Then the three roots of (44) are

$$z_1 + z_2, \qquad \omega z_1 + \omega^2 z_2 \quad and \quad \omega^2 z_1 + \omega z_2$$

where

$$z_1 = \sqrt[3]{-\frac{q}{2} + \sqrt{\left(\frac{p}{3}\right)^3 + \left(\frac{q}{2}\right)^2}}, \qquad z_2 = \sqrt[3]{-\frac{q}{2} - \sqrt{\left(\frac{p}{3}\right)^3 + \left(\frac{q}{2}\right)^2}} \tag{45}$$

(so that $z_1 z_2 = -p/3$) and ω is the cube root of 1, $\omega = -1/2 + i(\sqrt{3}/2)$.
(b)   *Let*

$$z^4 + pz^2 + qz + r = 0 \tag{46}$$

be a quartic equation with complex coefficients (p, q, r, not all 0). Then the roots of (46) are the four roots of the quadratic equations

$$z^2 + \xi z + \frac{1}{2}\left(p + \xi^2 - \frac{q}{\xi}\right) = 0$$

and

$$z^2 - \xi z + \frac{1}{2}\left(p + \xi^2 + \frac{q}{\xi}\right) = 0 \tag{47}$$

where ξ^2 is any nonzero root of the cubic equation

$$z^3 + 2pz^2 + (p^2 - 4r)z - q^2 = 0. \tag{48}$$

Proof.
(a) Set $z = y_1 + y_2$. Then

$$z^3 = y_1^3 + 3y_1^2 y_2 + 3y_1 y_2^2 + y_2^3$$

$$= y_1^3 + y_2^3 + 3y_1 y_2 z$$

or

$$z^3 - 3y_1 y_2 z - (y_1^3 + y_2^3) = 0. \tag{49}$$

Equation (49) is the same as (44) if

$$-3y_1 y_2 = p \tag{50}$$

and

$$-(y_1^3 + y_2^3) = q. \tag{51}$$

The problem is to find y_1 and y_2 that satisfy (50) and (51), in other words we want two numbers y_1^3 and y_2^3 whose product is $-p^3/27$ and whose sum is $-q$. It follows from Theorem 6.5 that y_1^3 and y_2^3 are the two roots of the quadratic equation

$$x^2 + qx - \frac{p^3}{27} = 0.$$

Hence y_1^3 and y_2^3 are equal to

$$\frac{1}{2}\left(-q \pm \sqrt{q^2 + \frac{4p^3}{27}}\right) = -\frac{q}{2} \pm \sqrt{\left(\frac{p}{3}\right)^3 + \left(\frac{q}{2}\right)^2}.$$

Thus $y_1 = u_1 z_1$ and $y_2 = u_2 z_2$ where z_1, z_2 are defined as in (45) and both u_1 and u_2 can be any of the cube roots of 1, namely 1, ω, or ω^2 (see Example 3.5). However, equation (50) implies (with appropriate choice of the cube roots for z_1 and z_2 so that $\sqrt[3]{(p/3)^3} = p/3$) that $u_1 u_2 = 1$. The result follows.
(b) The left-hand side of equation (46) can be expressed as a product of two quadratic polynomials

$$(z^2 + \xi z + \mu)(z^2 - \xi z + v) = z^4 + (\mu + v - \xi^2)z^2 + \xi(v - \mu)z + \mu v \tag{52}$$

if

$$\mu + v - \xi^2 = p, \qquad \xi(v - \mu) = q \qquad \text{and} \qquad \mu v = r.$$

Assume $\xi \neq 0$ and solve the first two equations for μ and v:

$$\mu = \frac{1}{2}\left(p + \xi^2 - \frac{q}{\xi}\right) \quad \text{and} \quad v = \frac{1}{2}\left(p + \xi^2 + \frac{q}{\xi}\right). \tag{53}$$

The third equation then gives

$$\frac{1}{4}\left(p + \xi^2 - \frac{q}{\xi}\right)\left(p + \xi^2 + \frac{q}{\xi}\right) = r,$$

i.e.,

$$\xi^6 + 2p\xi^4 + (p^2 - 4r)\xi^2 - q^2 = 0. \tag{54}$$

We can solve (54) as a cubic in ξ^2. Let ξ^2 be any nonzero root of (54) (if any) and let ξ be a square root of ξ^2. Substitute ξ in (53) and (52) and thus obtain two quadratic equations equivalent to the quartic equation (46):

$$z^2 + \xi z + \frac{1}{2}\left(p + \xi^2 - \frac{q}{\xi}\right) = 0$$

and

$$z^2 - \xi z + \frac{1}{2}\left(p + \xi^2 + \frac{q}{\xi}\right) = 0.$$

The above method fails only if all the roots of (54) are 0. But then (54) must be $\xi^6 = 0$ and $p = q = r = 0$ in which case all roots of (46) are 0.

EXAMPLES 6.12

(Each of the following equations can be solved by the method used in Example 6.8. However, we shall use the method given in the preceding theorem.)

(a)   Solve the cubic equation

$$x^3 - 6x^2 + 57x - 196 = 0. \tag{55}$$

Set $x = z + 2$. Then (55) becomes

$$z^3 + 45z - 98 = 0. \tag{56}$$

We have from formulas (45)

$$z_1 = \sqrt[3]{49 + \sqrt{15^3 + 49^2}} = \sqrt[3]{49 + 76} = 5$$

$$z_2 = \sqrt[3]{49 - 76} = -3.$$

Therefore the three roots of (56) are

$$5 - 3 = 2,$$

$$5\left(-\frac{1}{2} + i\frac{\sqrt{3}}{2}\right) - 3\left(-\frac{1}{2} - i\frac{\sqrt{3}}{2}\right) = -1 + i4\sqrt{3},$$

and

$$5\left(-\frac{1}{2} - i\frac{\sqrt{3}}{2}\right) - 3\left(-\frac{1}{2} + i\frac{\sqrt{3}}{2}\right) = -1 - i4\sqrt{3}.$$

Hence the roots of (55) are

$$4, \quad 1 + i4\sqrt{3} \quad \text{and} \quad 1 - i4\sqrt{3}.$$

(b)   Use Descartes' method (Theorem 6.13(b)) to solve the equation

$$z^4 - 3z^2 - 14z - 12 = 0. \tag{57}$$

We require a root of the cubic

$$z^3 - 6z^2 + 57z - 196 = 0.$$

In part (a) we found that 4 is a root of this cubic equation. Thus ξ in (47) can be chosen to be 2 and (57) can be written

$$[z^2 + 2z + \tfrac{1}{2}(-3 + 4 + \tfrac{14}{2})][z^2 - 2z + \tfrac{1}{2}(-3 + 4 - \tfrac{14}{2})] = 0$$

or

$$(z^2 + 2z + 4)(z^2 - 2z - 3) = 0.$$

Hence the roots of (57) are

$$-1 \pm i\sqrt{3}, \quad 3, \quad -1.$$

It would appear from Theorem 6.13 that with sufficient ingenuity one could find an expression involving only radicals and rational operations involving the coefficients for the roots of the general equation of degree 5. Indeed in 1675 the great Scottish mathematician James Gregory believed that he had developed a method for solving the general quintic equation and, in principle, the general equation of any degree. However, the story was not destined to have a happy ending. It is now known, with mathematical certainty, that such a method could not and cannot exist: the roots of a general polynomial equation of degree greater than four cannot be expressed in terms of radicals and rational operations involving the coefficients, not even in principle!

Quiz

Answer **true** or **false**:

1.   If x_1 is an indeterminate over R and x_2 is an indeterminate over $R[x_1]$ then x_2 is an indeterminate over R.

2.   If x_1 and x_2 are indeterminates over R then x_2 is an indeterminate over $R[x_1]$.

3. The function $x_1^2 + x_2^2 + x_1 x_2 x_3$ is symmetric.

4. The function $f(x_1, \ldots, x_n) = \sum_{\omega \in Q_{r,n}} (\prod_{i=1}^{r} x_{\omega_i})^2$ is symmetric.

5. The coefficient of z^{n-1} in $\prod_{i=1}^{n} (z - i)$ is $-n(n+1)/2$.

6. The product of the roots of $z^5 + 7z^3 + 5z^2 + 3z$ is -3.

7. At least one of the numbers $2, -2, 1, -1$ is a root of $z^9 - z^5 + 2$.

8. The polynomials $z^8 - 3z^5 + z^3 + 1$ and $3z^4 - z^3 - z^2 - 1$ have a root in common.

9. Any cubic polynomial with real coefficients has a real root.

10. If $a_4 z^4 + a_3 z^3 + a_2 z^2 + a_1 z + a_0$ where $a_4 \neq 0$ and a_j are real, $j = 0, \ldots, 4$, has no real roots, then $a_0 > 0$.

Exercises

1. Show that if x_1 is an indeterminate over R and x_2 is an indeterminate over $R[x_1]$ then x_1 is an indeterminate over $R[x_2]$.

2. Show that if $\psi(x_1, \ldots, x_p) \in R[x_1, \ldots, x_p]$ and $f_i(x_1, \ldots, x_p) \in R[x_1, \ldots, x_p]$, $i = 1, \ldots, p$, and each $f_i(x_1, \ldots, x_p)$ is symmetric then $\psi(f_1, \ldots, f_p)$ is symmetric.

3. If $E_r(\hat{x}_k)$ designates the rth elementary symmetric function of $x_1, \ldots, x_{k-1}, x_{k+1}, \ldots, x_p$ show that

$$E_r(\hat{x}_k) + x_k E_{r-1}(\hat{x}_k) = E_r(x_1, \ldots, x_p).$$

4. In the notation of Exercise 3 show that

$$\sum_{k=1}^{p} E_r(\hat{x}_k) = (p - r) E_r(x_1, \ldots, x_p).$$

5. Complete the formal induction indicated in the proof of Theorem 6.5.

6. If $c_k = \cos 2\pi k/n + i \sin 2\pi k/n, k = 1, \ldots, n$, then show that

$$E_t(c_1, \ldots, c_n) = 0, \qquad t = 1, \ldots, n - 1.$$

(*Hint*: The c_k are the roots of $z^n - 1$.)

7. Find all the rational zeros of the polynomial $f(z) = z^5 - 3z^3 - 2z^2 - 4z + 8$. Hence find all the zeros of $f(z)$.

8. Find all the multiple zeros of $f(z) = z^6 + 4z^5 + 6z^4 + 8z^3 + 9z^2 + 4z + 4$.

9. Let $c_1, \ldots, c_m$ be the distinct zeros of the polynomial

$$f(z) = \prod_{i=1}^{m} (z - c_i)^{k_i}.$$

Let $d(z) = \text{g.c.d.}(f(z), f'(z))$ and $f(z) = d(z)q(z)$. Show that

$$q(z) = \prod_{i=1}^{m} (z - c_i).$$

10. Given that $1 + i$ is a zero of $f(z) = z^4 - z^3 + z^2 + 2$ find the other zeros of $f(z)$.

11. Find the integer a such that the real root c of

$$z^3 + 6z^2 + 10z - 1 = 0$$

satisfies $a < c < a + 1$.

12. Use Sturm's Theorem to determine the number of real zeros of the polynomial

$$f(z) = z^4 - 5z^2 - 2z + 3:$$

(i)   between -2 and 0;

(ii)   between 0 and 2;

(iii)   between 2 and 4.

How many zeros of $f(z)$ are not real? How many real zeros are rational?

13. Solve the equation
$$z^3 - 9z - 28 = 0.$$

14. Use Theorem 6.13(b) to solve the equation

$$z^4 - 5z^2 - 2z + 3 = 0.$$

Hence verify your answers to Exercise 12.

Answers and Solutions

Quiz

1. **False.** This problem is easily verified by writing out both sides.

2. **True.** One of the factors is $\cos 3\pi/6$ which is 0.

3. **False.** The left side is $\cos 0 + \cos \pi/6 + \cos 2\pi/6 + \cos 3\pi/6 + \cos 4\pi/6 + \cos 5\pi/6 = 1 + \sqrt{3}/2 + 1/2 + 0 - 1/2 - \sqrt{3}/2 = 1$.

4. **True.** $\dbinom{n}{r} = \dfrac{n!}{(n-r)!\,r!} = \prod_{t=1}^{r} \dfrac{n-t+1}{t}$.

5. **False.** Take $r = 3$, then $(3^2)! = 9!$ while $(3!)^2 = 6^2 = 36$.

6. **True.**

$$\binom{2r}{r} = \frac{(2r)!}{(r!)^2} = \frac{[2r(2r-2)\cdots 2][(2r-1)\cdots 1]}{(r!)^2}$$

$$= \frac{2^r \cdot r! [(2r-1)\cdots 1]}{(r!)^2} = 2^r \cdot \frac{2r-1}{r} \cdot \frac{2r-3}{r-1} \cdots \frac{1}{1} \geq 2^r,$$

$$\text{since } \frac{2r-(2k+1)}{r-k} \geq 1 \quad \text{for} \quad k > 0.$$

7. **False.** Let $b = -a$, then $(a-a)^3 = a^3 + (-a)^3$; that is, $n = 3$.

8. **True.**

$$\binom{n}{r} = \frac{n!}{r!\,(n-r)!} = \frac{n!}{(r+1)!\,(n-r-1)!} \cdot \frac{r+1}{n-r} = \binom{n}{r+1} \cdot \frac{r+1}{n-r} < \binom{n}{r+1},$$

$$\text{since } 2r+1 < n, \text{ i.e., } \frac{r+1}{n-r} < 1$$

9. **True.** The result follows from $\binom{n}{r} + \binom{n}{r+1} = \binom{n+1}{r+1}$ for all $n > r \geq 0$ and the fact that $\binom{n}{r+1}$ is a positive integer.

10. **False.** The coefficient of $x^4 y^2$ is $\binom{6}{2} = 15$.

Exercises

1. (a) $\sum_{t=2}^{5} (-t)^2 = (-2)^2 + (-3)^2 + (-4)^2 + (-5)^2 = 54$.

    (b) $\sum_{t=1}^{4} 2t = 2(1 + 2 + 3 + 4) = 20$.

    (c) $\sum_{k=2}^{2} \dfrac{1}{k} = \dfrac{1}{2}$.

    (d) $\sum_{n=0}^{3} (-1)^n \dfrac{2^{2n}}{(2n)!} = 1 - \dfrac{2^2}{2!} + \dfrac{2^4}{4!} - \dfrac{2^6}{6!} = 1 - 2 + \dfrac{2}{3} - \dfrac{4}{45} = -\dfrac{19}{45}$.

    (e) $\sum_{s=1}^{20} s^2 / \sum_{t=1}^{20} t^2 = 1$.

    (f) $\sum_{s=1}^{4} s! / \sum_{t=2}^{4} t! = \dfrac{1! + 2! + 3! + 4!}{2! + 3! + 4!} = \dfrac{33}{32}$.

    (g) $(\prod_{s=1}^{10} s!)/(\prod_{t=3}^{10} t!) = 1! \, 2! \quad (\prod_{s=3}^{10} s!)/(\prod_{s=3}^{10} s!) = 2$.

    (h) $\prod_{i=1}^{4} (2i - 1) = 1 \cdot 3 \cdot 5 \cdot 7 = 105$.

    (i) $\prod_{i=1}^{15} \dfrac{2i-1}{2i+1} = \dfrac{\prod_{i=1}^{15}(2i-1)}{\prod_{i=1}^{15}(2i+1)} = \dfrac{\prod_{i=1}^{15}(2i-1)}{\prod_{i=2}^{16}(2i-1)} = \dfrac{1}{31}$.

2. (a) $-x + \dfrac{x^3}{3!} - \dfrac{x^5}{5!} + \dfrac{x^7}{7!}$.

    (b) $1 - 6x + 15x^2 - 20x^3 + 15x^4 - 6x^5 + x^6$.

    (c) $1 - x^6$.

3. $\binom{21}{19} = \dfrac{21!}{19! 2!} = \dfrac{21 \cdot 20}{2} = 210$.

4. $\binom{n}{3} = \dfrac{10}{21}\binom{n}{5}$; $\dfrac{n!}{3!\,(n-3)!} = \dfrac{10}{21} \cdot \dfrac{n!}{5!(n-5)!}$; $\dfrac{5! \cdot 21}{3! \cdot 10} = \dfrac{(n-3)!}{(n-5)!}$;

    $42 = (n-3)(n-4)$; $(n-10)(n+3) = 0$; $n = 10$, since $n \geq 0$.

5. $\binom{20}{3}(-2)^3 = -9120$.

6. Set $a = b = 1$ in Theorem 1.1. Then $\sum_{r=0}^{n} \binom{n}{r} = (1+1)^n = 2^n$. Setting $a = 1$ and $b = -1$ in the same theorem we get $\sum_{r=0}^{n} (-1)^r \binom{n}{r} = (1-1)^n = 0$.

7. $x^7 - 7x^5 + 21x^3 - 35x + 35x^{-1} - 21x^{-3} + 7x^{-5} - x^{-7}$.

8. For $n \geq 3$, $n^n = n \cdot n \cdot n \cdot n^{n-3} \geq (n+1) \cdot n \cdot (n-1) \cdot (n-2)! = (n+1)!$, since

$$\frac{n}{n+1} \cdot \frac{n}{n} \cdot \frac{n}{n-1} \cdot \frac{n}{n-2} \cdot \frac{n}{n-3} \cdots \geq 1.$$ This last statement is true since, clearly,

$$\frac{n}{n-k} \geq 1, \quad k = 2, 3, \ldots, \qquad \text{and} \qquad \frac{n}{n+1} \cdot \frac{n}{n} \cdot \frac{n}{n-1} = \frac{n^2}{n^2-1} \geq 1.$$

9.
$$\binom{n-2}{r} + 2\binom{n-2}{r-1} + \binom{n-2}{r-2} = \left[\binom{n-2}{r} + \binom{n-2}{r-1}\right]$$
$$+ \left[\binom{n-2}{r-1} + \binom{n-2}{r-2}\right]$$
$$= \binom{n-1}{r} + \binom{n-1}{r-1} = \binom{n}{r}.$$

10. Case 1: n even, then $\binom{n}{r}$ is greatest for $r = \dfrac{n}{2}$.

Case 2: n odd, then $\binom{n}{r}$ is greatest for $r = \dfrac{n+1}{2}$. (See the Pascal Triangle immediately preceding Theorem 1.1.)

11. The given statement is equivalent to the following:

$$\left(\frac{n+5}{2}\right)^{n+5} \geq (n+5)!$$

for all positive integers n. The proof is by induction on n. Notice that $((1+5)/2)^6 = 3^6 = 729 > 720 = 6!$. Hence the statement is true for $n = 1$. Assume it is true for all integers less than $k+1$. Then

$$\left(\frac{k+6}{2}\right)^{k+6} = \left(\frac{k+6}{2}\right)\left(\frac{k+6}{2}\right)^{k+5}$$
$$= \left(\frac{k+6}{2}\right)\left(\frac{k+5}{2} + \frac{1}{2}\right)^{k+5}$$
$$= \left(\frac{k+6}{2}\right)\left[\left(\frac{k+5}{2}\right)^{k+5} + \binom{k+5}{1}\left(\frac{k+5}{2}\right)^{k+4} \cdot \frac{1}{2} + \cdots\right]$$
$$\geq \frac{k+6}{2}\left[\left(\frac{k+5}{2}\right)^{k+5} + \binom{k+5}{1}\left(\frac{k+5}{2}\right)^{k+4} \cdot \frac{1}{2}\right]$$
$$= \frac{k+6}{2}\left[\left(\frac{k+5}{2}\right)^{k+5} + \left(\frac{k+5}{2}\right)^{k+5}\right]$$
$$\geq \frac{k+6}{2}[(k+5)! + (k+5)!]$$
$$= (k+6)!$$

Hence the result.

Quiz

1. **False.** Let $X = \{1\}$ and $Y = \{2\}$. Then $X \times Y = \{(1, 2)\}$ whereas $Y \times X = \{(2, 1)\}$.

2. **False.** Let $X = \{1, 2, 3\}$, $Y = \{2, 6\}$ and $Z = \{3, 6\}$. Then $(X \cup Y) \cap Z = \{3, 6\}$ while $X \cup (Y \cap Z) = \{1, 2, 3, 6\}$.

3. **True.** There are m choices for the first member of the ordered pair and for each such choice, there are n choices for the second member.

4. **False.** $X \cap Y$ need not be empty.

5. **False.** The equation is satisfied by $x = 0$.

6. **False.** $P(\varnothing) = \{\varnothing\}$.

7. **True.** The symmetric, transitive and reflexive properties obviously hold.

8. **True.** $X \subset Y$ if and only if $X = Y$ or X is a proper subset of Y. In either case $X \cup Y = Y$.

9. **False.** $2 \geq 1$ does not imply $1 \geq 2$.

10. **True.** Definition 2.7 (i) and (ii) are clearly satisfied. Suppose $x - y = n$ and $y - z = m$, then $x - z = (n + y) - (y - m) = n + m$, an integer. Therefore R is an equivalence relation.

Exercises

1. (a) set of all nonnegative integers.
   (b) N.
   (c) set of all nonpositive integers.
   (d) set of all positive even integers.
   (e) set of all even integers together with positive odd integers.
   (f) I.
   (g) $\{1, 2, 3, 4\}$.
   (h) $\varnothing$.
   (i) $\varnothing$.
   (j) the set of all rational numbers together with $\pm\sqrt{2}$.

2. From Quiz question 3, we have: $X \times Y$ has 12 elements; $Y \times X$ has 12 elements; $X \times X$ has 16 elements and $Y \times Y$ has 9 elements. These elements are all distinct. Next we compute that $(X \times Y) \cap (Y \times X) = \{(1, 1), (1, 2), (1, 3), (2, 1), (2, 2), (2, 3), (3, 1), (3, 2), (3, 3)\}$, 9 distinct elements.

3. $P(X) = \{\varnothing, \{1\}, \{2\}, \{3\}, \{4\}, \{1, 2\}, \{1, 3\}, \{1, 4\}, \{2, 3\}, \{2, 4\}, \{3, 4\}, \{1, 2, 3\}, \{1, 2, 4\}, \{1, 3, 4\}, \{2, 3, 4\}, \{1, 2, 3, 4\}\}$. Two partitions are $S_1 = \{\{1, 2, 3\}, \{4\}\}$ and $S_2 = \{\{2, 4\}, \{1, 3\}\}$.

4. A subset of X is completely determined once it is known whether each of the elements in X is in the subset or not. There are two possibilities for each of the n elements and thus there are 2^n possibilities for subsets.

5. Clearly $(n_1, s_1)R(n_1, s_1)$. Suppose $(n_1, s_1)R(n_2, s_2)$, then $n_1 s_2 = n_2 s_1$ and it follows that $(n_2, s_2)R(n_1, s_1)$. Let $(n_1, s_1)R(n_2, s_2)$ and $(n_2, s_2)R(n_3, s_3)$, then $n_1 s_2 = n_2 s_1$ and $n_2 s_3 = n_3 s_2$. But then, since the elements of S are nonzero, we have $\dfrac{n_2}{s_2} = \dfrac{n_1}{s_1}$ and $\dfrac{n_2}{s_2} = \dfrac{n_3}{s_3}$ or $n_1 s_3 = n_3 s_1$ and $(n_1, s_1)R(n_3, s_3)$.

6. Yes. Two real numbers x and y satisfy x R y if and only if they are not separated by an integer. Thus the equivalence classes are just the intervals $n \le x < n+1$, where n is any integer.

7. If x and y are in the element X of S and y and z also belong to X then clearly x and z must belong to X. This proves the transitive property. Reflexive and symmetric properties are obvious.

8. The power set consists of at least n singleton sets (sets with one element) and the empty set.

Section 1.3

Quiz

1. **True.** Suppose $fg(x_1) = fg(x_2)$, then $g(x_1) = g(x_2)$ which implies $x_1 = x_2$ since g is 1-1.

2. **True.** $Y \subset f(X)$ if and only if $Y = f(X)$, since it is always true that $f(X) \subset Y$.

3. **False.** See Example 3.2(c).

4. **True.** Let f be a 1-1 function onto a finite set Y and let $Y = \{y_1, \ldots, y_n\}$ be the range of f. Then f^{-1} exists and $\{f^{-1}(y_1), \ldots, f^{-1}(y_n)\}$, a finite set, is the domain of f.

5. **True.** Let $f(x) = \begin{cases} 2x + 1 & \text{if } x \ge 0 \\ -2x & \text{if } x < 0. \end{cases}$

    Then $f: I \to N$ is $1-1$ and onto N.

6. **False.** Let $X = \{0, 1, 2\}$ be the domain of $f: X \to X$ defined by $f(0) = f(2) = 0$, $f(1) = 1$. Let $V = \{0, 1\}$ and $W = \{1, 2\}$. Then $f(V) \cap f(W) = \{0, 1\} \cap \{1, 0\} = \{0, 1\}$ whereas $f(V \cap W) = f(\{1\}) = \{1\}$.

7. **True.** $z \in f(V \cup W)$ implies $z = f(x)$ where $x \in V \cup W$ and thus $z = f(x) \in f(V) \cup f(W)$. On the other hand, $z \in f(V) \cup f(W)$ implies $z = f(x)$ where $x \in V \cup W$ and hence $z = f(x) \in f(V \cup W)$.

8. **False.** $[-2.5] = -3 \ne -2 = -[2.5]$.

9. **False.** Let X and Y be the real numbers. Let $f(x) = x^2$ and $g(x) = x$. Then $fg(x) = f(x) = x^2 = g(x^2) = gf(x)$ and g is 1-1 onto but f is clearly not 1-1.

10. **True.** $fg(x) = fh(x)$ implies that $f(g(x)) = f(h(x))$, and thus $g(x) = h(x)$ since f is 1-1.

Exercises

1. (a) Since $\delta_{3,0} = 0$, $\delta_{0,\delta_{3,0}} = \delta_{0,0} = 1$.
   (b) Since $\delta_{5,5} = 1$, $\delta_{0,t} = \delta_{0,1} = 0$.
   (c) $\sum_{t=1}^{4} \delta_{1,t} \delta_{t,2} = 1 \cdot 0 + 0 \cdot 1 + 0 \cdot 0 + 0 \cdot 0 = 0$.
   (d) $\sum_{t=1}^{4} (\delta_{1,t} + \delta_{t,2})/2 = \frac{1}{2}(\sum_{t=1}^{4} \delta_{1,t} + \sum_{t=1}^{4} \delta_{t,2}) = \frac{1}{2}(1+1) = 1$.

2. $f|N$ is defined by $f(x) = x$.

3. $\sigma^{-1}(1) = 2$, $\sigma^{-1}(2) = 3$, $\sigma^{-1}(3) = 4$, $\sigma^{-1}(4) = 1$, $\sigma\tau(1) = 1$, $\sigma\tau(2) = 4$, $\sigma\tau(3) = 3$, $\sigma\tau(4) = 2$, and $\tau\sigma(1) = 3$, $\tau\sigma(2) = 2$, $\tau\sigma(3) = 1$, $\tau\sigma(4) = 4$.

4. $\sigma^3(1) = \sigma^2(\sigma(1)) = \sigma^2(4) = \sigma(\sigma(4)) = \sigma(3) = 2$. Similarly $\sigma^3(2) = 3$, $\sigma^3(3) = 4$, $\sigma^3(4) = 1$. Also $\sigma^4(1) = 1$, $\sigma^4(2) = 2$, $\sigma^4(3) = 3$ and $\sigma^4(4) = 4$.

5. Let $X = \{x_1, x_2, \ldots, x_n\}$. Since f is onto, $f(X) = \{f(x_1), f(x_2), \ldots, f(x_n)\} = X$. Suppose $f(x_1) = f(x_2)$. Then $f(X)$ has at most $n-1$ distinct elements whereas X has n distinct elements.

6. The value of $f(x)$ can be any integer $1, \ldots, n$, for each $x \in X$. Thus there are n^n possibilities for distinct f. Since $f(1)$ can be chosen in n ways and then $f(2)$ in $n-1$ ways, and so on, there are $n!$ $1-1$ functions.

Section 1.4

Quiz

1. **True.** Let $X = \{x_1, x_2, \ldots, x_n, \ldots\}$ and $Y = \{y_1, y_2, \ldots, y_n, \ldots\}$ be the two denumerable sets. Form the set $X \cup Y = \{x_1, y_1, x_2, y_2, \ldots\}$ where any element is omitted if it occurs previously in the sequence. Now $X \cup Y$ cannot be finite since $X \subset X \cup Y$. Also we can make the 1-1 correspondence $1 \leftrightarrow x_1$, $2 \leftrightarrow y_1$, $3 \leftrightarrow x_2$, $4 \leftrightarrow y_2, \ldots$.

2. **True.** If X is finite, $P(X)$ is finite. Suppose then that X is infinite. Note that X is equipotent to the subset of $P(X)$ consisting of the one element sets $\{x\}$, and therefore $P(X)$ is infinite. If $P(X)$ were denumerable then, by Theorem 4.3, X would have to be denumerable and thus equipotent to $P(X)$, contradicting Theorem 4.1.

3. **True.** This set is an infinite subset of the rational numbers. Apply Theorems 4.4 and 4.3.

4. **False.** By Theorem 4.1, $P(\mathrm{Re})$ is not equipotent to Re.

5. **True.** Consider $P(N)$. With each $X \in P(N)$ we can define a unique partition of N consisting of the two sets X and $Y = \{y \in N \,|\, y \notin X\}$. The correspondence $X \leftrightarrow (X, Y)$ is 1-1 from $P(N)$ onto the set of 2-element partitions of N. (We leave the consideration of $X = \varnothing$ to the purists.)

6. **False.** $P(P(\varnothing))$ is a two-element set consisting of $\varnothing$, $\{\varnothing\}$.

7. **True.** If S is denumerable then S is equipotent to N and hence $S \times S$ is equipotent to $N \times N$. By the first part of the proof of Theorem 4.4, the set $N \times N$ is denumerable and hence $S \times S$ is denumerable. Conversely, if $S \times S$ is

denumerable then the infinite subset $X = \{(x, x) \mid x \in S\}$ of $S \times S$ is also denumerable. Clearly X and S are equipotent.

8. **False.** The set N is an example.

9. **True.** Denote the set of rational numbers by S. The set considered here is precisely $S \times S$ and we can apply the result in Question 7.

10. **True.** As every student of trigonometry knows, $\sin x = 0$ if and only if x is an integer multiple of π. Hence the set of solutions is $\{0, \pi, -\pi, 2\pi, -2\pi, \ldots\}$, clearly denumerable.

Exercises

1. Clearly the set of triples is equipotent to $N \times (N \times N)$. Apply Question 7 (of the preceding quiz) twice.

2. This set is clearly infinite and a subset of the integers. Apply Theorem 4.3.

3. In the open interval (a_i, b_i) let $c_i = \dfrac{a_i + b_i}{2}$ and if c_i is not rational then let d_i be a rational number whose decimal expansion is equal to a sufficiently long segment of the decimal expansion of c_i so that d_i is also in (a_i, b_i). Thus in each (a_i, b_i) we can select a rational number and since these intervals are disjoint they can be put into 1-1 correspondence with a subset of the rational numbers. Apply Theorems 4.4 and 4.3.

4. Let X be an equivalence class and let $x \in X$. Then all the elements of X are of the form $x + r$ where r is a rational number.

5. We assume that the student is acquainted with the elementary properties of the prime natural numbers: $p_1 = 2, p_2 = 3, p_3 = 5, p_4 = 7, p_5 = 11, \ldots$. Namely, that these form an infinite set and that $p_i^n = p_j^m$ if and only if $i = j$ and $n = m$. Then define $X_i = \{p_i^m \mid m \in N\}$, $i = 1, 2, 3, \ldots$, and $X = \{n \in N \mid n \notin X_i, i = 1, 2, \ldots\}$. Clearly each X_i is denumerable and since $2 \cdot 3, 2 \cdot 3^2, 2 \cdot 3^3, \ldots$ are all elements of X, the subset X is denumerable. By definition of the X_i and X we have $X \cup X_1 \cup X_2 \cup \cdots = N$.

6. Y is not denumerable because any equation of the form $x - c = 0$, c any real number, is in Y. To prove the second part we establish a 1-1 correspondence between the set $I \times I$, where I is the set of integers, and Z: the pair (a, b) corresponds to $ax + b = 0$. We know that I is denumerable by Theorem 4.4 and thus $I \times I$ is denumerable by Quiz question 7.

7. With each sequence $\{a_1, a_2, \ldots, a_m\}$ associate the unique natural number $p_1^{a_1} \cdots p_m^{a_m}$ where the p_i are primes as in the solution to Exercise 5. This set of integers is clearly infinite and a subset of N, thus denumerable.

8. With each equation indicated, associate the unique n-tuple of rational numbers $(a_0, \ldots, a_{n-1})$. This correspondence obviously is 1-1. For a fixed n, the set of n-tuples of rational numbers is denumerable, as can be shown by a trivial induction based on Quiz question 7. Hence the set of all such indicated equations

that involve n rational coefficients is denumerable and can be ordered in a sequence $E_1^{(n)}, E_2^{(n)}, E_3^{(n)}, \ldots$. Now write out the array

$$E_1^{(1)} \quad E_2^{(1)} \quad E_3^{(1)} \quad E_4^{(1)} \quad \cdots$$

$$E_1^{(2)} \quad E_2^{(2)} \quad E_3^{(2)} \quad E_4^{(2)} \quad \cdots$$

$$E_1^{(3)} \quad E_2^{(3)} \quad E_3^{(3)} \quad E_4^{(3)} \quad \cdots$$

$$E_1^{(4)} \quad E_2^{(4)} \quad E_3^{(4)} \quad E_4^{(4)} \quad \cdots$$

$$\cdot \quad \cdot \quad \cdot \quad \cdot \quad \cdot \quad \cdot \quad \cdot \quad \cdot \quad \cdot \quad \cdot$$

Arrange these equations in a single sequence as in the proof of Theorem 4.4: $E_1^{(1)}, E_1^{(2)}, E_2^{(1)}, \ldots$. Now write out the finite number of real roots of the first equation followed by the finite number of real roots of the second equation and so on, omitting in this procedure any root that has occurred previously. Thus the set of algebraic numbers can be ordered in a single sequence and is therefore denumerable.

2

Section 2.1

Quiz

1. **True.** If $\sigma = (i_1 i_2)$ then $\sigma^2 = (i_1 i_2)(i_1 i_2) = e$.

2. **False.** $((13)(12))^2 = (123)^2 = (132) \neq e$.

3. **False.** $(1234)(3412) = (13)(24) \neq e$.

4. **True.** $257 = 64 \times 4 + 1$ and $\sigma^4 = e$. Hence $\sigma^{257} = \sigma^{64 \times 4 + 1} = (\sigma^4)^{64}\sigma = \sigma$.

5. **True.**

6. **True.** For, $\sigma_0 \sigma = \sigma_0 \varphi$ implies $\sigma = \varphi$. Hence f is 1-1 and therefore onto S_n.

7. **True.** $(i_1 i_2 \cdots i_k)^{-1} = (i_k i_{k-1} \cdots i_1)$.

8. **False.** $(1234)^2 = (13)(24)$.

9. **True.**

10. **True.**

Exercises

1. Set $\beta = \theta \sigma^{-1}$ and then $\beta \sigma = (\theta \sigma^{-1})\sigma = \theta(\sigma^{-1}\sigma) = \theta e = \theta$. Also, if $\beta_1 \sigma = \theta$ then $(\beta_1 \sigma)\sigma^{-1} = \theta \sigma^{-1}$, $\beta_1(\sigma \sigma^{-1}) = \theta \sigma^{-1}$, $\beta_1 e = \theta \sigma^{-1}$, $\beta_1 = \beta$.

2. $\sigma^2 = \begin{pmatrix} 1 & 2 & 3 & 4 \\ 3 & 4 & 1 & 2 \end{pmatrix}$ so $\sigma^4 = (\sigma^2)^2 = \begin{pmatrix} 1 & 2 & 3 & 4 \\ 3 & 4 & 1 & 2 \end{pmatrix}^2 = e$.

3. Let $\sigma \in S_n$ commute with every cycle of length 2 in S_n. We show first that if $\sigma(i) = j$ then $\sigma(j) = i$. For, if $\varphi = (i\,j)$ then $i = \varphi(j) = \varphi(\sigma(i)) = \sigma\varphi(i) = \sigma(j)$.

Suppose now that there exist i and j such that $\sigma(i) = j$ and $j \neq i$. Let k be different from i and j (since $n \geq 3$) and let $\tau = (j\,k)$. Then $\sigma\tau(j) = \sigma(k)$ and $\tau\sigma(j) = \tau(i) = i$. Hence $\sigma(k) = i$. But σ is 1-1 and $\sigma(j) = i$. Thus no such i and j can exist and $\sigma = e$.

4. Let $\sigma = \sigma_1 \cdots \sigma_m$ be the disjoint cycle decomposition of σ and suppose σ_i is of length k_i, $i = 1, \ldots, m$. Then if p is a multiple of each k_i, say, $p = k_i q_i$, then $\sigma^p = \sigma_1^p \cdots \sigma_m^p = \sigma_1^{k_1 q_1} \cdots \sigma_m^{k_m q_m} = e$. On the other hand if $\sigma^p = e$ then since $\sigma_1^p, \ldots, \sigma_m^p$ act on disjoint subsets they must be separately equal to e in order that their product be e. Now, divide p by k_i, $p = k_i q_i + r_i$, $0 \leq r_i < k_i$, so that $\sigma_i^p = (\sigma_i^{k_i})^{q_i} \sigma_i^{r_i} = \sigma_i^{r_i}$; and $\sigma_i^{r_i} = e$ if and only if $r_i = 0$.

Section 2.2

Quiz

1. **True.**

2. **False.** $\sigma = (143)(2586)$, hence $\varepsilon(\sigma) = (-1)^{2+3} = -1$.

3. **True.** $\varepsilon(\sigma^2) = \varepsilon(\sigma\sigma) = \varepsilon(\sigma)\varepsilon(\sigma) = \varepsilon(\sigma)^2 = 1$.

4. **True.** $\varepsilon(\sigma^{-1})\varepsilon(\sigma) = \varepsilon(\sigma\sigma^{-1}) = \varepsilon(e) = 1$.

5. **True.** $\alpha_{\sigma(1)} = \alpha_2 = 7$, $\alpha_{\sigma(2)} = \alpha_3 = 10$, $\alpha_{\sigma(3)} = \alpha_1 = 3$.

6. **True.** $\sigma\sigma^{m-1} = e$, $\sigma^{m-1} = \sigma^{-1}$.

7. **True.**

8. **True.** Let $\beta = \alpha^\sigma$. Then $\beta_i = \alpha_{\sigma(i)}$ and $\beta_{\mu(i)} = \alpha_{\sigma(\mu(i))} = \alpha_{\sigma\mu(i)}$.

9. **True.** For, $\sum_{i=1}^m \beta_i = \sum_{i=1}^m \alpha_{\sigma(i)} = \sum_{i=1}^m \alpha_i$, since the order of summation of the α_i is immaterial.

10. **True.** $\varepsilon(\sigma^5\mu^{24}) = \varepsilon(\sigma)^5\,\varepsilon(\mu)^{24} = 1^5(-1)^{24} = 1$.

Exercises

1. Let $\alpha = (\alpha_1, \ldots, \alpha_{15})$ be the digits in some order. The different numbers we obtain correspond to the different sequences α^σ, $\sigma \in S_{15}$. According to Example 2.3(d) there are $15!/2!5!8!$ such distinct sequences.

2. We count these as follows. Write down in succession α_i brackets of length i, $i = 2, \ldots, m$,

$$\overbrace{(xx)(xx)\cdots(xx)}^{\alpha_2} \cdots \overbrace{(xx\cdots x)(xx\cdots x)\cdots(xx\cdots x)}^{\alpha_i} \cdots$$

where the x represent the integers $1, \ldots, m$. We can construct the disjoint cycle factorization of a permutation $\sigma \in S_m$ by putting these integers in the brackets in some order. Of course, not all $m!$ of these arrangements represent different permutations; for example, $(12)(34)(567) = (21)(43)(567)$. Let h_α denote the number of distinct permutations so obtained and let σ be a fixed one of these distinct permutations. First, for each i we can change the order in which the α_i brackets of length i occur without altering σ. With each of these arrangements we can shift the integers in any individual cycle of length i ahead, one at a time, to obtain i different arrangements, again without altering σ. Thus there are

$$\alpha_2! \, 2^{\alpha_2} \cdots \alpha_m! \, m^{\alpha_m}$$

different arrangements of the integers $1, \ldots, m$ in the brackets, each of which represents σ. Hence

$$h_\alpha \prod_{i=2}^{m} \alpha_i! \, i^{\alpha_i} = m!$$

or

$$h_\alpha = \frac{m!}{\prod_{i=2}^{m} \alpha_i! \, i^{\alpha_i}}.$$

(Note that some of the α_j can be 0 and recall that $0! = 1$.)

3. For,

$$\varphi\sigma\varphi^{-1}(\varphi(x_{tj})) = \varphi\sigma(x_{tj})$$

$$= \varphi(x_{t,j+1}).$$

4. (a) If $\mu \in S_6$ then $\alpha^\mu = \alpha$, if and only if μ maps each of the sets $\{1, 2\}$, $\{3, 4\}$, $\{5, 6\}$ onto itself. Now $\sigma^2 = (135)(246)$, $\sigma^3 = (14)(25)(36)$, $\sigma^4 = (153)(264)$, $\sigma^5 = (165432)$, $\sigma^6 = e$. Thus $t = 6$, since no lower power of σ leaves these sets invariant. Similarly we find: (b) $t = 3$; (c) $t = 6$; (d) $t = 1$; (e) $t = 6$.

Section 2.3

Quiz

1. **False.** The value of a function at a point in its domain is uniquely defined and hence an incidence matrix of a function can have only one 1 in each column.

2. **False.** The product is a 3×3 matrix.

3. **False.** Take $\sigma = (12) \subset S_3$.

4. **True.** Clearly, from Theorem 3.1, $A(\sigma) = A(\mu)$ if and only if $I_n = A(e) = A(\sigma^{-1})A(\sigma) = A(\sigma^{-1})A(\mu) = A(\sigma^{-1}\mu)$. It is obvious from the definition of $A(\sigma^{-1}\mu)$ that $\sigma^{-1}\mu = e$ is equivalent to $A(\sigma^{-1}\mu) = I_n$.

5. **True.** In (10), if $a_{1k} = 0$, $k = 1, \ldots, n$, then $c_{1j} = 0$, $j = 1, \ldots, r$.

6. **False.** $\begin{bmatrix} 0 & 1 \\ 0 & 1 \end{bmatrix}\begin{bmatrix} 0 & 0 \\ 1 & 1 \end{bmatrix} = \begin{bmatrix} 1 & 1 \\ 1 & 1 \end{bmatrix}$.

7. **True.** First note that Theorem 3.7 (with 2 replacing 0) implies that there exist s rows and t columns of A, $s + t = n + 1$, at the intersections of which lie entries all of which are 2. Thus there are at least n entries equal to 2 in A. Since the remaining $n^2 - n$ entries are at least 1, the sum of all the entries is at least $2n + n^2 - n = n^2 + n$.

8. **True.** By Theorem 3.5 the (i, j) entry of $PA(\sigma)$ is $p_{i\sigma(j)}$ and $\sum_{j=1}^{n} p_{i\sigma(j)} = \sum_{j=1}^{n} p_{ij}$.

9. **True.** Again apply Theorem 3.5.

10. **True.** $A(\sigma\varphi) = A(\varphi\sigma)$ implies $\sigma\varphi = \varphi\sigma$ for all $\varphi \in S_n$ and hence we may use the result in Exercise 3 of Section 2.1.

Exercises

1. First note that each row and column of A must contain precisely two 1's and one 0. Suppose then that every diagonal of A contains a 0. Then, by Theorem 3.7, A contains s rows and t columns at the intersections of which are zeros, $s + t = 4$. The possibilities are $s = 3, t = 1; s = 1, t = 3; s = 2, t = 2$. The first two are excluded since no row or column consists of 0's, and the third possibility implies that two rows have two 0's each, also excluded.

2. See Example 1.1(d) in Chapter 4.

3. The (i, j) entry of $A(B + C)$ is

$$\sum_{k=1}^{n} a_{ik}(b_{kj} + c_{kj}) = \sum_{k=1}^{n} a_{ik}b_{kj} + \sum_{k=1}^{n} a_{ik}c_{kj}$$

and this last expression is the sum of the (i, j) entries of AB and AC respectively.

4. The computation is essentially the same as in the preceding solution.

5. The sum of the entries in any column of a sum of k permutation matrices is k. Here the sum of the entries in the first column is 3 while this sum for the second column is 1.

6. No. The reasoning is identical to that in the preceding solution.

7. The (i, j) entry of AJ is $\sum_{k=1}^{n} a_{ik}1 = \sum_{k=1}^{n} a_{ik}$. Thus all entries in the ith row of AJ are equal to the sum of the entries in the ith row of A.

8. The (i, j) entry of JA is $\sum_{k=1}^{n} 1a_{kj} = \sum_{k=1}^{n} a_{kj}$. Thus all entries in the jth column of JA are equal to the sum of the entries in the jth column of A.

9. In general, the number of rows in the incidence matrix of $f: X \to Y$ is the number of elements in Y. In this case there are $n!$ permutation matrices so that the incidence matrix for f possesses $n!$ rows.

10. The 1 may appear in any of n row positions in each of the columns and there are n^n such possibilities altogether.

11. These formulas follow immediately from the definitions.

12. We want to prove the following statement. Let P be an $n \times n$ matrix whose entries are all 0 and 1. Suppose there are s rows and t columns, $s + t = n + 1$, at the intersections of which the entries are all 0. Then every diagonal of P contains a 0. By Theorem 3.6 we can rearrange rows and columns of P so that

the 0 entries appear in rows numbered $1, \ldots, s$ and columns numbered $1, \ldots, t$:

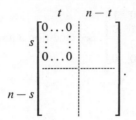

Suppose that the matrix contains a diagonal not containing a 0. Then all the elements of the diagonal which come from the first s rows must lie in the last $n - t$ columns. But in any diagonal there is exactly one element from each row and each column. Thus $s \leq n - t$, $s + t \leq n$, which contradicts $s + t = n + 1$.

Section 2.4

Quiz

1. **True.** Since P is a permutation matrix, DP is a matrix in which the number c_i appears in the $(i, \sigma(i))$ position, for an appropriate permutation σ, with 0 elsewhere. Thus in per (DP) there is at most one nonzero term, namely $c_1 \cdots c_n$.

2. **True.** The row and column sums are obviously unaltered.

3. **True.** The diagonals in PA and AP are the rearranged diagonals of A, according to Theorem 3.6.

4. **False.** per $(A) = 1$.

5. **True.** They correspond to the permutations $\begin{pmatrix} 1 & 2 & 3 & 4 \\ 1 & 2 & 3 & 4 \end{pmatrix}$, $\begin{pmatrix} 1 & 2 & 3 & 4 \\ 1 & 3 & 2 & 4 \end{pmatrix}$, $\begin{pmatrix} 1 & 2 & 3 & 4 \\ 4 & 2 & 3 & 1 \end{pmatrix}$, $\begin{pmatrix} 1 & 2 & 3 & 4 \\ 4 & 3 & 2 & 1 \end{pmatrix}$.

6. **False.** per $(J) = n!/n^n > 1/n^n$ for $n > 1$.

7. **True.** Any 2×2 doubly stochastic matrix is of the form

$$\begin{bmatrix} \theta & 1 - \theta \\ 1 - \theta & \theta \end{bmatrix}, \quad 0 \leq \theta \leq 1.$$

8. **True.** Write

$$A = \begin{bmatrix} \frac{1}{2} - \alpha & \frac{1}{2} + \alpha \\ \frac{1}{2} + \alpha & \frac{1}{2} - \alpha \end{bmatrix}, \quad B = \begin{bmatrix} \frac{1}{2} - \beta & \frac{1}{2} + \beta \\ \frac{1}{2} + \beta & \frac{1}{2} - \beta \end{bmatrix}.$$

Then

$$AB = \begin{bmatrix} \frac{1}{2} & \frac{1}{2} \\ \frac{1}{2} & \frac{1}{2} \end{bmatrix} \text{ is equivalent to the statement } \alpha\beta = 0.$$

Thus $\alpha = 0$ or $\beta = 0$ and A or B must be the indicated matrix.

9. **True.** Since $a_{ii} \leq 1$ it follows that $\sum_{i=1}^{n} a_{ii} = n$ if and only if $a_{ii} = 1$, $i = 1, \ldots, n$. Since each row sum is 1, it follows that $A = I_n$.

10. **False.** Let $P = \begin{bmatrix} 0 & 0 & 0 & 1 \\ 0 & 0 & 1 & 0 \\ 0 & 1 & 0 & 0 \\ 1 & 0 & 0 & 0 \end{bmatrix}$. See Question 5 above.

Exercises

1. Let $C = \theta A + (1 - \theta)B$. Then

$$\sum_{j=1}^{n} c_{ij} = \theta \sum_{j=1}^{n} a_{ij} + (1 - \theta) \sum_{j=1}^{n} b_{ij} = \theta + (1 - \theta) = 1.$$

Similarly for the column sums. Also, every entry of C is clearly nonnegative.

2. Let $C = AB$. Then

$$\sum_{j=1}^{n} \left(\sum_{k=1}^{n} a_{ik} b_{kj} \right) = \sum_{k=1}^{n} a_{ik} \sum_{j=1}^{n} b_{kj} = \sum_{k=1}^{n} a_{ik} = 1.$$

Similarly for the column sums.

3. Yes. Apply Theorem 4.3.

4. We use the notation of the proof of Theorem 4.2. Take

$$P_1 = \begin{bmatrix} 0 & 0 & 1 \\ 0 & 1 & 0 \\ 1 & 0 & 0 \end{bmatrix} \quad \text{and } a = \tfrac{1}{6}. \text{ Then } A_1 = \begin{bmatrix} \tfrac{4}{5} & \tfrac{1}{5} & 0 \\ 0 & 0 & 1 \\ \tfrac{1}{5} & \tfrac{4}{5} & 0 \end{bmatrix}.$$

Clearly $A_1 = \tfrac{1}{5}P_2 + \tfrac{4}{5}P_3$ where

$$P_2 = \begin{bmatrix} 0 & 1 & 0 \\ 0 & 0 & 1 \\ 1 & 0 & 0 \end{bmatrix} \quad \text{and} \quad P_3 = \begin{bmatrix} 1 & 0 & 0 \\ 0 & 0 & 1 \\ 0 & 1 & 0 \end{bmatrix}$$

and therefore $A = \tfrac{1}{6}P_1 + \tfrac{1}{6}P_2 + \tfrac{2}{3}P_3$. In fact, this is the only way to express A in form (7). Let

$$P_4 = \begin{bmatrix} 0 & 1 & 0 \\ 1 & 0 & 0 \\ 0 & 0 & 1 \end{bmatrix}, \quad P_5 = \begin{bmatrix} 0 & 0 & 1 \\ 1 & 0 & 0 \\ 0 & 1 & 0 \end{bmatrix}, \quad P_6 = I_3$$

and write $A = \sum_{j=1}^{6} c_j P_j, \quad \sum_{j=1}^{6} c_j = 1, \quad c_j \geq 0, \quad j = 1, \ldots, 6.$

Now $a_{21} = 0$ and hence $c_4 = c_5 = 0$; also $a_{33} = 0$ and hence $c_4 = c_6 = 0$. Thus $A = c_1 P_1 + c_2 P_2 + c_3 P_3$. Now, $a_{12} = \tfrac{1}{6}$ implies that $c_2 = \tfrac{1}{6}$ since both P_1 and P_3 have zero in the (1, 2) position. Similarly $a_{13} = \tfrac{1}{6}$ implies that $c_1 = \tfrac{1}{6}$. It follows that $c_3 = \tfrac{2}{3}$.

5. Clearly both AJ and JA have nonnegative entries. Let $B = AJ$ so that

$$\sum_{j=1}^{n} b_{ij} = \sum_{j=1}^{n}\left(\sum_{k=1}^{n} a_{ik}\frac{1}{n}\right) = \frac{1}{n}\sum_{j=1}^{n}\sum_{k=1}^{n} a_{ik} = \frac{1}{n}\sum_{j=1}^{n} 1 = \frac{n}{n} = 1.$$

Similarly $\sum_{i=1}^{n} b_{ij} = 1$ and B is doubly stochastic. An analogous computation shows that JA is doubly stochastic as well.

6. Let $A = \begin{bmatrix} \theta & 1-\theta \\ 1-\theta & \theta \end{bmatrix}$ where $0 \le \theta \le 1$. Then

$$\text{per }(xI - A) = \text{per}\left(\begin{bmatrix} x-\theta & \theta-1 \\ \theta-1 & x-\theta \end{bmatrix}\right) = x^2 - 2\theta x + 2\theta^2 - 2\theta + 1.$$

Thus the roots of the quadratic equation $\text{per }(xI - A) = 0$ are (by the quadratic formula) $\theta \pm i(1-\theta)$. Hence their absolute value squared is $\theta^2 + (1-\theta)^2 \le \theta^2 + (1-\theta)^2 + 2\theta(1-\theta) = (\theta + (1-\theta))^2 = 1.$

3

Section 3.1

Quiz

1. **False.** $-1(1, 1, \ldots, 1)$ is not in the set.

2. **False.** $-(n, n-1, \ldots, 1)$ is not in the set.

3. **True.** If x and y are in the set then clearly $x + y$ and rx are in the set for any number r.

4. **True.** If x and y are in the set and $z = \theta x + (1-\theta)y$, $0 \le \theta \le 1$, then

$$\sum_{i=1}^{n} z_i = \sum_{i=1}^{n}(\theta x_i + (1-\theta)y_i) = \theta\sum_{i=1}^{n} x_i + (1-\theta)\sum_{i=1}^{n} y_i > \theta + (1-\theta) = 1.$$

5. **False.** $(1, 0)$ and $(-1, 0)$ are in the set but $\dfrac{(1, 0) + (-1, 0)}{2} = (0, 0)$ is not.

6. **True.** Obvious.

7. **False.** Obvious.

8. **True.** Obvious.

9. **True.** See Theorem 1.3(b).

10. **False.** The vertices of the polyhedron S are $(-2, -1)$, $(-2, 3)$, $(1, -1)$, $(1, 3)$. The values of f at these four points are $-4, -12, 5, -3$, respectively. The smallest of these is $-12 = f((-2, 3))$.

Exercises

1. (c) If $A \in \Omega_n$ then

$$A = \sum_{j=1}^{m} \theta_j P_j, \qquad m = n!, \qquad \theta_j \ge 0, \qquad \sum_{j=1}^{m} \theta_j = 1.$$

Hence, from the definition of φ,

$$\varphi(A) = \sum_{j=1}^{m} \theta_j \varphi(P_j) \in H(\varphi(P_1), \ldots, \varphi(P_m)).$$

(d) X contains all of the n-tuples $r_i(\delta_{i1}, \ldots, \delta_{in})$, $i = 1, \ldots, n$, for any choice of nonnegative numbers r_i, $i = 1, \ldots, n$. Then any

$$(a_1, \ldots, a_n) = \frac{1}{n}[\sum_{i=1}^{n} na_i (\delta_{i1}, \ldots, \delta_{in})],$$

a convex combination of elements of X. Thus $P^n \subset H(X)$ and clearly $H(X) \subset P^n$.

2. Assume that f is linear and use induction on p. If $p = 2$ then (16) reduces to (14). Assume that (16) holds for fewer than p summands. Let $s = \sum_{j=1}^{p-1} \theta_j = 1 - \theta_p$. If $s = 0$ then both sides of (16) are identical. If $s > 0$, set $\varphi_j = \theta_j/s$, $j = 1, \ldots$, $p - 1$. Then $\varphi_j \geq 0, 1, \ldots, p - 1$, and

$$\sum_{j=1}^{p-1} \varphi_j = \sum_{j=1}^{p-1} \theta_j/s = 1.$$

Now, let g be the function f restricted to $H(a^1, \ldots, a^{p-1})$. Clearly g is linear. Therefore, by the induction hypothesis,

$$g(\sum_{j=1}^{p-1} \varphi_j a^j) = \sum_{j=1}^{p-1} \varphi_j g(a^j).$$

We compute

$$f(\sum_{j=1}^{p} \theta_j a^j) = f(\sum_{j=1}^{p-1} \theta_j a^j + \theta_p a^p)$$

$$= f(\sum_{j=1}^{p-1} \theta_j a^j) + \theta_p f(a^p)$$

$$= sf(\sum_{j=1}^{p-1} \varphi_j a^j) + \theta_p f(a^p)$$

$$= sg(\sum_{j=1}^{p-1} \varphi_j a^j) + \theta_p f(a^p)$$

$$= s\sum_{j=1}^{p-1} \varphi_j g(a^j) + \theta_p f(a^p)$$

$$= \sum_{j=1}^{p-1} \theta_j f(a^j) + \theta_p f(a^p)$$

$$= \sum_{j=1}^{p} \theta_j f(a^j).$$

3.   Using the notation in the proof of Theorem 1.3(b) we have

$$f(x) = f(\sum_{j=1}^{p} \theta_j a^j)$$

$$= \sum_{j=1}^{p} \theta_j f(a^j)$$

$$\geq \min_j f(a^j) \qquad \text{(by part (a)).}$$

4.   If

$$x = \sum_{j=1}^{n} \alpha_j a^j, \qquad y = \sum_{j=1}^{n} \beta_j a^j, \qquad r \in R \qquad \text{and} \qquad s \in R,$$

then

$$rx + sy = r \sum_{j=1}^{n} \alpha_j a^j + s \sum_{j=1}^{n} \beta_j a^j$$

$$= \sum_{j=1}^{n} (r\alpha_j + s\beta_j) a^j \in X.$$

5.   If $a \in H(X)$ and $b \in H(X)$ then there exist elements $x^1, \ldots, x^p$ in X and non-negative numbers $\alpha_i, \beta_i, i = 1, \ldots, p$,

$$\sum_{i=1}^{p} \alpha_i - \sum_{i=1}^{p} \beta_i = 1,$$

such that

$$a = \sum_{i=1}^{p} \alpha_i x^i, \qquad b = \sum_{i=1}^{p} \beta_i x^i.$$

Then for $0 \leq \theta \leq 1$ we have

$$\theta a + (1 - \theta) b = \sum_{i=1}^{p} (\theta \alpha_i + (1 - \theta) \beta_i) x^i$$

and

$$\sum_{i=1}^{p} (\theta \alpha_i + (1 - \theta) \beta_i) = \theta \sum_{i=1}^{p} \alpha_i + (1 - \theta) \sum_{i=1}^{p} \beta_i = 1.$$

6.   If $x = (x_1, \ldots, x_n)$ and $y = (y_1, \ldots, y_n)$ are in S, $0 \leq \theta \leq 1$, and $z = \theta x + (1 - \theta) y$ then

$$\sum_{j=1}^{n} a_{ij} z_j = \sum_{j=1}^{n} a_{ij} (\theta x_j + (1 - \theta) y_j)$$

$$= \theta \sum_{j=1}^{n} a_{ij} x_j + (1 - \theta) \sum_{j=1}^{n} a_{ij} y_j$$

$$= \theta b_i + (1 - \theta) b_i = b_i.$$

7. If $0 \le \theta \le 1$ then $a \le \theta a + (1 - \theta)b \le b$ by Theorem 1.3(a). Thus $H(a, b) \subset S$. If $x \in S$ then $x = [(b - x)/(b - a)]a + [(x - a)/(b - a)]b$. Set $\theta = (b - x)/(b - a)$ and then $1 - \theta = (x - a)/(b - a)$.

8. If f is linear then $f(\alpha x + \beta y) = \alpha f(x) + \beta f(y)$. Take $\alpha = \beta = 1$ and then $\alpha = 1$, $\beta = 0$, to obtain the two formulas in the exercise. The converse is also trivial.

9. The function f is not linear on C. However, it is obtained from a linear function by just adding the constant 3 to every function value, and hence the max and min are assumed at some v_i. We check that $f(v_1) = 3$, $f(v_2) = 0$, $f(v_3) = 4$, $f(v_4) = 5$. Thus $\max_{a \in C} f(a) = 5$, $\min_{a \in C} f(a) = 0$.

10. The polyhedron defined by these inequalities is the triangle $a^1 = (-2, -2)$, $a^2 = (1, -1)$, $a^3 = (2, 3)$. We compute $f(a^1) = -6$, $f(a^2) = 5$, $f(a^3) = 5$. Thus $\max_{a \in S} (f(a)) = 5$ and $\min_{a \in S} (f(a)) = -6$. The set of all points on the side joining a^2 and a^3 (i.e., all $z = \theta a^2 + (1 - \theta)a^3$, $0 \le \theta \le 1$) satisfy $f(z) = \theta f(a^2) + (1 - \theta) f(a^3) = 5$. On the other hand, if $\theta_1 > 0$ and $z = \theta_1 a^1 + \theta_2 a^2 + \theta_3 a^3$, $\theta_1 + \theta_2 + \theta_3 = 1$, $0 \le \theta_i \le 1$, $i = 1, 2, 3$, then $f(z) = \sum_{i=1}^{3} \theta_i f(a^i) = 6\theta_1 + 5(\theta_2 + \theta_3) = -6\theta_1 + 5(1 - \theta_1) = 5 - 11\theta_1 < 5$. Hence the required set is $\{z \in S \mid z = \theta a^2 + (1 - \theta)a^3, 0 \le \theta \le 1\}$.

11. Let x_1, x_2 and x_3 denote the numbers of pounds of each of the ingredients A, B and C respectively. The total cost of the mixture is $5x_1 + 2x_2 + 3x_3$. Also $x_1 + x_2 + x_3 = 100$ so that the total cost can be expressed as

$$f((x_1, x_2)) = 5x_1 + 2x_2 + 3(100 - x_1 - x_2)$$

$$= 2x_1 - x_2 + 300.$$

The conditions are

$$x_1 \ge x_2 + 10,$$

$$x_1 \le x_3 + 40,$$

$$x_2 \ge x_3,$$

that is,

$$x_1 - x_2 \ge 10,$$

$$2x_1 + x_2 \le 140,$$

$$2x_2 + x_1 \ge 100.$$

These define a triangle S whose vertices are $a^1 = (50, 40)$, $a^2 = (40, 30)$, $a^3 = (60, 20)$. Then $f(a^1) = 360$, $f(a^2) = 350$, $f(a^3) = 400$. Thus $\max_{a \in S} f(a) = 400$ and $\min_{a \in S} f(a) = 350$.

Section 3.2

Quiz

1. **False.** Take $a = b = 0$, $c = 1$, $d = 0$.
2. **False.** Take $a = 1$, $c = 1$, $b = 1$, $d = -2$.

3. **True.**

4. **True.** If $x > 0$ then $|x| = x$. Thus $x < 0$ and $|x| = -x$.

5. **True.** By Theorem 2.3,

$$\frac{1 + x^2 + x^4}{3} \geq \sqrt[3]{x^2 x^4} = x^2.$$

6. **False.** $x = -1$.

7. **True.**

8. **False.** This equality always holds for any x and y.

9. **True.** This is Theorem 2.6 with $n = 2$, $a_1 = a$, $a_2 = 1$, $b_1 = 1$, $b_2 = b$.

10. **False.** Take $a = -1$, $b = -2$, $c = 3$, $d = 1$.

Exercises

1. $(a + c) - (b + d) = (a - b) + (c - d)$ is the sum of two nonnegative numbers.

2. $\sqrt{30} + \sqrt{42} + \sqrt{56} + \sqrt{40} = \sqrt{5}\sqrt{6} + \sqrt{6}\sqrt{7} + \sqrt{7}\sqrt{8} + \sqrt{8}\sqrt{5} \leq \sqrt{5}\sqrt{5}$
   $+ \sqrt{6}\sqrt{6} + \sqrt{7}\sqrt{7} + \sqrt{8}\sqrt{8} = 26$. The lower inequality is similarly proved.

3. $$\frac{x + 2}{x^2 + x + 1} - \frac{x - 1}{x^2 - x + 1} = -\frac{(x^2 + 3x - 1)}{(x^2 + x + 1)(x^2 - x + 1)}.$$

   Now $x^2 + x + 1 > 0$ for all x and $x^2 - x + 1 > 0$ for all x. Hence the original inequality is equivalent to $x^2 + 3x - 1 < 0$ which in turn holds if and only if

   $$\frac{-3}{2} - \frac{\sqrt{13}}{2} < x < \frac{-3}{2} + \frac{\sqrt{13}}{2}.$$

4. If $x \geq 0$, $y \geq 0$ then $|x| + |y| < 1$ becomes $x + y < 1$. Similarly if $x \leq 0$, $y \geq 0$ then $-x + y < 1$. If $x \leq 0$, $y \leq 0$ then $-x - y < 1$. If $x \geq 0, \cdot y \leq 0$ then $x - y < 1$. These inequalities are satisfied if and only if (x, y) is inside the square whose vertices are $(1, 0)$, $(0, 1)$, $(-1, 0)$, $(0, -1)$.

5. Squaring both sides we have $x^2 + y^2 + 2xy = x^2 + y^2 + 1 + x^2 y^2$, $x^2 y^2 + 1 = 2xy$, $(xy - 1)^2 = 0$, $xy = 1$. If x were negative then y would have to be negative and the original statement would not hold. Thus $x > 0$. Conversely, if $x > 0$, $xy = 1$ then $y > 0$, and $0 = (xy - 1)^2 = x^2 y^2 - 2xy + 1$, $x^2 + y^2 + 2xy = x^2 + y^2 + 1 + x^2 y^2$. Since $x > 0$, $y > 0$, we have $(x^2 + y^2 + 2xy)^{1/2} = x + y$.

6. Since $(|a| - |b|)^2 \geq 0$ we have $\dfrac{a^2 + b^2}{2} \geq \left(\dfrac{|a| + |b|}{2}\right)^2$ and hence $\left(\dfrac{a^2 + b^2}{2}\right)^{1/2}$
   $\geq \dfrac{|a| + |b|}{2} \geq \dfrac{a + b}{2}$. Equality holds if and only if $|a| = |b|$, $a = |a|$, $b = |b|$, i.e., $a = b \geq 0$.

7. $\left(\prod_{i=1}^{n} \dfrac{p_i}{q_i}\right)^{1/n} \le \dfrac{1}{n} \sum_{i=1}^{n} \dfrac{p_i}{q_i} \le \dfrac{1}{n} n \max_i \dfrac{p_i}{q_i} = \max_i \dfrac{p_i}{q_i}$. Apply this result to $\left(\prod_{i=1}^{n} \dfrac{q_i}{p_i}\right)^{1/n}$
    to get the lower inequality.

8. Let $s_n = \sum_{i=1}^{n} a_i$. We show that $\prod_{i=1}^{n}(1 - a_i) \ge 1 - s_n$ by induction on n. The
    case $n = 1$ is obvious. Assume that the inequality holds for $n - 1$. Then

    $$\prod_{i=1}^{n}(1 - a_i) = (1 - a_n)\prod_{i=1}^{n-1}(1 - a_i)$$

    $$\ge (1 - a_n)(1 - s_{n-1})$$

    $$= 1 + a_n s_{n-1} - s_n \ge 1 - s_n.$$

9. Apply Theorem 2.3: $2x^2 + 2y^2 \ge 4xy$, $5x^2 + 5z^2 \ge 10xz$, $3y^2 + 3z^2 \ge 6yz$.
    Now add.

10. $(n!)^{1/n} = (n \cdot (n - 1) \cdots 1)^{1/n} \le \dfrac{n + (n - 1) + \cdots + 1}{n} = \dfrac{n(n + 1)}{2n} = \dfrac{n + 1}{2}$, by
    Theorem 2.3.

Section 3.3

Quiz

1. **True.** For, $\theta a \le \theta x \le \theta b$ and $(1 - \theta)a \le (1 - \theta)y \le (1 - \theta)b$ and thus $a = \theta a$
    $+ (1 - \theta)a \le \theta x + (1 - \theta)y \le \theta b + (1 - \theta)b = b$.

2. **True.** Apply Theorem 3.5 with $p = 5$ and $n = 2$.

3. **True.** $x_1^2 + x_2^2$ is convex (see (3)) and $g(t) = t^3$ is convex and increasing. Apply
    Theorem 3.6(d).

4. **False.** $f[((1, 0) + (0, 1))/2] = 1/4$ while $(f[(1, 0)] + f[(0, 1)])/2 = 0$.

5. **True.** $f(x) = |x|$ is convex.

6. **True.** $rf(\theta x + (1 - \theta)y) \le r(\theta f(x) + (1 - \theta)f(y)) = \theta rf(x) + (1 - \theta)rf(y)$.

7. **True.**

8. **True.** The inequality is equivalent to $t^n + n \ge 1$.

9. **False.** The function $g(x) = x^{3/2}$ is convex for $x \ge 0$ (see solution to Exercise 10).
    Also, $f(x) = x^2$ is convex for $x \ge 0$. But $h(x) = \dfrac{f(x)}{g(x)} = x^{1/2}$ is not convex:

    $$h\left(\dfrac{1 + 4}{2}\right) = \sqrt{\dfrac{5}{2}} > \sqrt{\dfrac{9}{4}} = \dfrac{h(1) + h(4)}{2}.$$

10. **False.** Let $f(x) = 1$, $x \ne \frac{1}{2}$, $f(\frac{1}{2}) = 2$. Then $f(f(x)) = 1$ for all x. Thus $f(f)$ is
    convex but clearly f is not.

Exercises

1. x^4 is convex and so is $5|x|$. Thus their sum is convex.

2. The function $|x|$ is convex and t^p is convex nondecreasing for $t \geq 0$, p a positive integer. Thus $|x|^p$ is convex.

3. The function $f(x) = \sum_{i=1}^{n} |x_i|^p$ is convex on all of R^n by the preceding exercise. It is obviously positively homogeneous of degree p. Thus by Theorem 3.4, $(\sum_{i=1}^{n} |x_i|^p)^{1/p}$ is convex on R^n and the inequality follows.

4. The latter expression is larger, as can be seen from Theorem 3.5 with $x_1 = 1$, $x_2 = 3$, $x_3 = 5$, $x_4 = 7$, $x_5 = 9$, $y_1 = 2$, $y_2 = 4$, $y_3 = 6$, $y_4 = 8$, $y_5 = 10$ and $p = 3$.

5. Let $\max_i (a_i + b_i) = a_k + b_k$. Then $a_k \leq \max_i a_i$ and $b_k \leq \max_i b_i$. Similarly let $\theta a_k = \max_i (\theta a_i)$. Then $\theta a_k \geq \theta a_i$ for all i. Thus $a_k \geq a_i$ and $a_k = \max_i a_i$. Hence $\theta a_k = \theta \max_i a_i$.

6. If $r \geq 1$ then $r - 1 \geq 0$ and $r^n \geq r^k$, $k = 0, \ldots, n-1$. Thus $nr^n \geq r^{n-1} + \cdots + r + 1$ so that the right-hand side of the identity is nonnegative. (It is the product of two nonnegative numbers.) If $r < 1$ then $r - 1 < 0$ and $r^n < r^k$, $k = 0, \ldots, n-1$. Thus the right side of the identity is a product of two negative numbers and this completes the argument.

7. By repeated applications of the preceding exercise we have

$$\frac{r^n - 1}{n} \geq \frac{r^{n-1} - 1}{n-1} \geq \frac{r^{n-2} - 1}{n-2} \geq \cdots \geq \frac{r^m - 1}{m}.$$

8. Since $\gamma = \dfrac{n}{m} > 1$ we know that $n > m$ and hence $\dfrac{r^n - 1}{n} \geq \dfrac{r^m - 1}{m}$ for any $r > 0$.

   Replace r by $r^{1/m}$ in this inequality to obtain $\dfrac{r^{n/m} - 1}{n} \geq \dfrac{r - 1}{m}$, or clearing of fractions, $r^\gamma - \gamma r + \gamma - 1 \geq 0$.

9. We write down a sequence of inequalities equivalent to the statement we want to prove: $x^\alpha \geq z^\alpha + \alpha(x - z)z^{\alpha-1}$; $x^\alpha \geq z^\alpha + \alpha x z^{\alpha-1} - \alpha z^\alpha$; $x^\alpha - z^\alpha - \alpha x z^{\alpha-1} + \alpha z^\alpha \geq 0$; $\dfrac{x^\alpha}{z^\alpha} - 1 - \alpha \dfrac{x}{z} + \alpha \geq 0$; $r^\alpha - 1 - \alpha r + \alpha \geq 0$; $r^\alpha + \alpha - 1 \geq \alpha r$. With γ replaced by α this is precisely the inequality in the preceding exercise.

10. Let x and y be two nonnegative numbers and let $0 \leq \theta \leq 1$. Set $z = \theta x + (1 - \theta)y$. Then by the preceding exercise,

$$f(x) = x^\alpha \geq z^\alpha + \alpha(x - z)z^{\alpha-1},$$

$$f(y) = y^\alpha \geq z^\alpha + \alpha(y - z)z^{\alpha-1}.$$

Multiply the first of these inequalities by θ, the second by $(1-\theta)$ and add to obtain

$$\theta f(x) + (1-\theta)f(y) \geq z^\alpha + \alpha z^{\alpha-1}\{\theta(x-z) + (1-\theta)(y-z)\}$$

$$= z^\alpha + \alpha z^{\alpha-1}\{\theta x + (1-\theta)y - z\}$$

$$= z^\alpha$$

$$= (\theta x + (1-\theta)y)^\alpha$$

$$= f(\theta x + (1-\theta)y).$$

11. Use the notation of Theorem 3.5. If p is rational, $p \geq 1$, then, as above, $f(x) = \sum_{i=1}^{n} x_i^p$ is convex on the cone C consisting of all $x = (x_1, \ldots, x_n)$, $x_i \geq 0$. Then f is homogeneous of degree p and hence $g(x) = (f(x))^{1/p}$ is convex on C by Theorem 3.4 (the proof given on p. 97 works for any $p \geq 1$). The Minkowski inequality is just $g((x+y)/2) \leq (g(x) + g(y))/2$.

4

Section 4.1

Quiz

1. **False.** 1 is the multiplicative identity.

2. **True.** Let $(a, b) = ae_1 + be_2 \in R$. Then $(a, b) \otimes (1, 0) = (ae_1 + be_2) \otimes e_1 = (ae_1 + be_2) = e_1 \otimes (ae_1 + be_2)$.

3. **True.** Suppose $\begin{bmatrix} a & -b \\ b & a \end{bmatrix}\begin{bmatrix} c & -d \\ d & c \end{bmatrix} = \begin{bmatrix} 0 & 0 \\ 0 & 0 \end{bmatrix}$ but $\begin{bmatrix} a & -b \\ b & a \end{bmatrix} \neq \begin{bmatrix} 0 & 0 \\ 0 & 0 \end{bmatrix} \neq \begin{bmatrix} c & -d \\ d & c \end{bmatrix}$.
The product being the zero matrix implies $ac - bd = 0$ and $ad + bc = 0$. Thus $ac^2 - cbd = 0$ and $ad^2 + cbd = 0$ and hence $a(c^2 + d^2) = 0$. Thus $a = 0$ or $c = d = 0$. If $a = 0$ then $bd = bc = 0$ and hence either $b = 0$ or $d = c = 0$. In any event $a = b = 0$ or $c = d = 0$.

4. **True.** Since real numbers are commutative we have

$$\begin{bmatrix} a & -b \\ b & a \end{bmatrix}\begin{bmatrix} c & -d \\ d & c \end{bmatrix} = \begin{bmatrix} ac - bd & -(ad + bc) \\ ad + bc & ac - bd \end{bmatrix}$$

$$= \begin{bmatrix} ca - db & -da + cb \\ da + cb & ca - db \end{bmatrix} = \begin{bmatrix} c & -d \\ d & c \end{bmatrix}\begin{bmatrix} a & -b \\ b & a \end{bmatrix}.$$

5. **True.** See the multiplication table (4).

6. **True.** From (4) we can verify that $3 \otimes 3 = 1$.

7. **True.** Let a and b be nonzero elements in R_1 such that $a \otimes b = 0 \in R_1$. Then $\varphi(a)$ and $\varphi(b)$ are nonzero; for if $\varphi(a)$ were 0, we would have $a = 0$ since φ is 1-1 and $\varphi(0) = 0$. Thus $\varphi(a \otimes b) = \varphi(0) = 0$, the zero of R_2. But $\varphi(a \otimes b) = \varphi(a) \times \varphi(b) = 0$ implies that R_2 has zero divisors.

8. **True.** The identity in R is $\begin{bmatrix} 1 & 0 \\ 0 & 1 \end{bmatrix}$ and as was shown, for any $\begin{bmatrix} a & -b \\ b & a \end{bmatrix} \in R$,

$$\begin{bmatrix} a & -b \\ b & a \end{bmatrix} \begin{bmatrix} \dfrac{a}{a^2+b^2} & \dfrac{b}{a^2+b^2} \\ -\dfrac{b}{a^2+b^2} & \dfrac{a}{a^2+b^2} \end{bmatrix} = \begin{bmatrix} 1 & 0 \\ 0 & 1 \end{bmatrix}.$$

Since R is commutative we have shown that every element of R has an inverse and hence is a unit.

9. **False.** See Quiz question 10 where $1 = -1$.

10. **True.** Clearly (i) and (iii) of Definition 1.1 are satisfied. The additive identity is obviously 0. The additive inverse of 0 is 0, and of 1 is 1. Properties (ii) and (vi) can be verified in a manner analogous to the proofs in Example 1.1(e).

Exercises

1. Let $a \otimes b = r_1$, where $ab = 4q + r_1$, $0 \leq r_1 < 4$, then $(a \otimes b) \otimes c = r_1 \otimes c = r_2$ where $r_1 c = 4Q + r_2$, $0 \leq r_2 < 4$. Thus $(ab - 4q)c = 4Q + r_2$ or $abc = 4(qc + Q) + r_2$; that is, r_2 is the remainder obtained upon dividing the ordinary product abc by 4. In a similar way it can be verified that $a \otimes (b \otimes c)$ is also the remainder obtained upon dividing abc by 4.

2. $a \in R_1$ implies $a - a = 0 \in R_1$ and $0 - a = -a \in R_1$. The commutative law for addition and the associative laws hold in R_1 because they hold in the ring R.

3. The first part is verified in the same way as Example 1.1(g). Regarding $A = \begin{bmatrix} a & -b \\ b & a \end{bmatrix} \neq 0$ as a matrix with real number entries we know that its unique inverse is given by $\begin{bmatrix} \dfrac{a}{a^2+b^2} & \dfrac{b}{a^2+b^2} \\ \dfrac{-b}{a^2+b^2} & \dfrac{a}{a^2+b^2} \end{bmatrix}$. In order that this matrix have integer entries, $a^2 + b^2$ must divide a and b. We know that $a/(a^2+b^2)$ is a nonzero integer if and only if $a = \pm 1$ and $b = 0$. But then $A = \begin{bmatrix} \pm 1 & 0 \\ 0 & \pm 1 \end{bmatrix}$. On the other hand if $a = 0$ then $b/(a^2+b^2)$ is a nonzero integer if and only if $b = \pm 1$ and then $A = \begin{bmatrix} 0 & \pm 1 \\ \pm 1 & 0 \end{bmatrix}$.

4. Let r_1 and s_1 be in R_1 and let $\varphi(r_1) = r_2$ and $\varphi(s_1) = s_2$. Then

$$\varphi(r_1 + s_1) = \varphi(r_1) + \varphi(s_1) = r_2 + s_2 \quad \text{and} \quad \varphi(r_1 s_1) = \varphi(r_1)\varphi(s_1) = r_2 s_2.$$

Therefore

$$\varphi^{-1}(r_2 + s_2) = r_1 + s_1 = \varphi^{-1}(r_2) + \varphi^{-1}(s_2)$$

and

$$\varphi^{-1}(r_2 s_2) = r_1 s_1 = \varphi^{-1}(r_2)\varphi^{-1}(s_2).$$

5. Let R, S, and T be in α such that $\varphi : R \to S$ and $\theta : S \to T$ are isomorphisms. It can be easily verified that $\theta\varphi : R \to T$ is an isomorphism. This proves the transitive property. The reflexive and symmetric properties are obvious.

6. (a) $(ae_1 + be_2) \otimes (3e_1 + 4e_2) = e_1$ implies $3a - 4b = 1$ and $4a + 3b = 0$ which gives $a = \frac{3}{25}$, $b = \frac{-4}{25}$.

   (b) $z = \frac{3}{25} e_1 - \frac{4}{25} e_2$ as computed in (a).

   (c) Let $z = ae_1 + be_2$. Then $(3e_1 + 4e_2) \otimes z = 2e_1 - 4e_2$ gives $3a - 4b = 2$ and $4a + 3b = -4$, that is, $a = -\frac{2}{5}$, $b = -\frac{4}{5}$.

   (d) $(ae_1 + be_2)^2 = ae_1 + be_2$ implies $a^2 - b^2 = a$ and $2ab = b$. If $b \neq 0$, we do not get a real solution for a. In case $b = 0$, we get $a = 1$ or $a = 0$. Hence $z = e_1$ or $z = 0$.

7. Let $A = \begin{bmatrix} a & c \\ b & d \end{bmatrix}$. Then

$$\begin{bmatrix} 3 & -4 \\ 4 & 3 \end{bmatrix}\begin{bmatrix} a & c \\ b & d \end{bmatrix} = \begin{bmatrix} 2 & 4 \\ -4 & 2 \end{bmatrix}$$

implies

$$3a - 4b = 2, \qquad 4a + 3b = -4, \qquad 3d + 4c = 2 \qquad \text{and} \qquad 4d - 3c = -4.$$

By Exercise 6(c) we get

$$a = -\tfrac{2}{5}, \qquad b = -\tfrac{4}{5}, \qquad c = \tfrac{4}{5} \qquad \text{and} \qquad d = -\tfrac{2}{5}.$$

8. The required matrices are $\begin{bmatrix} 1 & 0 \\ 0 & 1 \end{bmatrix}$ and $\begin{bmatrix} 0 & 0 \\ 0 & 0 \end{bmatrix}$. For, since $z^2 = z \otimes z = z$ we have from Example 1.2, $\varphi(z^2) = \varphi(z)\varphi(z) = \varphi(z)$ and, because $z = e_1$ or $z = 0$, we have $A = \varphi(e_1) = \begin{bmatrix} 1 & 0 \\ 0 & 1 \end{bmatrix}$ or $A = \varphi(0) = \begin{bmatrix} 0 & 0 \\ 0 & 0 \end{bmatrix}$.

9.

$\oplus$	0	1	2	3	4	5
0	0	1	2	3	4	5
1	1	2	3	4	5	0
2	2	3	4	5	0	1
3	3	4	5	0	1	2
4	4	5	0	1	2	3
5	5	0	1	2	3	4

$\otimes$	0	1	2	3	4	5
0	0	0	0	0	0	0
1	0	1	2	3	4	5
2	0	2	4	0	2	4
3	0	3	0	3	0	3
4	0	4	2	0	4	2
5	0	5	4	3	2	1

10. The proof is similar to that given in Example 1.1(e).

11. The units are 5 and 1.

12. 2, 3, 4.

Section 4.2

Quiz

1. **True.** Let $d = (a, b, c)$. Then $d \mid a$ and $d \mid b$ and hence $d \mid (a, b)$.

2. **True.** This follows from Theorem 2.8.

3. **False.** $[372][777] = [676]$.

4. **True.** $mx \equiv 1 \bmod n$ if and only if $mx - ny = 1$, for some integer y. This is true if and only if $(m, n) = 1$.

5. **False.** $[4]_6[3]_6 = [2]_6[3]_6$ but $[4]_6 \neq [2]_6$.

6. **False.** Take $a = 2$, $b = 3$, $m = n = 6$.

7. **True.** $p \nmid a$ implies $(p, a) = 1$ and the result follows from Theorem 2.11.

8. **False.** Let $a = 3$ and $m = 6$.

9. **False.** Let $a = n = 3$ and $b = m = 2$, then $ma + nb = c = 12 \neq 1 = (2, 3)$.

10. **False.** Let $a = 6$, $b = 3$ and $c = 2$.

Exercises

1. $3{,}451 = 1{,}411 \times 2 + 629; \quad 1{,}411 = 629 \times 2 + 153; \quad 629 = 153 \times 4 + 17;$
   $153 = 17 \times 9$. Hence $(3{,}451, 1{,}411) = 17$.

2. $17 = 629 - 153 \times 4 = 629 - (1{,}411 - 629 \times 2) \times 4 = 629 \times 9 - 1{,}411 \times 4$
   $= (3{,}451 - 1{,}411 \times 2) \times 9 - 1{,}411 \times 4 = 3{,}451(9) + 1{,}411(-22)$.

3. Define $\varphi(n) = [n]_4$ for $n = 0, 1, 2, 3$. Then φ is the required isomorphism.

4. (All residue classes will be taken mod 3.) Observe that $[10^n] = [1]$ and therefore
   $[a_n 10^n + \cdots + a_1 10 + a_0] = [a_n][1] + \cdots + [a_1][1] + [a_0] = [a_n + \cdots + a_1 + a_0]$
   $= [0]$ if and only if $a_n + \cdots + a_1 + a_0$ is divisible by 3.

5. (All residue classes taken mod 13.) $[3^{2n} + 3^n + 1][3^n - 1] = [3^{3n} - 1] = [27]^n$
   $+ [-1] = [1]^n + [-1] = [0]$. Since 13 is prime, Theorem 2.10(b) tells us I_{13} has
   no zero divisors. Thus either $[3^n - 1] = [0]$ or $[3^{2n} + 3^n - 1] = [0]$. If $3 \nmid n$ then
   $n = 3m + 1$ or $n = 3m + 2$ for some nonnegative integer m. If $n = 3m + 1$,
   $[3^n - 1] = [3^{3m+1} - 1] = [3][27]^m + [-1] = [3][1]^m + [-1] = [2] \neq [0]$. If $n =$
   $3m + 2$, $[3^n - 1] = [3^{3m+2} - 1] = [9][27]^m + [-1] = [9][1]^m + [-1] = [8] \neq$
   $[0]$. Therefore $[3^{2n} + 3^n + 1] = [0]$ if $3 \nmid n$.

6. $(28, 64) = 4 = 7 \times 28 - 3 \times 64$. Therefore $[28][28] = [16]$ and the solutions
   are $[28 + 16t]$, $t = 0, 1, 2, 3$.

7. By Quiz question 4, there exist integers m and n such that $am \equiv 1 \bmod c$
   and $bn \equiv 1 \bmod c$. Therefore $(am)(bn) \equiv 1 \bmod c$ or $(ab, c) = 1$.

Section 4.3

Quiz

1. **True.** Let $z = x + iy$. Then z is real implies $y = 0$ and $\bar{z} = x = z$. If $z = \bar{z}$ then
   $x + iy = x - iy$, and $y = -y$ implies $y = 0$, i.e., z is real.

2. **False.** Let $z = -2$. Then $|z| = 2 \neq -2 = \text{Re}\,(z)$.

3. **False.** Let $z_1 = z_2 = i$.

4. **True.** $(-i)^2 = i^2 = -1$.

5. **True.** $|z_1 z_2| = |z_1||z_2| = 1$.

6. **False.** Let $z_1 = 1$, $z_2 = i$.

7. **True.** $\cos \pi + i \sin \pi = -1 + i \cdot 0 = -1$.

8. **True.** $z = (-b \pm \sqrt{b^2 - 4ac})/2a$ satisfies the given equation.

9. **False.** Let $z = 1 + i$.

10. **True.** Let $z_1 = x_1 + iy_1 = r_1(\cos \theta_1 + i \sin \theta_1) = z_2 = x_2 + iy_2 = r_2(\cos \theta_2 + i \sin \theta_2)$. Then $r_1 = |z_1| = |z_2| = r_2$. Also $\cos \theta_1 = \cos \theta_2$, $\sin \theta_1 = \sin \theta_2$ and hence $\theta_1 = \theta_2 + 2k\pi$ for some integer k. Since $-\pi < \theta_1 \leq \theta_2 \leq \pi$ we must have $k = 0$ and $\theta_1 = \theta_2$.

Exercises

1. $1/z = \bar{z}/z\bar{z} = \bar{z}/|z|^2$.

2. In figure (2) following Theorem 3.3, with $\theta = \pi/3$, the length of NP is $\sqrt{3}/2$ and that of ON is $\frac{1}{2}$. Therefore $\sin \pi/3 = \sqrt{3}/2$, $\cos \pi/3 = \frac{1}{2}$ and $\tan \pi/3 = \sqrt{3}$.

3. $z^n = 2^{93}(\cos 93\pi/6 + i \sin 93\pi/6)$ implies $\text{Re}\,((\sqrt{3} + i)^{93}) = 2^{93} \cos 93\pi/6 = 0$, and $\text{Im}\,((\sqrt{3} + i)^{93}) = 2^{93} \sin 93\pi/6 = -2^{93}$.

4. $$z = \frac{i4\sqrt{3}}{1 + i\sqrt{3}} = \frac{i4\sqrt{3}(1 - i\sqrt{3})}{(1 + i\sqrt{3})(1 - i\sqrt{3})} = 3 + i\sqrt{3} = 2\sqrt{3}\left(\cos \frac{\pi}{6} + i \sin \frac{\pi}{6}\right).$$

5. Use Theorem 3.3(g):
$$|z_1 z_2 z_3 \cdots z_k| = |z_1| \cdot |z_2 z_3 \cdots z_k|$$
$$= |z_1||z_2||z_3 \cdots z_k| = \cdots = |z_1||z_2| \cdots |z_k|.$$

6. Write $z_1 = z_1 - z_2 + z_2$. Then Theorem 3.3(h) gives $|z_1| \leq |z_1 - z_2| + |z_2|$, that is, $|z_1| - |z_2| \leq |z_1 - z_2|$. Similarly $z_2 = -(z_1 - z_2) + z_1$ gives $|z_2| - |z_1| \leq |z_1 - z_2|$.

7. If $z_2 \neq 0$, then
$$\left|\frac{z_1}{z_2}\right|^2 = \left(\frac{z_1}{z_2}\right)\left(\frac{\bar{z}_1}{\bar{z}_2}\right) = \frac{z_1 \bar{z}_1}{z_2 \bar{z}_2} = \frac{|z_1|^2}{|z_2|^2}.$$

8. $-1 + i = \sqrt{2}\,(\cos 3\pi/4 + i \sin 3\pi/4)$. Therefore, by Theorem 3.8, all the 2/3 powers are given by
$$2^{1/3}\left(\cos\left(\frac{\pi}{2} + \frac{4}{3}\pi k\right) + i \sin\left(\frac{\pi}{2} + \frac{4}{3}\pi k\right)\right), \qquad k = 0, 1, 2.$$

9. We have $-1 = \cos \pi + i \sin \pi$ and therefore, according to Theorem 3.7, the required roots are the n complex numbers

$$\cos \frac{1}{n}(2k+1)\pi + i \sin \frac{1}{n}(2k+1)\pi, \qquad k = 0, 1, \ldots, n-1.$$

10. Let $\omega = \cos 2\pi/n + i \sin 2\pi/n$. Then $\cos 2h\pi/n + i \sin 2h\pi/n = \omega^h = \cos 2k\pi/n + i \sin 2k\pi/n = \omega^k$ implies $\omega^{h-k} = 1$ and therefore $((h-k)/n)(2\pi)$ is an integer multiple of 2π and $h - k$ is an integer multiple of n.

11. Let $d = (p, n)$ and let $p = qd$ and $n = kd$. Then $z = \cos 2p\pi/n + i \sin 2p\pi/n = \cos 2q\pi/k + i \sin 2q\pi/k$ is a kth root of 1 and $1 \leq k \leq n$. Hence z is a primitive nth root of 1 if and only if $k = n$, i.e., $d = 1$.

12. Let $u = \cos 2p\pi/n + i \sin 2p\pi/n$ be a primitive nth root of 1. Then $u, u^2, \ldots, u^{n-1}$ are nth roots of 1. We show that they are all distinct. Suppose that $u^h = u^k$ for distinct positive integers h and k, $h < n$, $k < n$. Then $\cos 2ph\pi/n + i \sin 2ph\pi/n = \cos 2pk\pi/n + i \sin 2pk\pi/n$ and, by Exercise 10, we can conclude that $p(h-k)$ is divisible by n. But, by Exercise 11, $(p, n) = 1$ and therefore $h - k$ must be divisible by n which is not possible since $h < n$ and $k < n$.

13. Observe that Re $(z) = |z|$ if and only if z is a nonnegative real number. We see from the proof of Theorem 3.3(h) that $|z_1 + z_2| = |z_1| + |z_2|$ if and only if Re $(z_1 \bar{z}_2) = |z_1 \bar{z}_2|$, that is, if and only if $z_1 \bar{z}_2$ is a nonnegative real number. If either z_1 or z_2 is real then both must be real and the result follows easily. A similar argument works if either is pure imaginary. Suppose that $z_1 = a_1 + ib_1$ and $z_2 = a_2 + ib_2$ where none of a_1, b_1, a_2, b_2 is 0. Then $z_1 \bar{z}_2 = a_1 a_2 + b_1 b_2 + i(a_2 b_1 - a_1 b_2)$ which is a nonnegative real number if and only if $a_1 a_2 + b_1 b_2 \geq 0$ and $a_2 b_1 - a_1 b_2 = 0$. Thus $a_1 = k a_2$ and $b_1 = k b_2$ for some real number k. But then $a_1 a_2 + b_1 b_2 = k(a_2^2 + b_2^2)$ which is nonnegative if and only if $k \geq 0$.

14. Let $C_1 = \{m + in \mid m, n \text{ integers}\}$. C_1 is a subset of the complex numbers and since the ordinary sum, product and difference of two integers is an integer, we conclude by Exercise 2, Section 4.1, that C_1 is a ring. Let R_1 be the ring of matrices of the form $\begin{bmatrix} m & -n \\ n & m \end{bmatrix}$. Define $\varphi : C_1 \to R_1$ by $\varphi(m + in) = \begin{bmatrix} m & -n \\ n & m \end{bmatrix}$. Then φ is an isomorphism (see Example 1.2).

15. We have $\varphi(z_1 + z_2) = \overline{z_1 + z_2} = \bar{z}_1 + \bar{z}_2 = \varphi(z_1) + \varphi(z_2)$ and $\varphi(z_1 z_2) = \overline{z_1 z_2} = \bar{z}_1 \cdot \bar{z}_2 = \varphi(z_1) \cdot \varphi(z_2)$. Furthermore, if $\varphi(z_1) = \varphi(z_2)$, that is, $\bar{z}_1 = \bar{z}_2$, then $z_1 = z_2$. Hence φ is 1-1. Last, $z = \varphi(\bar{z})$ for any complex number z and thus φ is onto.

Section 4.4

Quiz

1. **True.** $(z + 1)(z^6 + z^4 - z^3 + 2z^2 - 2z + 2) = z^7 + z^6 + z^5 + z^3 + 2.$

2. **True.** $a_r(c) = \begin{bmatrix} 0 & 0 \\ 0 & 0 \end{bmatrix}$ and $a_i(c) = \begin{bmatrix} 7 & -8 \\ 4 & -7 \end{bmatrix}.$

3. **True.** Let $d(z) = \prod_{i=1}^{r} (p_i(z))^{m_i}$ be the unique factorization of $d(z)$ into primes. The result follows by Theorem 4.10.

4. **False.** $\frac{1}{2}(\sqrt{2})^2 - 1 = 0$.

5. **False.** $i^2 + 1 = 0$.

6. **False.** Let $a(z) = b(z) = \begin{bmatrix} 0 & 1 \\ 0 & 0 \end{bmatrix}$ and $c(z) = \begin{bmatrix} 0 & 2 \\ 0 & 0 \end{bmatrix}$.

7. **False.** See Example 4.1.

8. **False.** Let $a(z) = b(z) = \begin{bmatrix} 0 & 1 \\ 0 & 0 \end{bmatrix} z$.

9. **True.** Since z is an indeterminate, it commutes with everything in $R[z]$.

10. **True.** Let $c = -I_2$ and I_2 in succession.

11. **True.** Any factor of a linear polynomial is in R or is an associate of the polynomial.

12. **True.** $z^2 + 1$ cannot have any real factors, for if $(z - a) \mid (z^2 + 1)$ then $a^2 + 1 = 0$, impossible for real a.

13. **False.** $z^3 + 1 = (z + 1)(z^2 - z + 1)$.

14. **False.** The g.c.d. of two polynomials is monic.

15. **True.** We use Theorem 4.9(b). Let $a(z) = q_1(z)d(z)$, $b(z) = q_2(z)d(z)$ where $(q_1(z), q_2(z)) = 1$. Then $a(z)^2 = q_1(z)^2 d(z)^2$, $b(z)^2 = q_2(z)^2 d(z)^2$, $(q_1(z)^2, q_2(z)^2) = 1$ and hence $d(z)^2 = (a(z)^2, b(z)^2)$.

Exercises

1. Suppose $n \geq m$. Then $\sum_{i=0}^{n} a_i z^i = \sum_{i=0}^{m} b_i z^i$ implies $\sum_{i=0}^{n} (a_i - b_i)z^i = 0$, where $b_{m+1} = b_{m+2} = \cdots = b_n = 0$ and therefore, since z is an indeterminate, $a_i - b_i = 0$, $i = 0, 1, \ldots, n$, that is, $a_i = b_i$ for $i = 0, 1, \ldots, m$ and $a_i = 0$ for $i = m + 1, \ldots, n$.

2. Let $d(z) = (a(z), b(z), c(z))$. $d(z)$ divides each of $a(z)$ and $b(z)$ and hence it divides $(a(z), b(z))$. If $p(z) \mid (a(z), b(z))$ and $p(z) \mid c(z)$ then $p(z)$ divides each of $a(z), b(z)$ and $c(z)$ and hence it divides $d(z)$. Thus $d(z) = ((a(z), b(z)), c(z))$.

3. Let $d(z) = (a(z), b(z))$. Then $c(z) \mid a(z)$, $c(z) \mid b(z)$ imply $c(z) \mid d(z)$. Since $c(z) \neq d(z)$, we have $\deg c(z) < \deg d(z)$.

4. $a([2]) = [1][2]^3 + [1][2] + [2] = [2] + [2] + [2] = [0]$ and $b([2]) = [2][2] + [2] = [1] + [2] = [0]$. Similar verification holds for $[c] = [0]$ and $[c] = [1]$. However $a(z)$ and $b(z)$ are not equal since their degrees differ.

5. Let

$$A = \begin{bmatrix} a_{11} & a_{12} \\ a_{21} & a_{22} \end{bmatrix} \quad \text{and} \quad B = \begin{bmatrix} b_{11} & b_{12} \\ b_{21} & b_{22} \end{bmatrix}.$$

Then let $a(z) = (zI_2 - B)(z^2 I_2 - (a_{11} + a_{22})zI_2 + (a_{11}a_{22} - a_{12}a_{21})I_2)$. The formula (20) implies that $a_i(B)$ is the zero matrix. We directly verify that

$a_r(A) = (A - B)(A^2 - (a_{11} + a_{22})A + (a_{11}a_{22} - a_{12}a_{21})I_2)$. But observe that $A^2 - (a_{11} + a_{22})A + (a_{11}a_{22} - a_{12}a_{21})I_2$ is the zero matrix.

6. The $(1, 1)$ entry of $a_r(A)$ is $2a + 4c + 1$. Since $2a + 4c = -1$ has no integer solutions (why?), $a_r(A)$ is never 0. Similarly the $(1, 1)$ entry of $a_l(A)$ is $2a - 2b + 1$ and $2a - 2b = -1$ has no integer solutions. Thus $a_l(A) \neq 0$.

7. $z^6 - 10z^4 + 3z^3 + z^2 + 3z - 1 = (z^4 + 5z^3 + 5z^2 - 2z)(z^2 - 5z + 10)$

$$+ (-20z^3 - 59z^2 + 23z - 1),$$

$$z^4 + 5z^3 + 5z^2 - 2z = (-20z^3 - 59z^2 + 23z - 1)\left(-\frac{z}{20} - \frac{41}{400}\right)$$

$$+ \frac{41}{400}(z^2 + 3z - 1),$$

$$-20z^3 - 59z^2 + 23z - 1 = \tfrac{41}{400}(z^2 + 3z - 1)\tfrac{400}{41}(-20z + 1).$$

Thus the g.c.d. is $z^2 + 3z - 1$.

8. We have $b(z) = za(z) + r_1(z)$, where $r_1(z) = 2z^2 - z - 2$; $a(z) = (\tfrac{1}{2}z^2 + \tfrac{1}{4}z + \tfrac{1}{8})r_1(z) + r_2(z)$, where $r_2(z) = \tfrac{5}{8}z + \tfrac{5}{4}$; $r_1(z) = (\tfrac{16}{5}z - 8)r_2(z) + 8$. Thus 8 is a g.c.d. of $a(z)$ and $b(z)$ and $(a(z), b(z)) = 1$. Hence

$$8 = r_1(z) - (\tfrac{16}{5}z - 8)r_2(z)$$

$$= r_1(z) - (\tfrac{16}{5}z - 8)(a(z) - (\tfrac{1}{2}z^2 + \tfrac{1}{4}z + \tfrac{1}{8})r_1(z))$$

$$= \tfrac{8}{5}(z^3 - 2z^2 - z)r_1(z) + \tfrac{8}{5}(-2z + 5)a(z)$$

$$= \tfrac{8}{5}[(z^3 - 2z^2 - z)(b(z) - za(z)) + (-2z + 5)a(z)]$$

$$= \tfrac{8}{5}[(z^3 - 2z^2 - z)b(z) + (-z^4 + 2z^3 + z^2 - 2z + 5)a(z)]$$

and thus

$$1 = (\tfrac{1}{5}z^3 - \tfrac{2}{5}z^2 - \tfrac{1}{5}z)b(z) + (-\tfrac{1}{5}z^4 + \tfrac{2}{5}z^3 + \tfrac{1}{5}z^2 - \tfrac{2}{5}z + 1)a(z).$$

9. We use the Euclidean Algorithm:

$$z^4 + z^3 + 2z - 4 = (z^3 + 2z^2 - z - 2)(z - 1) + (3z^2 + 3z - 6),$$

$$z^3 + 2z^2 - z - 2 = (3z^2 + 3z - 6)\left(\frac{z}{3} + \frac{1}{3}\right),$$

and therefore

$$(a(z), b(z)) = z^2 + z - 2 = (z - 1)(z + 2).$$

Next,

$$z^5 + z^3 - 2z = (z^3 + 2z^2 - z - 2)(z^2 - 2z + 6) + (-12z^2 + 12),$$

$$z^3 + 2z^2 - z - 2 = (-12z^2 + 12)\left(-\frac{z}{12} - \frac{2}{12}\right),$$

and thus

$$(a(z), c(z)) = z^2 - 1 = (z - 1)(z + 1).$$

234   **Answers and Solutions**

Finally,

$$z^5 + z^3 - 2z = (z^4 + z^3 + 2z - 4)(z - 1) + (2z^3 - 2z^2 + 4z - 4),$$

$$(z^4 + z^3 + 2z - 4) = (2z^3 - 2z^2 + 4z - 4)\left(\frac{z}{2} + \frac{2}{2}\right)$$

and therefore

$$(b(z),\ c(z)) = z^3 - z^2 + 2z - 2 = (z - 1)(z^2 + 2).$$

Now, from the above we can factorize $a(z)$, $b(z)$ and $c(z)$:

$$a(z) = (z - 1)(z + 2)(z + 1), \qquad b(z) = (z - 1)(z + 2)(z^2 + 2)$$

and

$$c(z) = (z - 1)(z + 1)(z^2 + 2)z.$$

Therefore $(a(z),\ b(z),\ c(z)) = z - 1$. Next, we compute directly $((a(z),\ b(z)),\ c(z))$:

$$z^5 + z^3 - 2z = (z^2 + z - 2)(z^3 - z^2 - 4z - 6) + (12z - 12),$$

$$z^2 + z - 2 = (12z - 12)\left(\frac{1}{12} z + \frac{1}{6}\right).$$

Therefore $((a(z),\ b(z)),\ c(z)) = z - 1 = (a(z),\ b(z),\ c(z))$. The other two equalities are verified in the same way.

10. From the solution of Exercise 9 we have

$$(a(z),\ b(z)) = z^2 + z - 2 = \frac{1}{3}[b(z) - (z - 1)a(z)].$$

Thus

$$z - 1 = \frac{1}{12} [c(z) - (z^2 + z - 2)(z^3 - z^2 + 4z - 6)]$$

$$= \frac{1}{12} [c(z) - \frac{1}{3} (z^3 - z^2 + 4z - 6)(b(z) - (z - 1)a(z))]$$

$$= \frac{1}{36}(z - 1)(z^3 - z^2 + 4z - 6)a(z) - \frac{1}{36}(z^3 - z^2 + 4z - 6)b(z) + \frac{1}{12} c(z).$$

Section 4.5

Quiz

1. **True.** The elements of R^X are functions on X to R and not elements of R.

2. **True.** We prove $f(x) = 0$ by induction on x. Now, $(f \otimes f)(0) = f(0)f(0) = 0$ so $f(0) = 0$. Suppose $f(0) = \cdots = f(x - 1) = 0$. Then $(f \otimes f)(2x) = \sum_{u+v=2x} f(u)f(v) = f(0)f(2x) + f(1)f(2x - 1) + \cdots + f(x)f(x) + \cdots + f(2x - 1)f(1) + f(2x)f(0)$. Now $f \otimes f = 0$ and, by induction, $f(0) = \cdots = f(x - 1) = 0$. Thus we have $f(x)f(x) = 0$ and hence $f(x) = 0$.

3. **False.** Let $f(0) = 2$, $f(x) = 0$, $x \neq 0$. Then clearly $f \otimes f = 0$ but f is not the zero function.

4. **True.** Established in the proof of Theorem 5.1(d).

5. **False.** In the proof of Theorem 5.1(d) it is established that $(f \otimes z)(0) = 0$ for any f. Thus if $r \neq 0$ then $(f_r \otimes z)(0) \neq r$.

6. **False.** In the proof of Theorem 5.1(d) it is established that $(f \otimes z^k)(0) = 0$. Hence if $r \neq 0$ then $(f_r \otimes z^2 \otimes f_r)(0) = (z^2 \otimes (f_r \otimes f_r))(0) = 0 \neq r^2$.

7. **True.** $(f \otimes f_i)(x) = \sum_{u+v=x} f(u) f_i(v) = f(x) f_i(0) = f(x)i = f(x)$.

8. **False.** $(z^2 \otimes f)(3) = f(1)$.

9. **True.** This is precisely the statement of Theorem 5.1(d).

10. **True.** z commutes with everything in R_1 by Theorem 5.1(d), and hence z^2 does also.

Exercises

1. (iii) $(f \oplus g)(x) = f(x) + g(x) = g(x) + f(x) = (g \oplus f)(x)$. (iv) The function f whose value at each x is 0 is the additive identity. (v) $-f$ is the function whose value at each x is the negative of $f(x)$. (vi) We prove one of the distributive laws. The other is similarly proved. $(f \otimes (g \oplus h))(x) = \sum_{u+v=x} f(u)(g(v) + h(v))$
    $= \sum_{u+v=x} f(u)g(v) + f(u)h(v) = \sum_{u+v=x} f(u)g(v) + \sum_{u+v=x} f(u)h(v) = (f \otimes g)(x)$
    $+ (f \otimes h)(x) = ((f \otimes g) \oplus (f \otimes h))(x)$.

2. We write down the elements of X^X denoted by f, g, h, k. $f(0) = 0$, $f(1) = 0$; $g(0) = 0$, $g(1) = 1$; $h(0) = 1$, $h(1) = 0$; $k(0) = 1$, $k(1) = 1$. We compute

$\oplus$	f	g	h	k
f	f	g	h	k
g	g	f	k	h
h	h	k	f	g
k	k	h	g	f

$\otimes$	f	g	h	k
f	f	f	f	f
g	f	h	g	k
h	f	g	h	k
k	f	k	k	f

    For example, $(g \otimes h)(0) = g(0)h(0) + g(1)h(1)$ (since $1 + 1 = 0$ in X). Thus $(g \otimes h)(0) = 0$. Also $(g \otimes h)(1) = g(0)h(1) + g(1)h(0) = 1$. Thus $g \otimes h = g$.

Section 4.6

Quiz

1. **True.** It is given that x_2 is an indeterminate over $R[x_1]$. Thus

$$\sum_{k=0}^{n} a_k(x_1)x_2^k = 0$$

implies that

$$a_0(x_1) = \cdots = a_n(x_1) = 0.$$

In particular, this is so in case each $a_k(x_1)$ is in $R \subset R[x_1]$.

2. **False.** Take $x_1 = x_2$.

3. **False.** Let $\sigma = (2 \quad 3)$ and $f(x_1, x_2, x_3) = x_1^2 + x_2^2 + x_1 x_2 x_3$. Then $f(x_{\sigma(1)}, x_{\sigma(2)}, x_{\sigma(3)}) = x_1^2 + x_3^2 + x_1 x_2 x_3 \neq f(x_1, x_2, x_3)$.

4. **True.** Each term $(x_{\sigma(\omega_1)} \cdots x_{\sigma(\omega_r)})^2$ of $f(x_{\sigma(1)}, \ldots, x_{\sigma(n)})$ appears exactly once in $f(x_1, \ldots, x_n)$.

5. **True.** By formula (25), the coefficient of z^{n-1} is $-E_1(1, 2, \ldots, n) = -(1 + 2 + \cdots + n) = -n(n+1)/2$.

6. **False.** The product of the roots is the constant term or its negative. Here the constant term is 0.

7. **False.** Substitute each of $2, -2, 1, -1$, for z.

8. **True.** Each polynomial has 1 as a root.

9. **True.** If the polynomial $a_3 z^3 + a_2 z^2 + a_1 z + a_0$, a_j real, has a complex root a with a nonzero imaginary part then, by Theorem 6.8, the number $\bar{a}$ is also a root. The product of all three roots is $-a_0$ and therefore the third root is $-a_0 / a\bar{a} = -a_0 / |a|^2$, a real number.

10. **False.** By Theorem 6.8, the four roots of the polynomial are of the form $a, \bar{a}, b, \bar{b}$. By formula (25), $a_0 / a_4 = |a|^2 |b|^2 > 0$. Thus a_0 has the same sign as a_4.

Exercises

1. Suppose $\sum_{k=0}^{n} a_k(x_2) x_1^k = 0$ where $a_k(x_2) \in R[x_2]$. Set $a_k(x_2) = \sum_{j=0}^{m} \alpha_{kj} x_2^j$, $\alpha_{kj} \in R$, and the notation is chosen so that m is the same for every $a_k(x_2)$, $k = 0, \ldots, n$, (append zero coefficients if necessary). Then we compute that

$$0 = \sum_{k=0}^{n} a_k(x_2) x_1^k$$

$$= \sum_{k=0}^{n} \sum_{j=0}^{m} \alpha_{kj} x_2^j x_1^k$$

$$= \sum_{j=0}^{m} \left(\sum_{k=0}^{n} \alpha_{kj} x_1^k \right) x_2^j.$$

Hence $\sum_{k=0}^{n} \alpha_{kj} x_1^k = 0$, $j = 0, \ldots, m$, because x_2 is an indeterminate over $R[x_1]$. But x_1 is an indeterminate over R and hence $\alpha_{kj} = 0$, $k = 0, \ldots, n$, $j = 0, \ldots, m$, and hence $a_k(x_2) = 0$, $k = 0, \ldots, n$.

2. Let $F(x_1, \ldots, x_p) = \psi(f_1(x_1, \ldots, x_p), \ldots, f_p(x_1, \ldots, x_p))$. If $\sigma \in S_p$ then

$$F(x_{\sigma(1)}, \ldots, x_{\sigma(p)}) = \psi(f_1(x_{\sigma(1)}, \ldots, x_{\sigma(p)}), \ldots, f_p(x_{\sigma(1)}, \ldots, x_{\sigma(p)}))$$

$$= \psi(f_1(x_1, \ldots, x_p), \ldots, f_p(x_1, \ldots, x_p))$$

$$= F(x_1, \ldots, x_p).$$

3. The terms in $E_r(x_1, \ldots, x_p)$ can be separated into two sets: those that involve x_k and those that do not. A typical term involving x_k can be written as $x_k x_{\omega_1} x_{\omega_2} \cdots x_{\omega_{r-1}}$ where $\omega = (\omega_1, \ldots, \omega_{r-1}) \in Q_{r-1, p}$ and k does not appear in ω, i.e., $k \notin \omega$. Thus the sum of all terms involving x_k can be written as

$$x_k \sum_{\substack{\omega \in Q_{r-1, p} \\ k \notin \omega}} \prod_{t=1}^{r-1} x_{\omega_t} = x_k E_{r-1}(\hat{x}_k).$$

The terms that do not involve x_k are precisely those of the form $x_{\omega_1} \cdots x_{\omega_r}$, $\omega \in Q_{r, n}$, $k \notin \omega$. Their sum is just

$$\sum_{\substack{\omega \in Q_{r, n} \\ k \notin \omega}} \prod_{t=1}^{r} x_{\omega_t} = E_r(\hat{x}_k).$$

Thus $E_r(x_1, \ldots, x_p) = E_r(\hat{x}_k) + x_k E_{r-1}(\hat{x}_k)$.

4. Sum both sides of

$$E_r(\hat{x}_k) + x_k E_{r-1}(\hat{x}_k) = E_r(x_1, \ldots, x_p)$$

on k to obtain

$$\sum_{k=1}^{p} E_r(\hat{x}_k) = p E_r(x_1, \ldots, x_p) - \sum_{k=1}^{p} x_k E_{r-1}(\hat{x}_k).$$

Now let $Q_{r, p}^k$ denote those elements in $Q_{r, p}$ that involve k. Then clearly $x_k E_{r-1}(\hat{x}_k) = \sum_{\omega \in Q_{r, p}^k} \prod_{t=1}^{r} x_{\omega_t}$ and moreover each $\omega \in Q_{r, p}$ lies in precisely r of the $Q_{r, p}^k$, namely those for which $k = \omega_i$, $i = 1, \ldots, r$. Hence

$$\sum_{k=1}^{p} x_k E_{r-1}(\hat{x}_k) = \sum_{k=1}^{p} \sum_{\omega \in Q_{r, p}^k} \prod_{t=1}^{r} x_{\omega_t}$$

$$= r \sum_{\omega \in Q_{r, p}} \prod_{t=1}^{r} x_{\omega_t}$$

$$= r E_r(x_1, \ldots, x_p).$$

5. In the notation of the proof of Theorem 6.5, the induction hypothesis is: any polynomial of degree $n - 1$ or less can be written as a product of first degree terms. Thus let $q(z) = \prod_{i=1}^{n-1}(z - c_i)$, ($q(z)$ is monic since $q(z)(z - c_n) = a_n^{-1} f(z)$). Then

$$a_n^{-1} f(z) = q(z)(z - c_n)$$

$$= \prod_{i=1}^{n-1}(z - c_i)(z - c_n)$$

$$= \prod_{i=1}^{n}(z - c_i).$$

6. From Example 3.5 we know that the indicated numbers are precisely all the roots of the polynomial $z^n - 1$. By formula (25),

$$E_k(c_1, \ldots, c_n) = 0, \qquad k = 1, \ldots, n - 1.$$

7. By Theorem 6.9, the rational zeros of $f(z)$ (if any) are divisors of 8. We compute $f(-1) \neq 0$, $f(1) = 0$, $f(-2) = 0$, $f(2) = 0$, $f(-4) \neq 0$, $f(4) \neq 0$, $f(-8) \neq 0$, $f(8) = 0$. Hence the only rational zeros are 1, -2, 2. By Theorem 4.4, $z - 1$, $z + 2$, $z - 2$ are divisors of $f(z)$ and thus $(z - 1)(z + 2)(z - 2) = z^3 - z^2 - 4z + 4$ is a divisor of $f(z)$. Thus we can factorize $f(z) = (z^3 - z^2 - 4z + 4)$ $(z^2 + z + 2)$. It follows that the other two zeros of $f(z)$ are $\frac{1}{2}(-1 - i\sqrt{7})$, $\frac{1}{2}(-1 + i\sqrt{7})$.

8. We use the Euclidean Algorithm to compute a g.c.d. of $f(z)$ and $f'(z) = 6z^5 + 20z^4 + 24z^3 + 24z^2 + 18z + 4$:

$$f(z) = (\tfrac{1}{6}z + \tfrac{1}{9})f'(z) + r_1(z)$$

where $r_1(z) = -\frac{2}{9}z^4 + \frac{4}{3}z^3 + \frac{10}{3}z^2 + \frac{4}{3}z + \frac{32}{9}$;

$$f'(z) = (-27z - 252)r_1(z) + r_2(z)$$

where $r_2(z) = 450(z^3 + 2z^2 + z + 2)$, $r_1(z) = \frac{1}{4050}(-2z + 16)r_2(z)$.

Hence $d(z) = $ g.c.d.$(f(z), f'(z)) = z^3 + 2z^2 + z + 2$. We find that $d(-2) = 0$ and $d(z) = (z + 2)(z^2 + 1)$. Thus the repeated roots of $f(z)$ are: -2 (double), i (double) and $-i$ (double). In fact, $f(z) = (z + 2)^2(z^2 + 1)^2$.

9. We can assume without loss of generality that $k_1 \geq \cdots \geq k_m$. Let

$$k_j > 1 \text{ for } j = 1, \ldots, t \qquad \text{and} \qquad k_{t+1} = \cdots = k_m = 1.$$

Then, by Theorem 6.7,

$$f'(z) = r(z) \prod_{i=1}^{t} (z - c_i)^{k_i - 1}$$

where $r(z)$ is a polynomial for which $(z - c_i) \nmid r(z)$, $i = t + 1, \ldots, m$. Hence

$$d(z) = \prod_{i=1}^{t} (z - c_i)^{k_i - 1}$$

and

$$f(z) = d(z) \prod_{i=1}^{m} (z - c_i).$$

10. By Theorem 6.8, the number $1 - i$ is a zero of $f(z)$. Thus, by Theorem 4.4, $(z - 1 - i)(z - 1 + i) = z^2 - 2z + 2$ is a factor of $f(z)$. We compute

$$f(z) = z^4 - z^3 + z^2 + 2 = (z^2 - 2z + 2)(z^2 + z + 1)$$

and the other two zeros of $f(z)$ are $\frac{1}{2}(-1 - i\sqrt{3})$ and $\frac{1}{2}(-1 + i\sqrt{3})$.

11. Use Sturm's method:

$$f_0(z) = z^3 + 6z^2 + 10z - 1,$$

$$f_1(z) = 3z^2 + 12z + 10.$$

Now,

$$f_0(z) = (\tfrac{1}{3}z + \tfrac{2}{3})f_1(z) - f_2(z) \qquad \text{where} \qquad f_2(z) = 4z + \tfrac{23}{3};$$

$$f_1(z) = (\tfrac{3}{4}z + \tfrac{25}{26})f_2(z) - f_3(z) \qquad \text{where} \qquad f_3(z) = -95/48.$$

Set

$$g_0(z) = -\tfrac{48}{95}(z^3 + 6z^2 + 10z - 1),$$

$$g_1(z) = -\tfrac{48}{95}(3z^2 + 12z + 10),$$

$$g_2(z) = -\tfrac{16}{95}(12z + 23),$$

$$g_3(z) = 1.$$

Then

$$g_0(0) > 0, \qquad g_1(0) < 0, \qquad g_2(0) < 0, \qquad g_3(0) > 0;$$

$$g_0(1) < 0, \qquad g_1(1) < 0, \qquad g_2(1) < 0, \qquad g_3(1) > 0.$$

Hence $S(0) - S(1) = 1$ and the equation $z^3 + 6z^2 + 10z - 1 = 0$ has a real root between 0 and 1.

12. We use the notation of Theorem 6.12. Here $f_0(z) = z^4 - 5z^2 - 2z + 3$ and $f_1(z) = 4z^3 - 10z - 2$. We compute

$$f_0(z) = (\tfrac{1}{4}z)f_1(z) - (\tfrac{5}{2}z^2 + \tfrac{3}{2}z - 3).$$

Hence $f_2(z) = \tfrac{5}{2}z^2 + \tfrac{3}{2}z - 3$ and

$$f_1(z) = (\tfrac{8}{5}z - \tfrac{24}{25})f_2(z) - (\tfrac{94}{25}z + \tfrac{122}{25}).$$

We have $f_3(z) = \tfrac{94}{25}z + \tfrac{122}{25}$. Therefore

$$f_2(z) = \left(\frac{125}{188}z - \frac{1025}{2209}\right)f_3(z) - f_4(z)$$

where $f_4(z) = 1{,}625/2{,}209$. Thus we can conclude that the four roots of $f(z)$ are distinct. If $c = 1/f_4(z)$ then

$$g_0(z) = c(z^4 - 5z^2 - 2z + 3),$$

$$g_1(z) = c(4z^3 - 10z - 2),$$

$$g_2(z) = \frac{c}{2}(5z^2 + 3z - 6),$$

$$g_3(z) = \frac{2c}{25}(47z + 61),$$

$$g_4(z) = 1.$$

We compute

$$g_0(-2) > 0, \quad g_1(-2) < 0, \quad g_2(-2) > 0, \quad g_3(-2) < 0, \quad g_4(-2) > 0;$$

$$g_0(0) > 0, \quad g_1(0) < 0, \quad g_2(0) < 0, \quad g_3(0) > 0, \quad g_4(0) > 0;$$

$$g_0(2) < 0, \quad g_1(2) > 0, \quad g_2(2) > 0, \quad g_3(2) > 0, \quad g_4(2) > 0;$$

$$g_0(4) > 0, \quad g_1(4) > 0, \quad g_2(4) > 0, \quad g_3(4) > 0, \quad g_4(4) > 0.$$

Hence $S(-2) = 4$, $S(0) = 2$, $S(2) = 1$ and $S(4) = 0$ and, by Sturm's theorem, $f(z)$ has two real zeros between -2 and 0, one real zero between 0 and 2, and one between 2 and 4. Thus all the zeros of $f(z)$ are real. All rational roots of $f(z)$ must, by Theorem 6.9, be divisors of 3. The only candidates are -1, 1, 3 (because -3 cannot be a root by the preceding argument). We verify by direct computation that none of $f(-1), f(1), f(3)$ is 0. Hence $f(z)$ has no rational zeros.

13. The equation is already in reduced form. From formula (45) we compute $z_1 = -1$, $z_2 = -3$. Thus the roots of $z^3 - 9z - 28 = 0$ are $-4, 2 + i\sqrt{3}$ and $2 - i\sqrt{3}$. Alternatively, we may use Theorem 6.9 here to determine if the equation has a rational root (possible rational roots: -1, 1, -2, 2, -4, 4, -7, 7, -14, 14, -28, and 28) and find that -4 is a root. We use Theorem 4.4, and compute $z^3 - 9z - 28 = (z + 4)(z^2 - 4z - 7)$ and thus the other two roots are zeros of $z^2 - 4z - 7$, namely, $2 \pm i\sqrt{3}$.

14. In the notation of Theorem 6.13(b): $p = -5$, $q = -2$ and $r = 3$. Thus the equation (48) is $z^3 - 10z^2 + 13z - 4 = 0$ and we see by inspection that 1 is a root. Take $\xi = 1$. The equations (47) become $z^2 + z - 1 = 0$ and $z^2 - z - 3 = 0$. Thus the roots of the given equation are $\frac{1}{2}(-1 \pm \sqrt{5})$ and $\frac{1}{2}(1 \pm \sqrt{13})$. We check that $-2 < \frac{1}{2}(-1 - \sqrt{5}) < 0$, $-2 < \frac{1}{2}(1 - \sqrt{13}) < 0$, $0 < \frac{1}{2}(-1 + \sqrt{5}) < 2$ and $2 < \frac{1}{2}(1 + \sqrt{13}) < 4$.

Index

This unique book presents a highly original concept for a course in algebra at an introductory (pre-calculus) level. The degree of abstraction, rigor and interesting topics included affords an excellent background for further mathematical development. Some of the topics—particularly those from the areas of combinatorial analysis and convexity —are often considered too advanced for freshmen level courses in college algebra and too elementary for junior-senior level courses in modern algebra. This results in the omission of these important topics from the mathematical training of many students.

No attempt has been made to develop a rigid axiomatic approach to the study of mathematics at this level. The authors feel there are many new and exciting ideas in the subject matter itself such as convex sets, convex functions and the classical inequalities that should be given priority.

The book is divided into four chapters, each of which is essentially self-contained and independent of the others.

Chapter I, Numbers and Sets, deals with the elementary language of mathematics: induction, summation and product notation, sets and functions, and elementary theory of cardinality.

Chapter II, Combinatorial Analysis, presents a fairly complete theory of permutations on a finite set. The concept of an incidence matrix is also introduced and the definitions of matrix product and sum are motivated by their combinatorial applications.

Chapter III, Convexity, has as its goal the investigation of important and classical inequalities for real numbers; e.g., the arithmetic-geometric mean inequality, Minkowski's inequality, the trian-